Study Guide with ActivPhysics 2

Volume 2

Alan Van Heuvelen
The Ohio State University

Paul D'Alessandris
Monroe Community College

Jeffrey J. Braun
University of Evansville, Indiana

Christopher Wozny
Waycross College, Georgia

Physics with Modern Physics for Scientists and Engineers

Wolfson • Pasachoff

An Imprint of Addison Wesley Longman, Inc.

San Francisco, California • Reading, Massachusetts
New York • Harlow, England • Don Mills, Ontario • Sydney
Mexico City • Madrid • Amsterdam

ACKNOWLEDGMENTS

Publisher: Robin Heyden
Sponsoring Editor: Sami Iwata
Project Coordinators: Bridget Biscotti Bradley, Catherine Flack
Accuracy Checkers: Gordon Aubrecht and Mike Ziegler, The Ohio State University
Senior Production Editor: Larry Olsen
Copyeditor: Brian Jones
Cover Designer: Yvo Riezebos Design
Director of Marketing: Stacy Treco
Channel Marketing Manager: Gay Meixel
Cover Photo: Copyright © Image Bank

ISBN 0-321-05147-5

1 2 3 4 5 6 7 8 9 10-CRS-03 02 01 00 99

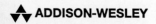 **ADDISON-WESLEY**

1301 Sansome Street
San Francisco, California 94111

Studying Physics

Physics is a complex subject encompassing a great variety of phenomena. It will challenge many of your long-held, common-sense beliefs about how the world works. It will introduce you to phenomena on scales too tiny to see with the unaided eye and so vast that they are difficult to comprehend. Underlying the subject of physics are a rather small number of fundamental laws. Success in physics comes from learning the underlying principles and applying them to a wide variety of situations. The crucial steps toward achieving success are:

- Developing an intuitive feel for the concepts.
- Developing problem-solving skills to apply the concepts and make quantitative predictions.

Each of you will eventually discover the study techniques that work best for you, but successful physics students tend to have one thing in common: They are *active* participants in the learning process. An hour spent in an active study procedure is far more beneficial than an hour spent in a passive process. Effective studying, however, can include activities from *both* columns in the following table:

Passive process	Active process
1. Listening to a lecture.	1. Taking notes during a lecture.
2. Underlining (or highlighting) while reading the text	2. Writing review notes and summarizing a chapter in your notes.
3. Having someone tell you how to solve a problem or just reading through the solution to a problem.	3. Working through a homework or *ActivPhysics* problem.
4. Watching the instructor solve a problem on the board.	4. Explaining a problem to another student
5. Checking the correctness of your answer against the solution	5. Determining whether your answer is physically reasonable.

This *Study Guide* will be a powerful ally as you work through your physics course, whatever your learning style or needs. We have combined:

- An overview of the material from your textbook—equation summaries, key definitions, and hints on avoiding common pitfalls; and
- Interactive simulations on the *ActivPhysics* CD-ROM to provide visualization of physical processes and allow you to change variables, test assumptions, make predictions, and develop intuition that only such hands-on activity makes possible.

We have also provided support in the form of guides to *ActivPhysics* that show you the topics in your course where *ActivPhysics* will be most useful. These guides will help you use the simulations and worksheets in ways that complement your personal learning style and increase your understanding of the material.

How To Use This *Study Guide*

Study Guide with ActivPhysics is encyclopedic in scope. It is designed to provide you with a range of options for each topic in your course. It is intended to be a reference for you so that you can choose and use those parts that best address your needs. These needs are likely to change as you work through your physics course. The *Study Guide* is divided into three parts:

Part I Study Guide matches your textbook chapter by chapter to provide a useful overview and summary of material. The Summary of Equations sections include the significant equations in each chapter of your textbook. These sections include a short discussion that covers new variables and conditions for use. The Definitions section lists all the terms you should understand after studying a topic. The Avoiding Pitfalls section gives hints and suggestions for avoiding common mistakes. Each chapter of Part I concludes with suggestions about where *ActivPhysics* simulations can help you most.

Part II Guide to *ActivPhysics* This part of the *Study Guide with ActivPhysics* will guide you to use *ActivPhysics* in a way that will complement your personal learning style, whether methodical or intuitive. Each part of your course will provide different challenges, and *ActivPhysics* is designed to help you meet those challenges. Read the Introduction and Game Plan sections to give you an overview before you spend time with the *ActivPhysics* simulations. The icons in the margins of your textbook indicate key topics that *ActivPhysics* can reinforce, and those icons plus this Guide will provide a map for using *ActivPhysics*.

Part III *ActivPhysics* Use the *ActivPhysics* CD-ROM and worksheets to help you visualize a physical process and analyze problems. You can use the questions as you would a homework problem. By changing simulation variables, making predictions, and drawing diagrams, you will develop intuition and imagery that will help you to understand the material presented in your class and to solve problems. *ActivPhysics* will support you each step of the way with an Advisor section that provides hints and solutions.

Study Tips for Learning Physics

1. *Budget enough time.* A useful rule of thumb is to spend between two and three hours outside of class for each hour spent in class. While some other courses may not require this much time and effort outside of class, physics simply cannot be learned by listening to a lecture or reading the text. You must become an active practitioner of the science.

2. *Go to class.* This may seem obvious to you, but there is indeed a strong correlation between students who do not go to class and students who do poorly in the course. A few professors are superb lecturers, with a well-organized plan, spellbinding oration, and dramatic demonstrations. A few professors are unsure of themselves, possess little eloquence, and seem rather disorganized. Most fall somewhere in the middle. But you should realize that every professor chooses as the topic for the day's lecture the ideas and concepts he or she feels are the most important or that most need explanation. By coming to class *every* day, you see for yourself the topics that most need your attention when you return to your room to study.

3. *Read the chapter before coming to class.* You will undoubtedly receive a syllabus that tells you the sequence of topics and, perhaps, the date on which the instructor expects to deal with that chapter or section. By reading over the chapter *before* going to the lecture, you accomplish two objectives: (1) You will have heard the terms and concepts before and you will find it easier to see where the lecture is headed. (2) You will know which parts of the chapter seem fairly straightforward and which parts seem rather difficult or confusing to you. You can then pay particular attention to those sections that have given you trouble and can ask questions immediately. (If you haven't read the chapter, it is too easy to tell yourself, "Well, this will make sense when I get around to reading this section."

4. *Take notes.* You don't have to be a stenographer and record every word of a lecture. Rather, be sure you write down the topics the instructor is emphasizing. When he or she intrpdices new material or presents an alternative approach to a topic, then you should get very busy. If, however, you know that the example being worked on the board is straight out of the book, then it is not necessary to copy down every word and symbol from the board. (By the way, if you have not already read the chapter, how would you know if the lecture is straight from the book or is presenting new and priceless information?)

5. *Don't recopy notes.* When you get back to your study area, don't waste your valuable time recopying or typing out your class notes. There are much more beneficial things to do, such as the following.

6. *Re-read the chapter.* That afternoon or evening, re-read the chapter and work through the sample problems. You should be able to cover up the solution and solve the problems yourself. If not, re-read the solution and try again. It is important to actually *write out* your solutions.

7. *Work the assigned problems.* Now you are ready to attempt the homework problems. Give each problem your best effort before turning to the back of the book or to your friends. Once you have finished the problem, or reached a dead end, then seek help. Help may come from a number of places.

   a. Occasionally, a look at the answer in the back of the book will trigger something in your mind, and you will be able to get started again.

   b. Use the *ActivPhysics* simulations to help you visualize a physical process or concept, and use the questions as you would a homework problem. The Advisor section will give hints, and many of the application exercises include the full solution in an Advisor section. You will quickly discover that the best way to truly understand the problem is to try to solve it without the assistance of the Advisor, but the Advisor is there to provide support should you need it. *ActivPhysics* simulations and questions are written in a way that promotes and encourages student interaction and discussion, and you can learn a lot by working with other students.

   c. Working with a group of students can sometimes be a blessing and sometimes be a curse. The crucial element for success in study groups is for each person to spend time alone working on the problems *before* meeting with the others.

   d. Also, your instructor will be glad to help you with your difficulties, *if he or she sees you have been working diligently on your own before coming in for help.* Even in large universities where other pressures tend to make the professor less accessible, study centers exist, teaching assistants abound, and many other resources have been set up to help you.

Physics is a subject that has challenged some of the greatest scientific minds through the centuries, but it also, in many ways, is the simplest and most fundamental of the sciences. Whether this is the first of many physics courses or this is the only course you will take, success requires an effort on your part. Arnold Sommerfeld was one of the greatest physics teachers of all time, and his advice to Werner Heisenberg (then a student of his) still applies today: "Just do the exercises diligently, then you will know what you have understood, and what you have not."

PART I

Study Guide

JEFFREY BRAUN

Connections to *ActivPhysics* by Christopher Wozny

CHAPTER 23   ELECTRIC CHARGE, FORCE, AND FIELD

Three fundamental concepts are introduced in this chapter, and they will serve as the basis for the next twelve chapters. The first two concepts are *electric charge* and the electrostatic force that electrically charged objects exert on each other. The mathematical description of this force is known as Coulomb's law. We then develop a deeper understanding of the nature of the electrostatic interaction by explaining electrostatic forces in terms of a third concept, the *electric field*. We say that every charge surrounds itself with an electric field and that it is this charge's electric field that exerts the force on other charges in the vicinity.

DEFINITIONS

You should know the definition of each of these terms. (The number in parentheses is the text chapter and section in which the term is introduced.)

(23-2) *Electric charge*, like mass, is an inherent property of matter. Just as the mass of an object determines the strength of the gravitational force exerted on the object when it is placed within a gravitational field, the electric charge of an object determines the strength of the electrostatic force exerted on the object when it is placed in an electric field. (This begs the question a bit, since we haven't yet defined electric fields, but the essential idea can be seen by comparison with gravity.) Unlike mass, electric charge comes in two types (+ and −), because we observe both attractive and repulsive electric forces.

(23-2) The amount of electric charge carried by a proton is referred to as the *elementary charge* (e), which is found to equal 1.602×10^{-19} coulomb. The charge on all matter (electrons, protons, or anything made up of protons and/or electrons) is found to be an integral multiple of this quantity.

(23-2) The *coulomb* is the SI unit of electric charge. It can be thought of as the total charge on 6.242×10^{18} ($= 1 / 1.602 \times 10^{-19}$) protons. (The actual definition involves the SI unit of current, the ampere, which will be developed later.)

(23-2) The *law of conservation of electric charge* states that the total electric charge in the universe is constant. Electrically charged particles (electrons and positrons, for example) are continually being created in the universe, but whenever one electrically charged particle is created, another particle with precisely equal and opposite charge is formed at the same time, so the total charge in the universe does not change.

(23-3) *Coulomb's law* describes the dependence of the electrostatic force on charge and distance. Specifically, Coulomb's law states that the electrostatic force between two electrically charged particles is

- Directly proportional to the charge on either particle (thus, proportional to the product: $F \propto q_1 q_2$).
- Inversely proportional to the square of the distance between the two particles (thus, $F \propto 1/r^2$).
- Attractive if the charges have opposite sign, and repulsive if they carry like charges.

(23-3) The *superposition principle* states that electric forces add vectorially. Specifically, if two charges (q_1 and q_2) exert forces $\mathbf{F}_{12}$ and $\mathbf{F}_{21}$ on each other, then bringing a third charge q_3 into their vicinity adds its own forces ($\mathbf{F}_{13}$ and $\mathbf{F}_{23}$) but does not affect the forces that were already present. (The superposition principle is obeyed approximately by gravitational forces, exactly by electric and magnetic forces, and not at all by the strong nuclear force.)

(23-4) We visualize every charge as surrounding itself with an *electric field*, and any other charge in its vicinity experiences a force because it interacts with the electric field of the first charge. Mathematically, we define the strength and direction of the electric field at any point in space by placing a small test charge q_0 at the field point and then observing the electrostatic force $\mathbf{F}$ that acts on q_0. The electric field at that location is defined to be

$$\mathbf{E} \equiv \frac{\mathbf{F}}{q_0}.$$

(23-5) An *electric dipole* consists of two equal and opposite charges held a fixed distance apart.

(23-5) The *dipole moment* of a dipole is defined to be the product of the magnitude of either of the two charges and their separation. (For two charges $\pm q$, separated by a distance d, their dipole moment is $p = qd$.) In some cases, it is useful to treat the dipole moment as a vector quantity, and the direction of the vector dipole moment is defined to point from the negative charge toward the positive charge.

(23-6) An (electrical) *conductor* is a material that contains a large number of charged particles that are free to move in response to an applied electric field.

(23-6) An (electrical) *insulator* is a material that contains few mobile charge carriers.

SUMMARY OF EQUATIONS

1. Coulomb's law:

$$\mathbf{F}_{12} = \frac{kq_1q_2}{r^2}\hat{\mathbf{r}} \qquad \text{(Text Eq. 23-1)}$$

$\mathbf{F}_{12}$ represents the electrostatic force exerted by q_1 on q_2, r the distance between the two charges. $\hat{\mathbf{r}}$ is a unit vector that points from q_1 to q_2. (If both charges have the same sign, the product is positive and q_2 is pushed away from q_1. If they carry opposite charges, the product is negative and q_2 is pulled toward q_1.) The Coulomb's law constant (k) has the value

$$k = 8.987 \times 10^9 \text{ N} \cdot \text{m}^2 / \text{C}^2.$$

(For computational purposes, this is usually rounded to 9.0×10^9.)

2. Definition of electric field:

$$\mathbf{E} \equiv \frac{\mathbf{F}}{q} \qquad \text{(Text Eq. 23-3a)}$$

The electric field at any point in space is defined as the force per unit charge that would act on a tiny charge q resting at that point. (Note: The SI units of electric field are $[E] = $ N/C.)

3. Electric field of a point charge:

$$\mathbf{E} = \frac{kq}{r^2}\hat{\mathbf{r}} \qquad \text{(Text Eq. 23-4)}$$

This follows immediately from Coulomb's law and the definition of electric field ($\mathbf{E} \equiv \mathbf{F}/q$). The above expression gives the electric field at a distance r from a point charge q. ($\hat{\mathbf{r}}$ is a unit vector pointing from the location of q toward the point at which the electric field is needed.) Note that the electric field of a positive charge points radially outward, whereas the electric field of a negative charge points radially inward.

4. Electric field of a continuous charge distribution:

$$\mathbf{E} = \int \frac{k\,dq}{r^2}\hat{\mathbf{r}} \qquad \text{(Text Eq. 23-8b)}$$

Any continuous charge distribution can be considered to be a large number of point charges dq, each producing its own electric field. By vectorially adding all these fields (i.e., integrating), we obtain the resultant electric field of the entire charge distribution.

5. Definition of dipole moment:

$$\mathbf{p} \equiv q\mathbf{d} \qquad \text{(Text Eq. 23-6)}$$

The dipole moment produced by a pair of equal and opposite point charges ($\pm q$), separated by a distance d is defined to be the product of the positive charge and the dipole separation vector ($\mathbf{d}$), which is the displacement vector drawn from the negative to the positive charge.

6. Electric field produced by a dipole:

$$\text{(along} \perp \text{bisector)} \quad \mathbf{E} = \frac{k\mathbf{p}}{r^3} \qquad \text{(Text Eq. 23-7a)}$$

$$\text{(along axis)} \quad \mathbf{E} = \frac{2k\mathbf{p}}{r^3} \qquad \text{(Text Eq. 23-7b)}$$

These expressions give the electric field at large distances r, measured from the center of a dipole (1) at a point on the perpendicular bisector of the dipole (i.e., along its "side"), and (2) at a point on the axis of the dipole (i.e., along either end.) Note that the electric field of a dipole is, at large distances, inversely proportional to the *cube* of the distance.

7. Dipole in a uniform external electric field:

$$\boldsymbol{\tau} = \mathbf{p} \times \mathbf{E} \qquad \text{(Text Eq. 23-11)}$$
$$U = -\mathbf{p} \cdot \mathbf{E} \qquad \text{(Text Eq. 23-12)}$$

These equations describe the interaction between an electric dipole and a uniform electric field. Equation 23-11 describes the torque exerted on the dipole, and Equation 23-12 gives the potential energy of the system. Note that this expression defines the potential energy to be zero when $\mathbf{p}$ and $\mathbf{E}$ are perpendicular. When $\mathbf{p}$ turns toward the direction of $\mathbf{E}$, the potential energy decreases (below zero); when $\mathbf{p}$ turns away from the direction of $\mathbf{E}$, the potential energy increases (toward positive values.)

AVOIDING PITFALLS

1. **Elementary charge:** The magnitude of the charge on an electron or proton occurs in so many problems, it will save you a lot of time if you remember this number:

$$e = 1.602 \times 10^{-19} \text{ C}.$$

(Don't forget that the charge on an *electron* is $-e$.)

2. **Units:** Static charges are almost always measured in microcoulombs (μC), but the value of k in Coulomb's law requires charges to be measured in *coulombs*, not microcoulombs. Also, most electrostatic equipment is tabletop-sized, so dimensions are often given in centimeters. Again, k assumes SI units of meters.

3. **Proportional relationships:** A common exam or homework problem is one where the electrostatic force is given for a particular set of conditions, and then one or more of the charges is doubled, tripled, etc. These problems are straightforward if you remember that the force is directly proportional to the product of the

charges, and inversely proportional to the *square* of the distance between them. Thus,

- If *either* charge is doubled, the force doubles.
- If *both* charges are doubled, the force quadruples.
- If the separation is doubled, the force *reduces* by a factor of 4.

4. **Using Coulomb's law:** In complicated problems, use Coulomb's law to find the magnitude of the forces, one pair of charges at a time. Then use the vector diagram as a guide to the directions of the individual forces, and add the forces (or fields) by components.

5. **Symmetry:** Keep your eyes open for the symmetry of these problems. By not repeating long calculations for repetitive parts of a problem, you save time and reduce the chance of making arithmetic errors.

6. **Electric field vs. electric force:** Remember that the electric *force* between two charges is, like any force, an interaction between *two* objects— a single, isolated electric charge doesn't have anything to exert a force on. However, each charge, even a single, isolated one, has its own electric *field*.

7. **Direction of forces and fields:** Once again, remember that the force exerted on a positive charge is parallel to the electric field, whereas the force exerted on a negative charge (*e.g.*, an electron) is in the direction *opposite* the electric field.

8. **Dipole moment:** The dipole moment formula is expressed in two common forms ($\mathbf{p} = q\mathbf{d}$ and $p = 2qa$). In the first expression, $\mathbf{d}$ represents the vector drawn from the negative to the positive charge; in the second version, a is the distance from the center of the dipole to each charge; thus, their separation is $d = 2a$.

9. **Dipole potential energy:** The potential energy of a dipole in an external electric field can be written as $U = -\mathbf{p} \cdot \mathbf{E}$ *only if* the choice of $U = 0$ for $\theta = 90°$ has been made. Otherwise, you will have to use $U_B - U_A = -(pE \cos\theta_B - pE \cos\theta_A)$.

10. **Problem-solving overview:** If you think this is a rather difficult chapter, you are probably right. The major difficulty lies in the fact that electrical phenomena are not as visible as springs, ramps, and carts. The electric-field concept seems rather abstract at first. Because of this, in addition to listing possible pitfalls, I am including a kind of problem-solving overview to help you see how the trees make up this forest.

In this chapter, you have encountered three types of problems:

1. Problems in which the positions of several charges are given, and you are asked for the forces they exert on each other.

2. Problems in which the field is given and the force on a given charge is needed (or vice versa).

3. Problems in which you are asked for the electric field produced by a given charge distribution.

The first type follows directly from Coulomb's law. Just remember that the forces are vectors, and in general need to be added component by component.

Problems of the second type are also straightforward and follow directly from the definition of electric field,

$$\mathbf{F}_{12} = q_1 \mathbf{E}_2.$$

The most common pitfall is forgetting that the force on a negative charge points in the *opposite* direction from the electric field. (Thus, an upward-pointing electric field will push a proton upward, but pull an electron downward.)

Problems of the third type can be very difficult. That's the bad news. The good news is that in an introductory course such as this, there usually isn't enough time to get into the really messy situations. So most of the problems you will encounter will involve one-dimensional situations, or they will be highly symmetric distributions where a lot of cancellation will occur.

Basically, there are three types of electric-field calculations: (1) finding the resultant field from a few point charges, (2) finding the field from a continuous charge distribution by direct integration, and (3) using Gauss's law to find the resultant field from a continuous charge distribution. (The third technique—Gauss's law—is discussed in detail in the next chapter.)

1. *Electric field from point charges*: These problems are sometimes tedious but straightforward. The field from each point charge has a magnitude

$$E = \frac{kq}{r^2},$$

and points directly away from a positive charge and directly toward a negative charge. Remember that r is the straight-line distance from q to the field point and that you will, in general, have to resolve each field into its x- and y-components to find the resultant field:

$$(E_{\text{tot}})_x = (E_1)_x + (E_2)_x + (E_3)_x + \dots$$
$$(E_{\text{tot}})_y = (E_1)_y + (E_2)_y + (E_3)_y + \dots$$

2. *Electric field of a continuous charge distribution*: In general, the charge may be distributed along a

line, over a surface, or throughout a volume. Your starting point in all of these will be the integral

$$E = \int dE = \int \frac{k\,dq}{r^2}\,\hat{r}\,.$$

where r is the distance from each element of charge dq to the field point. Remember that $E = \int dE$ is just a shorthand way of writing three separate scalar equations ($E_x = \int dE_x$, $E_y = \int dE_y$, $E_z = \int dE_z$). In many of your problems, two of these components will obviously be zero, so you really have only one (scalar) integral to evaluate.

The remaining integral will contain dq, and the first step is to express dq in terms of the relevant charge density:

Line charges: $dq = \lambda\,d\ell$.

Surface charges: $dq = \sigma\,dA$.

Volume charges: $dq = \rho\,dV$.

If the density is uniform, then $\lambda = q_{tot}/L$, or $\sigma = q_{tot}/A$, or $\rho = q_{tot}/V$, and it can be taken out of the integral; if not, substitute its algebraic expression.

Finally, the crucial step in these problems: Express all the variables in terms of a single variable of integration. Typically, you will have $d\ell$ (or dA or dV),θ, r, and x (or y or z) in the integrand, and a careful diagram will lead you to their functional relationships. Once this has been done, all that remains is to evaluate the integral.

It's a good idea to check your answer by comparing your solution to known electric fields of similar situations. If you have a numerical answer, see if an equivalent point charge placed at the center of a solid distribution gives a similar value. If you have an algebraic solution, see if reducing the dimensions of your charge distribution produces the point-charge field ($E = kq/r^2$).

 Connections to *ActivPhysics*

The activities in Unit 11 of *ActivPhysics* deal directly with the key concepts presented in this chapter. Activity 11.1 *Electric Force: Coulomb's Law* builds Eq. 23-1 by varying the positions, magnitudes, and signs of two charges and observing the effects on the resulting force, using images similar to those shown in Figure 23-7. Activities 11.2 *Electric Force: Superposition Principle* and 11.3 *Electric Force: Superposition Principle (Quantitative)* add a third charge to the picture, as in Figure 23-9. The problems presented in Activity 11.3 are similar to Problems 9–11, 14, 15, 19, 20, and 23 in the text.

The first part of Activity 11.4 *Electric Field: A Point Charge* (up through question 2) parallels the discussion of Section 23-4, The Electric Field, and employs the same line of argument as the text for presenting the concept of an electric field, including the analogy to the gravitational field. Completing the exercise should enhance your understanding of Figure 23-14b. The electric field of a two point charge distribution, the electric dipole, is discussed in the next section of the text and presented in Activity 11.5 *Electric Field: Due to a Dipole*; and a simple electric field word problem is the subject of the short Activity 11.6 *Electric Field: Problems*. Activities 11.9 and 11.10 both explore the motion of a charge in a uniform electric field, and animate Figure 23-26. This simulation can be used to verify the results of the calculations in Example 23-10 and Problems 57–61, 75, and 76.

CHAPTER 24   GAUSS'S LAW

This chapter develops our understanding of the electric field by concentrating on a remarkable theorem about electric fields—Gauss's law. We begin by introducing the concept of electric flux through the model of electric field lines. Once electric flux has been defined mathematically, we find that there is a simple relationship between the electric flux through any closed surface and the net charge inside the surface. The remainder of the chapter then uses Gauss's law to deduce the electric field from certain given charge distributions, and to compute the electrostatic charge distribution when conductors are present.

DEFINITIONS

You should know the definition of each of these terms. (The number in parentheses is the text chapter and section in which the term is introduced.)

(24-1) An *electric field line* is a line drawn to be everywhere parallel to the electric field in a region. Each field line starts on a positive charge and follows the direction of the electric field until it ends on a negative charge or radiates out toward infinity. In the field-line approach, electric field intensity is related to the spacing of the field lines, and the number of field lines drawn is proportional to the magnitude of the charge.

(24-2) *Electric flux* (through a given surface) is mathematically defined as the surface integral of electric field over the surface: $\phi = \int \mathbf{E} \cdot d\mathbf{A}$. In the field-line approach, the flux is measured by the number of electric field lines poking through the surface.

(24-3) *Gauss's law* states that the electric flux through any *closed* surface is proportional to the net charge enclosed by the surface:

$$\oint \mathbf{E} \cdot d\mathbf{A} = \frac{q_{encl}}{\varepsilon_0}.$$

The electric field appearing in the integrand is the *net* electric field, resulting from all charges in the vicinity.

(24-6) *Electrostatic equilibrium* is a condition in which all the free (mobile) charges in a material are, on the average, in equilibrium. In a conductor, this requires the average electric field within the material to be zero.

SUMMARY OF EQUATIONS

1. Definition of electric flux—uniform field:

$$\phi = \mathbf{E} \cdot \mathbf{A} = E A \cos\theta \quad \text{(Text Eq. 24-1)}$$

The electric flux (ϕ) through any plane area **A** produced by a uniform electric field **E** is given by the scalar (dot) product of the electric field and the vector representing the area. (**A** is normal to the surface, and its magnitude equals the area of the surface. For an open surface, **A** can be drawn on either side, but for a closed surface, **A** is always drawn on the *outer* surface.)

2. Definition of electric flux—nonuniform field:

$$\phi = \int_{\text{surface}} \mathbf{E} \cdot d\mathbf{A} \quad \text{(Text Eq. 24-2)}$$

If, on the surface through which the flux is needed, we find that E or θ varies from point to point, then we can't simply multiply field and area. In such cases, we split the surface into infinitesimal patches $d\mathbf{A}$, each small enough so that E and θ are essentially constant over the patch $d\mathbf{A}$. Then the flux through each patch is $d\phi = \mathbf{E} \cdot d\mathbf{A}$ and we sum (integrate) the flux through all the patches to obtain the total flux through the surface.

3. Gauss's law:

$$\oint \mathbf{E} \cdot d\mathbf{A} = \frac{q_{encl}}{\varepsilon_0} \quad \text{(Text Eq. 24-4)}$$

Gauss's law states that the electric flux through any *closed* surface is proportional to the net charge enclosed by the surface. The electric field appearing in the integrand is the *net* electric field, resulting from all charges in the vicinity.

The proportionality constant ε_0 is known as the "permittivity of free space," and is simply the reciprocal of 4π times the familiar Coulomb's law constant k:

$$\varepsilon_0 \equiv \frac{1}{4\pi k} \quad \text{(Text Eq. 24-3)}$$

This has the SI value $\varepsilon_0 = 8.854 \times 10^{-12} \text{ C}^2/\text{N} \cdot \text{m}^2$.

4. Electric fields from given charge distributions: As shown in your text, Gauss's law can be used to deduce the electric field produced by several specific charge distributions:

a. *Field outside a spherically symmetric charge distribution:*

$$E = \frac{1}{4\pi\varepsilon_0} \frac{Q}{r^2} \quad \text{(Text Eq. 24-6)}$$

This includes, as a special case, the field of a point charge.

b. *Field outside a cylindrically symmetric charge distribution:*

$$E = \frac{\lambda}{2\pi\varepsilon_0 r} \qquad \text{(Text Ex. 24-4)}$$

This includes, as a special case, the field of a uniformly charged, infinitely long line of charge. Recall that λ represents the charge per unit length: $[\lambda] = C/m$.

c. *Field on either side of a uniform sheet of charge:*

$$E = \frac{\sigma}{2\varepsilon_0} \qquad \text{(Text Eq. 24-10)}$$

While *exactly* true only for a uniformly charged sheet that is infinite in size, this works quite well for the field at points near the central area of a finite sheet of charge. In this expression, σ represents the surface charge density (charge per unit area): $[\sigma] = C/m^2$.

d. *Field outside the surface of a charged conductor:*

$$E = \frac{\sigma}{\varepsilon_0} \qquad \text{(Text Eq. 24-11)}$$

If a conductor carries a surface charge density σ, the electric field just outside the surface is σ/ε_0. (The field *inside* a conductor is zero.)

AVOIDING PITFALLS

1. **Inventing the Gaussian surface:** If you're asked to find the electric field at some point, one face of your Gaussian surface must pass through that point. The other surfaces should lie in regions where you know that (1) the electric field is parallel to the Gaussian surface (so $\phi = 0$ for that part of the surface) or (2) the electric field has a known, constant magnitude (so $\phi = EA\cos\theta$ for that part of the surface). Obviously, any region in which you know that $E = 0$ (e.g., inside any conductor) will make the flux zero through that part of the surface.

You will encounter Gauss's law in three situations: problems with plane symmetry, problems with cylindrical symmetry, and problems with spherical symmetry. In each case, your first task is to invent a Gaussian surface each of whose sides are perpendicular or parallel to the electric field.

a. *Plane symmetry (sheets of charge):* Since the electric field of a large, flat sheet of charge points perpendicularly away from (or toward) the sheet, the choice is what I call a "Gaussian shoebox," symmetrically straddling the sheet of charge with one end face passing through the field point, as shown in Figure 24.1. Notice that there is no flux through the sides of the box, and the flux through *each* of the end faces is $\phi_1 = \phi_2 = EA$.

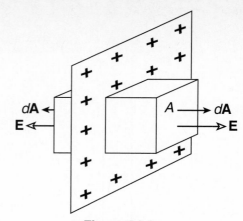

Figure 24.1
"Gaussian shoebox."

b. *Cylindrical symmetry (lines or rods of charge):* The field points radially away from the line, so the choice is a "Gaussian oatmeal box" surrounding the line of charge and passing through the field point, as shown in Figure 24.2. Now there is no flux through the end faces, and the flux through the cylindrical surface is $\phi = EA = E(2\pi rL)$.

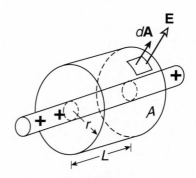

Figure 24.2
"Gaussian oatmeal box."

c. *Spherical symmetry (point charges or balls of charge):* This time, the field points radially away from the center, so we choose a "Gaussian sphere" that passes through the field point, as shown in Figure 24.3.

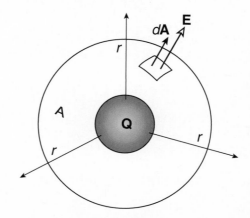

Figure 24.3
"Gaussian sphere."

At all points on the surface of the Gaussian sphere, the field is uniform and points radially outward, so $\phi = EA = E(4\pi r^2)$.

Inventing the proper Gaussian surface gets easier with experience and practice, so work as many of these problems as you can.

2. **Computing the enclosed charge:** Once you have chosen the proper Gaussian surface and found the total flux through the surface (in terms of E), all that remains is to evaluate the amount of enclosed charge. If the charge density (λ, σ, or ρ) is constant, you simply multiply the charge density by the length, area, or volume enclosed by the Gaussian surface:

$$q_{encl} = \lambda\, L_{encl}$$
$$q_{encl} = \sigma\, A_{encl}$$
$$q_{encl} = \rho\, V_{encl}$$

If, however, the charge density varies from point to point, you will have to integrate the charge density over the region enclosed by the Gaussian surface:

$$q_{encl} = \int_{encl} \lambda\, d\ell$$

$$q_{encl} = \int_{encl} \sigma\, dA$$

$$q_{encl} = \int_{encl} \rho\, dV$$

3. **Sheets of charge vs. charged metal sheets:** Why is the electric field near a "sheet of charge" $E = \sigma/2\varepsilon_0$, whereas the field near the surface of a charged metal sheet is $E = \sigma/\varepsilon_0$? There is a subtle difference in how σ, the surface charge density, is defined for "sheets of charge" and "charged metal sheets." Consider a 1 meter by 1 meter sheet of charge containing a total charge $Q = 1\,\mu C$. Its charge density is defined to be $\sigma = 1\,\mu C/m^2$. Now place a 1 μC charge on a 1 meter by 1 meter metal sheet. The charge now spreads equally over both $1-m^2$ sides, so the surface charge density *on each side* is $\sigma = 0.5\,\mu C/m^2$. Note that *both cases produce the same electric field!* The factor of 2 difference in these two equations is due to the different interpretation of σ in the two cases.

 Connections to *ActivPhysics*

Section 24-1 begins by examining electric field lines. Activity 11.4 contains three different simulations. The first simulation introduces the concept of a field based on Coulomb's law of electric force, which was discussed in the previous chapter (see Connections to *ActivPhysics* for Chapter 23). The second simulation is able to reproduce Figures 24-2, 24-3, and 24-4. The electric field of two uniformly and oppositely charged plates (Figure 24-35) is shown in the third simulation. The other two activities that explore the character and behavior of electric fields were recommended for the previous chapter but can also be viewed here.

Section 24-2 presents the concept of electric flux, as does Activity 11.7 *Electric Flux;* and Section 24-3 introduces Gauss's law, which is also the subject of Activity 11.8 *Gauss's Law.* Both of these activities will be very helpful for visual and active learners. The text of *ActivPhysics* closely parallels the discussion of the chapter, and the combination of both perspectives and discussions should make these abstract topics more understandable.

CHAPTER 25 ELECTRIC POTENTIAL

In this chapter, we introduce the concepts of energy and electric potential to our study of electrostatics—first, as an easier method of solving problems than computing electric fields, and then, as a method of handling problems that would otherwise be impossible. We start with the concept of work as developed in Chapter 7, applying this specifically to the case of electrostatic forces. The work done per unit charge is an essential concept, and it is given its own name: potential difference.

DEFINITIONS

You should know the definition of each of these terms. (The number in parentheses is the text chapter and section in which the term is introduced.)

(25-1) The *work* done by a force **F** as a particle is moved from point A to point B is defined by the path integral

$$W_{AB} \equiv \int_A^B \mathbf{F} \cdot d\ell.$$

(25-2) The (electrical) *potential difference* between two points A and B is defined to be the amount of work per unit charge that would be done by an external force while moving a small charge q slowly from point A to point B. Symbolically,

$$\Delta V_{A \to B} \equiv \frac{W_{AB}}{q}.$$

(25-2) The *volt* is the SI unit of potential difference:

$$1 \text{ volt} \equiv \frac{1 \text{ joule}}{1 \text{ coulomb}}.$$

(25-2) *Voltage* is a term that refers to the work done per unit charge. In electrostatic situations, voltage and potential difference are synonymous.

(25-2) The *electron volt* is a unit of energy (not potential) that equals the kinetic energy of a particle carrying a charge $q = e$ that has been accelerated from rest through a potential difference of 1 volt. The SI equivalence is $1 \text{ eV} = 1.602 \times 10^{-19}$ J.

(25-3) The *potential* at any point A is defined to be the potential difference between that point and the reference point where the potential was defined to be zero: $V_A \equiv \Delta V_{ref \to A}$.

(25-4) The locus of all points in space that are at the same (given) potential forms an *equipotential surface.*

(25-5) *Corona discharge* occurs when the air surrounding a charged object becomes electrically conducting, allowing the charge to "leak off" the object. This happens when the electric field exceeds the dielectric strength of the air and the air molecules become ionized, forming a conducting path for the charge.

SUMMARY OF EQUATIONS

1. Potential difference between two points in an electric field:

$$\Delta V_{A \to B} = -\int_A^B \mathbf{E} \cdot d\ell \quad \text{(Text Eq. 25-2a)}$$

Electrical potential difference is defined as (-1) times the work per unit charge done by the electric field as a charge moves from point A to point B. (This can also be thought of as $(+1)$ times the work per unit charge done by an external force *against* the electric field as the charge is moved from A to B.)

2. Potential difference in a uniform electric field:

$$\Delta V_{A \to B} = -\mathbf{E} \cdot \ell \quad \text{(Text Eq. 25-2b)}$$

If the electric field **E** is uniform, the integral becomes a simple product, where ℓ represents the displacement vector drawn from point A to point B.

3. Potential difference in the field of a point charge:

$$\Delta V_{A \to B} = kq \left(\frac{1}{r_B} - \frac{1}{r_A} \right) \quad \text{(Text Eq. 25-3)}$$

The potential difference between two points in the radial electric field of a point charge depends only on the difference in the radial distance from the charge.

4. Electric potential of a point charge:

$$V(r) = \frac{kq}{r} \quad \text{(Text Eq. 25-4)}$$

By defining the electric potential to be zero at $r = \infty$, we obtain a simple expression for the electric potential at a distance r from a point charge.

5. Electric potential due to several point charges:

$$V = \sum_i \frac{kq_i}{r_i} \quad \text{(Text Eq. 25-6)}$$

Because electric fields obey the superposition principle, we can also superimpose the potentials from a number of individual charges. Again, this assumes the definition that $V = 0$ when $r = \infty$. Also, the r_i in this equation represents the distance from each point charge q_i to the point at which the potential is being evaluated.

6. Electric potential due to a continuous charge distribution:

$$V = \int \frac{k\, dq}{r} \qquad \text{(Text Eq. 25-8)}$$

A continuous charge distribution can be broken up into an infinite number of infinitesimal (point) charges dq. Summing the potential from each element of charge gives the total potential.

7. Finding the electric field from a given potential:

$$E_\ell = -\frac{dV}{d\ell} \qquad \text{(Text Eq. 25-10)}$$

In this expression, E_ℓ represents the component of $\mathbf{E}$ in the direction of $d\ell$, and dV the change in potential that occurs when you move through a small displacement $d\ell$. For example, the x-component of $\mathbf{E}$ would be $E_x = -dV/dx$, while the y-component of $\mathbf{E}$ would be $E_y = -dV/dy$.

AVOIDING PITFALLS

1. **Signs of charges:** When we were working with electric fields and forces, we computed the magnitude of the (vector) quantities by using the absolute value of each charge. Now, when working with the electric potential, which is a signed scalar quantity, we need to be more careful with the signs. There is no direction to keep track of, so all the information about positive or negative potentials is carried by the sign of the charge. Therefore, we *must* carry the + and − signs along with the values of q.

2. **Combining potentials:** Electric potentials add as scalars, not as vectors. This is, of course, much simpler than vector addition, but we have to be careful to include all + and − signs in finding the total potential of a point.

3. **Choice of zero potential:** As in mechanics, only *changes* in potential are significant. Thus, the location of the zero-potential point is ours to choose. We usually define $V = 0$ at an infinite distance from our charges. However, there is one situation in which we cannot do this: If the charge distribution itself extends to infinity, such as with "infinitely long lines of charge," or with "infinite sheets of charge," then we must choose some nearby point as our zero of potential.

4. **Zero fields and zero potentials:** If the electric field happens to be zero at a particular point, that does *not* mean the potential is necessarily zero at that point. Similarly, if the potential happens to be zero at some particular point,

that does *not* mean the electric field must also be zero there.

We can, however, say this: If the electric field is zero throughout some region, then the potential is *constant* throughout that region. Conversely, if the potential is constant throughout some region, then we know $\mathbf{E} = 0$ throughout that region. (One common example of this is a conductor in electrostatic equilibrium. The electric potential of such a conductor is uniform (but not necessarily zero) over its entire extent, and $\mathbf{E} = 0$ throughout its volume.)

5. **Potential and the direction of E:** Remember that the electric field always points in the direction of *decreasing* potential (i.e., toward the more negative values of potential).

6. **Potential vs. distance:** Recall that the electric field of a point charge is inversely proportional to the *square* of the distance: $E \propto 1/r^2$. The electric potential, however, is inversely proportional to the *first* power of distance: $V \propto 1/r$. This results from the fact that potential is the integral of electric field, and the integration raises the power of r or x by 1. For example, the field of a large, uniformly charged sheet is uniform ($E \propto x^0$), while the potential in such a field is directly proportional to the distance: ($V \propto x$).

7. **W$_{app}$ vs. W$_E$:** You will encounter some problems that ask for the work done *by the electric field* as a charge is moved, and other problems that ask for the work *we do (against the electric field)* as a charge is moved. Assuming the charge is moved slowly (so it remains in equilibrium at all times), these amounts of work are the same but *opposite in sign!* The work done *by* the electric field is $W_E = -q\,\Delta V$; but the work done *against* the electric field (by an external agent) is $W_{app} = +q\,\Delta V$.

 Connections to *ActivPhysics*

Activities 11.11 *Electric Potential: Qualitative Introduction* and 11.12 *Electric Potential, Field, and Force* explore the same topics as this chapter. If the *ActivPhysics* simulations and discussion on electricity have helped you to understand the concepts of Chapters 23 and 24, then that trend should continue for this chapter. These two activities return to the simulations of a point charge, two point charges (a dipole), and two charged parallel plates adding equipotential lines. The text of the simulations discusses how to map equipotential lines and an appropriate voltage, the zero of a potential, and the relationship between the potential and the electric field.

CHAPTER 26 ELECTROSTATIC ENERGY AND CAPACITORS

In this chapter, we build on the concept of electric potential that we introduced in Chapter 25. We extend the concept of electric potential to the potential energy of extended charge distributions and to the idea of the energy contained in the electric field itself. We then develop the relationship between the potential difference and the charge on a pair of oppositely charged conductors, and define the capacitance of the system.

DEFINITIONS

You should know the definition of each of these terms. (The number in parentheses is the text chapter and section in which the term is introduced.)

(26-1) The *electrostatic potential energy* of a charge distribution is defined as the amount of work needed to assemble the given charge distribution, starting with the individual charges at infinite separations from each other. (This again assumes that the potential energy of infinitely separated charges has been defined to be zero.)

(26-3) The *electrostatic energy density* is the energy per unit volume contained by an electric field.

(26-4) Any pair of conductors separated by an insulator (*e.g.*, air) constitutes a *capacitor*.

(26-4) The *capacitance* (*C*) of a capacitor is defined as $C \equiv Q/V$, where V is the potential difference between the two conductors when they carry charges of $\pm Q$.

(26-4) The *farad* is the SI unit of capacitance, defined as $1\,F = 1\,C/V$.

(26-6) Each capacitor has a maximum voltage that its insulation can withstand without experiencing dielectric breakdown, and this maximum safe voltage is known as the *working voltage*.

(26-6) If one lead from a capacitor (or any two-lead circuit element) is connected directly to a lead from another capacitor, *and* the second leads from the two are also directly connected together, then the two are in *parallel*.

(26-6) If one lead from each of two capacitors (or any two-lead circuit elements) are connected together, but the other leads are *not* connected together, then the two are in *series*. (Note: Nothing else can be connected to the point of connection between the two capacitors.)

(26-7) A *dielectric material* is a substance whose molecules behave as dipoles when placed in an electric field.

(26-7) When a dielectric material is placed in an electric field E_0, the polarization within the dielectric reduces the net electric field to some new value E. The *dielectric constant* of a material is defined as the factor by which the field is reduced: $E \equiv E_0/\kappa$.

SUMMARY OF EQUATIONS

1. Electrostatic potential energy of two point charges:

$$U = \frac{kq_1 q_2}{r} \qquad \text{(Text Eq. 26-1)}$$

First, we define the potential energy of two charges to be zero when they are infinitely far apart. Then their potential energy when separated by a distance r is the amount of work needed to bring them in from infinity to the separation r.

2. Energy density of an electric field in empty space:

$$u_E = \tfrac{1}{2}\varepsilon_0 E^2 \qquad \text{(Text Eq. 26-3)}$$

The energy density (energy per unit volume) in an electric field in empty space is proportional to the square of the electric field amplitude.

If uniform, the energy density may be multiplied by the volume to find the total energy contained in a particular region. If nonuniform, the energy density can be integrated over the volume to find the total energy contained in that region:

$$U = \tfrac{1}{2}\varepsilon_0 \int E^2 \, dV. \qquad \text{(Text Eq. 26-4)}$$

3. Definition of capacitance:

$$C \equiv \frac{Q}{V} \qquad \text{(Text Eq. 26-5)}$$

If an amount of charge $+Q$ is placed on one conductor and a charge $-Q$ is placed on another conductor, then a potential difference V will exist between the two. We define the ratio of charge to voltage to be the *capacitance* of the two conductors. (The unit of capacitance is the *farad*, defined as follows: 1 farad = 1 coulomb/volt.)

4. Capacitance of a parallel-plate capacitor:

$$C = \frac{\varepsilon_0 A}{d} \qquad \text{(Text Eq. 26-6)}$$

This equation gives the capacitance of the most common type of capacitor, the parallel-plate capacitor. While *exactly* correct only for infinitesimal plate separation (or infinite plate area), either of which produces a uniform electric field in the region between the plates, this will work very well whenever the plate separation is small compared to the dimensions of the plates.

5. Energy stored in a charged capacitor:

$$U = \tfrac{1}{2}QV = \tfrac{1}{2}CV^2 = \tfrac{1}{2}Q^2/C \quad \text{(Text Eq. 26-8)}$$

The first expression is equivalent to $U = QV_{av}$, since the voltage increases linearly as a capacitor is charged. The others follow by substitution of $C = Q/V$.

6. Equivalent capacitance of parallel capacitors:

$$C_P = C_1 + C_2 + C_3 + \ldots \quad \text{(Text Eq. 26-9b)}$$

Note that the parallel capacitance will always be *greater* than the largest of the individual capacitors, and adding more capacitors in parallel *increases* the total capacitance.

7. Equivalent capacitance of series capacitors:

$$\frac{1}{C_S} = \frac{1}{C_1} + \frac{1}{C_2} + \frac{1}{C_3} + \ldots \quad \text{(Text Eq. 26-10b)}$$

Note that the series capacitance will always be *less* than the smallest of the individual capacitors, and adding more capacitors in series *reduces* the total capacitance.

8. Definition of dielectric constant:

$$\kappa \equiv \frac{E_0}{E} \quad \text{(Text Sect. 26-7)}$$

A fixed charge distribution produces, in empty space, an electric field E_0. Now introduce a dielectric material into the region, which reduces the electric field within the dielectric material to a value E. The dielectric constant of the material is the factor by which the electric field has been reduced.

9. Effect of a dielectric on capacitance:

$$C = \kappa\, C_0 \quad \text{(Text Eq. 26-11)}$$

In this equation, C_0 is the capacitance when the conductors are separated by empty space, and C is the capacitance after the space has been entirely filled with a dielectric material (of dielectric constant **k**). Since **k** > 1 for all dielectrics, the effect of a dielectric is to increase the capacitance.

10. Effect of a dielectric on the energy density of an electric field:

$$u_E = \tfrac{1}{2}\kappa\varepsilon_0 E^2 \quad \text{(Text Eq. 26-13)}$$

In this equation, E is the macroscopic electric field with the dielectric present. Remember that E is smaller than E_0, the field that would exist in the region without the dielectric, by a factor of κ. Since $u \propto E^2$, the effect of introducing a dielectric is to *reduce* the energy density in that region.

AVOIDING PITFALLS

1. **Energy of charge distributions:** The energy of a charge distribution is stored in its electric field, but there are two ways of computing this value: (1) If the resulting electric field is simple enough that we know its magnitude at all points, it may be simplest to compute the potential energy from the energy density in the electric field ($u = \tfrac{1}{2}\varepsilon_0 E^2$). (2) However, if we have only a few charges (which actually results in a rather complex field), it will probably be simpler to compute the work required to assemble the charges.

2. **Signs of charges:** Since work and potential energy are both scalar quantities, they can be either positive or negative, but there is no *direction* to either of these quantities. Whether the energy of a charge distribution is, in fact, positive or negative is determined by the sign of the charges, so one must be careful to include the plus or minus sign with all values of charge.

3. **Computing capacitance:** Remember that capacitance is a property of any two conductors in proximity, and is defined as $C = Q/V$. The actual capacitance of any arrangement is determined by factors like the size, shape, and location of the two conductors—*not* by the applied voltage or amount of accumulated charge.

   The formula $C = \varepsilon_0 A/d$, while important and frequently applicable, can only be used when the electric field in the region between the two conductors is uniform, and is zero elsewhere. (This will occur only if the two plates are everywhere equidistant and carry equal and opposite charges, as in the parallel-plate capacitor.) When the electric field is not uniform, one must resort to the definition of capacitance ($C = Q/V$) and compute the potential difference (produced by an arbitrary charge Q) from $V = -\int \mathbf{E} \cdot d\boldsymbol{\ell}$.

4. **Dielectrics in capacitors:** Remember that the effect of a dielectric material is to reduce the electric field strength within the material from E to E/κ. (This is a consequence of the induced surface charge densities that appear on the faces of the dielectric, and the resulting partial cancellation of the applied electric field by the electric field of these induced charges.)

5. **Energy in dielectrics:** If, in free space, the electric field is E_0, then the energy density is $u_0 = \tfrac{1}{2}\varepsilon_0 E_0^2$. Within a dielectric medium, the electric field is reduced to $E = E_0/\kappa$, but the energy density is *not* just $u = \tfrac{1}{2}\varepsilon_0 E^2 = \tfrac{1}{2}\varepsilon_0 E_0^2/\kappa^2$. Instead, the energy density is given by $u = \kappa(\tfrac{1}{2}\varepsilon_0 E^2) = \tfrac{1}{2}\varepsilon_0 E_0^2/\kappa$.

6. **Energy in capacitors:** The energy in a capacitor is given by $U = QV/2$. Note that this could be thought of as $U = Q\bar{V}$, where $\bar{V}$ is the average voltage across the capacitor plates during the charging process. Then, by combining $U = QV/2$ with $C = Q/V$, we can express U in terms of any combination of Q, V, and C.

7. **Series capacitors:** When connected in series ("end-to-end"), the charge on any capacitor plate can only come from the adjoining plate on its neighbor, so *the charge on each capacitor in series is the same*. As a result, the voltage across each capacitor is inversely proportional to its capacitance, and their capacitances add as reciprocals:

$$\frac{1}{C_S} = \frac{1}{C_1} + \frac{1}{C_2} + \frac{1}{C_3} + \ldots$$

When using this formula, don't forget that the sum of the reciprocals on the right-hand-side of this equation gives you $1/C_S$, not C_S. If you remember that the equivalent capacitance of any series connection is always *less* than the smallest individual capacitor, you have a quick check that will catch this common pitfall.

When two capacitors are in series, the equivalent series capacitance can be written as the product over the sum:

$$C_S = \frac{C_1 C_2}{C_1 + C_2}.$$

However, this can only be done with *two* capacitors. Note that, for the equivalent series capacitance of three capacitors,

$$C_S \neq \frac{C_1 C_2 C_3}{C_1 + C_2 + C_3}.$$

(The units don't even match, for one thing.)

8. **Parallel capacitors:** When connected in parallel ("side-by-side"), each capacitor is connected to the same potential difference, so *the voltage is the same for all capacitors in parallel*. As a consequence of this, the charge on each capacitor will be proportional to its capacitance, and parallel capacitances add directly:

$$C_P = C_1 + C_2 + C_3 + \ldots$$

9. **Altered capacitors:** A favorite homework and/or exam question goes something like this: A parallel-plate capacitor is charged up by a battery. Then something about the capacitor is changed—its plates are moved closer together or farther apart, or perhaps some dielectric material is inserted into the gap. You are then asked to tell what happens to its charge, voltage, capacitance, or stored energy. The key to these

problems is to notice whether the capacitor remains connected to the battery while the modifications are made, or if it is first disconnected from the battery.

If the capacitor remains connected to the battery, then the voltage across the plates will be kept fixed (at the battery's voltage), and the charge on the plates will vary proportionately with the capacitance. However, if the capacitor is disconnected from the battery before the modifications are made, then the charge is fixed. (It's trapped on the plates and can't go anywhere.) Now, as the capacitance is changed, the potential difference across the plates will be inversely proportional to the capacitance: If the capacitance increases, the voltage goes down.

 Connections to *ActivPhysics*

The first three sections of Chapter 23 approach the subject of electrical energy from a theoretical point of view. Activity 11.13 *Electrical Potential Energy and Potential* considers the same subject from a practical point of view, by considering the motion of a charged particle in the electric field of two oppositely charged parallel plates (Figure 26-4). An advantage of the *ActivPhysics* approach is that the uniform electric field between the parallel plates is similar to the uniform gravitational field that results in projectile motion. Therefore, concepts of potential energy and the conversion of potential to kinetic energy through work can be applied by analogy to the electric field.

The second half of the chapter introduces the subject of capacitors. The parallel plate system encountered in the previous activity is one type of capacitor. *ActivPhysics* has two activities that explore the behavior of capacitors, 12.6 *Capacitance* and 12.7 *Series and Parallel Capacitors*. Unit 12 of *ActivPhysics* covers the topic of DC circuits, which isn't encountered until Chapter 28. The simulations for these two activities employ the conventional symbols of circuit diagrams (like those shown in Figure 26-29); however, a knowledge of circuit diagrams or the *ActivPhysics* method for constructing your own working circuit simulations isn't necessary to successfully complete the activities. Once the DC circuit is connected, the instantaneous current flowing through the circuit is displayed as well as the voltage across each capacitor in the circuit. Activity 12.7 in particular contains an excellent set of simulations that visualize the fundamental behavior of capacitors connected in series and in parallel in a DC circuit, as discussed on pages 672–674 of the text.

CHAPTER 27 ELECTRIC CURRENT

In this chapter, we begin our study of electric charges in motion—electric currents. After defining current, we look at the factors that affect the rate of charge motion and develop the ideas of conductivity and resistance. Finally, we consider energy transformations and compute the power losses in a current-carrying conductor.

DEFINITIONS

You should know the definition of each of these terms. (The number in parentheses is the text chapter and section in which the term is introduced.)

(27-1) Electric charge in motion comprises an *electric current*, and the current (*I*) is defined as *dq/dt*, the time rate of charge transfer.

(27-1) The *drift speed* is defined as the time-average speed (v_d) of the charge carriers that comprise an electric current. (This can vary from values near the speed of light in cathode-ray tubes to fractions of a millimeter per second in metallic conductors.)

(27-1) The *current density* (*J*) is defined as the ratio of current to cross-section area: $J \equiv I/A$.

(27-2) The *conductivity* of any material is defined as the ratio of the current density to the applied electric field: $\sigma \equiv J/E$.

(27-2) Many materials share the property that the conductivity is not affected by the strength of the applied electric field. Materials for which σ is constant are known as *ohmic materials*, since they follow Ohm's law.

(27-2) The *resistivity* (ρ) of a material is the reciprocal of its conductivity: $\rho \equiv 1/\sigma$. Thus, resistivity is the ratio of electric field to current density: $\rho = E/J$.

(27-2) In a *metallic conductor*, the atoms are held in a rigid crystalline lattice arrangement, and one or more electrons from each atom drifts freely through the lattice of metal ions. The electric current (produced by an externally applied electric field) consists of these free electrons moving in the direction opposite the applied electric field.

(27-2) *Ionic solutions*: Many compounds, when dissolved in water, dissociate into positive and negative ions. When an external electric field is applied, the positive and negative ions drift in opposite directions, and the resulting current is due to the motion of these migrating ions.

(27-2) A *plasma* consists of a gas at such a high temperature that many of the molecules are ionized. Then the resulting plasma of positive ions and free electrons can conduct an electric current if an external electric field is applied.

(27-2) A *semiconductor* is a material whose conductivity lies somewhere between that of a conductor and an insulator. However, if a small percentage of the normal Group IV semiconductor atoms (usually silicon or germanium) are replaced by Group V atoms (arsenic, for example), there is an extra electron at each lattice site that is not used for bonding, and this fifth electron is easily moved through the semiconductor by an external electric field. Since the electric current is due to the motion of negative objects, these semiconductors are known as *N-type semiconductors*.

(27-2) Recall that an N-type semiconductor is formed by doping silicon with a Group V impurity atom, which has five valence atoms available for bonding. If, instead, silicon is doped with a Group III impurity atom with only three valence electrons available, the "missing" electron (called a "hole") at each impurity atom acts like a positive charge. As electrons jump from hole to hole in response to an externally applied electric field, the location of the hole itself moves steadily in the direction of the field. Thus, an electric current appears in response to an electric field. Since the current is due to the motion of a positive object ("the hole"), we call these *P-type semiconductors*.

(27-2) Some materials have the remarkable property that, at low enough temperatures, their resistivity totally disappears. In other words, their conductivity becomes infinite, so they are called *superconductors* when in this state.

(27-3) The *resistance* (*R*) of a particular object is defined as the ratio of the potential difference to the current passing through that object: $R \equiv V/I$.

(27-3) *Ohm's law* states that the conductivity ($\sigma = J/E$) of many materials is independent of the applied electric field. This law is often written in terms of the resistance, current, and potential difference. In these terms, Ohm's law states that the resistance ($R = V/I$) of many materials is independent of the voltage or current.

(27-4) *Electrical power*: Power, whether mechanical, electrical, or any other type, is defined as the time rate of energy transfer: $P = W/t$. In electrical circuits, this is conveniently expressed as the product of current (charge per unit time) and potential difference (energy per unit charge): $P = VI$.

(27-4) The *kilowatt-hour* is a unit of energy, defined as the total energy transferred at the rate of 1 kW for a period of 1 hour.

SUMMARY OF EQUATIONS

1. Definition of steady electrical current:

$$I \equiv \frac{\Delta q}{\Delta t} \qquad \text{(Text Eq. 27-1a)}$$

In this definition, Δq represents the amount of charge passing through any area in a time Δt. Note that 1 coulomb/second = 1 ampere (1 C/s = 1 A).

If the current changes with time, we use the *instantaneous current*:

$$I \equiv \frac{dq}{dt} \qquad \text{(Text Eq. 27-1b)}$$

2. Relationship between current and drift speed:

$$I = n A q v_d \qquad \text{(Text Eq. 27-2)}$$

In this equation,
n = number of free charge carriers per unit volume: $[n] = \text{m}^{-3}$
A = cross-section area through which the current is present: $[A] = \text{m}^2$
q = (net) charge on each free charge carrier: $[q] = \text{C}$
v_d = mean drift velocity of the free charge carriers: $[v_d] = \text{m/s}$

3. Definition of current density:

$$J \equiv \frac{I}{A} \qquad \text{(Text Eq. 27-3a)}$$

We can use Eq. 27-2 to express current density in terms of drift velocity, obtaining $J = nqv_d$. If the direction of the current density is significant in a problem, we can write current density as a vector pointing in the direction of the product $q\mathbf{v}_d$: $\mathbf{J} = n q \mathbf{v}_d$.

4. Microscopic Ohm's law: Definition of conductivity:

$$\mathbf{J} = \sigma \mathbf{E} \qquad \text{(Text Eq. 27-4a)}$$

This equation is a statement that, in ohmic materials, the current density is directly proportional to the applied electric field. While not true for all materials, it does rather accurately describe the behavior of most materials that are called on to carry an electric current. Keep in mind that the conductivity (σ) is temperature dependent, and increased currents often lead to heating effects in the conductor. (Note: *Resistivity* (ρ) is defined as the reciprocal of the conductivity: $\rho = 1/\sigma$.)

5. Macroscopic Ohm's law: Definition of resistance:

$$V = I R \qquad \text{(Text Eq. 27-6)}$$

This equation defines the resistance (R) of any object in terms of the potential difference (V) between the ends of the conductor and the current (I) carried by the conductor. Technically, $R \equiv V/I$ is the definition of electrical resistance. Ohm's law is the statement that this ratio is independent of V or I for many materials. The SI unit of resistance is the ohm: $1\ \Omega = 1$ V/A.

6. Resistance of a conductor with uniform cross section:

$$R = \frac{\rho \ell}{A} \qquad \text{(Text Eq. 27-7)}$$

The electrical resistance (R) of a particular sample of a uniform conductor is directly proportional to the material's resistivity (ρ), directly proportional to the sample's length (ℓ), and inversely proportional to the sample's cross-sectional area (A). With $[R]$ = V/A, $[\ell]$ = m , and $[A]$ = m^2, the units of resistivity become $[\rho] = \Omega \cdot \text{m}$.

7. Power carried by a current:

$$P = VI \qquad \text{(Text Eq. 27-8)}$$

When the charges comprising a current move through a (positive) potential difference V, energy is given to the charges at the rate $P = VI$. Note that the product of energy gain per unit charge (V) and charge transfer per unit time (I) gives energy transfer per unit time (P).

This equation can be combined with Ohm's law to produce three equivalent expressions for power: $P = VI = I^2 R = V^2/R$.

AVOIDING PITFALLS

1. **Conventional current:** When the direction of a current is indicated in a circuit, by convention this is the direction that *positive* charges would move. If the current is actually carried by positive charge carriers, this is what you would expect. However, currents in metallic conductors are normally carried by (negative) electrons, and their actual motion is *opposite* the direction of conventional current! Thus, for example, a (conventional) current pointing north could consist of positive charges drifting northward, or of negative charges drifting southward, or a combination of the two.

2. **Thermal vs. drift speed:** The free electrons moving around inside the lattice structure of a metallic conductor undergo two distinct types of motion. First, at room temperature the electrons have a very high-speed random thermal motion with speeds around 100,000 m/s. Since these high-speed motions are, however, in random directions, there is no net displacement. But when an electric field is applied to the wire, then a very small drift velocity is superimposed on the high speed thermal motions. It is this gradual,

overall, drift of the electrons in the direction opposite the electric field that constitutes the current, and these drift speeds are very small—on the order of fractions of a millimeter per second. Keep in mind that the random thermal motion has a very high speed (which is determined by the temperature), but zero average *velocity*, and so contributes nothing to the current. The drift velocity is very small and is determined by the applied electric fields (or, equivalently, by the potential difference). But since there are so many free electrons per cubic meter in metallic conductors, this small drift speed of each conduction electron gives rise to an appreciable electrical current.

3. **Ohm's law:** The familiar equation $V = IR$ is not, technically speaking, Ohm's law. The resistance of *any* object is defined as V/I. Ohm's law states that, for certain materials, this ratio (called the resistance) is independent of current and voltage.

4. **Current and drift speed:** The current through a conductor is given in terms of microscopic parameters by $I = nAqv_d$. In this equation, n represents the *density* of charge carriers, not the total number of charge carriers in the sample. As such, n has units of m^{-3}. Also, this is the density of *free* charge carriers, so it is not the total number of electrons per unit volume, but the number of *free* electrons per unit volume. In metals, there are usually one or two free electrons per atom, but in semiconductors, the density of free charge carriers can be varied over a very wide range by temperature changes or by adding impurities to the basic semiconductor material.

5. **Resistivity and resistance:** The resistivity ρ (units $= \Omega \cdot m$) of a material is a measure of the difficulty with which a current passes through a given *substance*; the resistance R (units $= \Omega$) depends on the resistivity, length, and cross-section area of a particular *piece* of the material. Thus, all copper wires have essentially the same resistivity, but a long, thin copper wire has a higher resistance than a short, thick copper wire.

    Also note that the units of resistivity are $\Omega \cdot m$, not Ω/m.

6. **Units of current and power:** Remember that both current and power are expressed in units of a quantity per *second*. ($1 A = 1 C/s$, $1 W = 1 J/s$). Be careful in problems dealing with total charge or energy transfers when the time is expressed in minutes or hours.

7. **Kilowatt-hour:** Remember that 1 kW·hr is a unit of energy, not of power. It is, in fact, the total energy transferred in one hour when energy is transferred at a rate of 1 kilowatt. (The kilowatt is, however, a power unit: a time *rate* of energy usage, equal to 1000 joules of energy per second.)

 Connections to *ActivPhysics*

There are no *ActivPhysics* activities that examine the behavior of free charges in conducting materials, which are discussed in this chapter.

In this chapter, we apply the concepts of electric current, potential difference, and resistance to the study of direct-current electric circuits. We introduce Kirchhoff's laws, an important problem-solving technique for analyzing complex circuits, and we learn how electric meters are used. Finally, we look at the effect of a capacitor in an electric circuit, encountering time-varying currents and voltages.

DEFINITIONS

You should know the definition of each of these terms. (The number in parentheses is the text chapter and section in which the term is introduced.)

(28-2) In an electrical circuit, any device that increases the electrical potential energy of the moving charges by some fixed amount is known as a source of *emf* (electromotive force). The emf itself, as used in calculations, is actually the increase in electric potential (measured in volts) due to the action of the source of emf.

(28-4) Essentially a statement of conservation of energy as applied to electric circuits, *Kirchhoff's loop law* (or "voltage law") states that the sum of all the changes in electric potential around any closed loop is zero: $\sum V = 0$.

(28-4) As used in electric circuits, a *node* is any point where currents can split or join together. Nodes are also called "branch points" or "junctions" in many texts.

(28-4) Essentially a statement that charge doesn't pile up at the nodes in a circuit, *Kirchhoff's node law* (or "current law") says that the sum of all the currents entering any node equals the sum of all the currents leaving that node. Or, as we have been using it, if we define entering currents as being positive and leaving currents as being negative, we can then say that the algebraic sum of all the currents at any node is zero: $\sum I = 0$.

(28-5) A *voltmeter* is a device that measures the potential difference between the two points its leads are touching. In practice, it is usually a very sensitive current-measuring device in series with a very high resistance resistor.

(28-5) An *ammeter* is a device that measures the current passing through the meter. To measure the current in a circuit, the circuit must be broken and the ammeter connected in series with the branch whose current you want to measure. In practice, it is usually a very sensitive current-measuring device with a very low-resistance shunt.

(28-5) An *ohmmeter* is a device that measures the resistance of a circuit component by connecting a

known emf across the component and then measuring the resulting current.

(28-5) A device that combines the functions of voltmeter, ammeter, and ohmmeter in one instrument is known as a *multimeter*.

(28-6) The *time constant* is a characteristic period of time that measures how slowly the charge on a capacitor is changing. Specifically, it is the time needed for the charge on a capacitor to decrease by a factor of *e*. This turns out to be equal to the product RC.

SUMMARY OF EQUATIONS

1. Equivalent resistance of *series* resistors:

$$R_{series} = R_1 + R_2 + R_3 + \ldots \qquad \text{(Text Eq. 28-1)}$$

The equivalent resistance of any number of resistors connected in series is found by adding their individual resistances. Note that this implies that each additional resistor added in series *increases* the total resistance.

2. Equivalent resistance of *parallel* resistors:

$$\frac{1}{R_{parallel}} = \frac{1}{R_1} + \frac{1}{R_2} + \frac{1}{R_3} + \ldots \qquad \text{(Text Eq. 28-3b)}$$

The (reciprocal of the) equivalent resistance of any number of resistors connected in parallel is found by adding the reciprocals of their individual resistances. Note that each additional resistor added in parallel increases the value of $1/R_{parallel}$, which *decreases* the equivalent resistance.

When you have two resistors in parallel, Eq. 28-3b may be solved for $R_{parallel}$, obtaining

$$R_{parallel} = \frac{R_1 R_2}{R_1 + R_2} \qquad \text{(Text Eq. 28-3c)}$$

the product over the sum. Note that this expression is valid only for *two* resistors.

3. Current and capacitor voltage while charging a capacitor:

$$I = \frac{\mathscr{E}}{R} e^{-t/RC} \qquad \text{(Text Eq. 28-5)}$$

$$V_C = \mathscr{E}\left(1 - e^{-t/RC}\right) \qquad \text{(Text Eq. 28-6)}$$

When a capacitor C is connected in series with a battery of emf $\mathscr{E}$ *and a resistor* R, the current exponentially decreases with time from an initial value of $I_0 = \mathscr{E}/R$ (when the capacitor is empty) toward zero. The voltage across the capacitor increases with time, asymptotically approaching the battery voltage $\mathscr{E}$ as a limit.

The product RC, which occurs in the denominator of the exponent, is a quantity that has the dimensions of time, and is known as the "time constant" of the circuit. (With $[R]$ = ohms, and $[C]$ = farads, then $[t]$ = seconds.)

4. Current and capacitor voltage while discharging a capacitor:

$$I = \frac{V_0}{R} e^{-t/RC} \qquad \text{(Text Eq. 28-7)}$$

$$V_C = V_0 e^{-t/RC} \qquad \text{(Text Eq. 28-6)}$$

A capacitor C is first charged to a potential difference V_0. It is then connected to a resistor R, allowing the charge to flow through the resistor from one plate to the other. The current and the charge remaining on the capacitor both decrease exponentially with time toward zero.

AVOIDING PITFALLS

1. **Parallel resistors:** Remember that the formula for the parallel resistors $(1/R_{\text{parallel}} = 1/R_1 + 1/R_2 + 1/R_3 + \ldots)$ gives the *reciprocal* of the parallel resistance, not the resistance itself.

    If you use the "product over sum" rule for parallel resistors,

$$R_P = \frac{R_1 R_2}{R_1 + R_2}$$

don't forget that this only works for *two* resistors at a time. That is,

$$R_P \neq \frac{R_1 R_2 R_3}{R_1 + R_2 + R_3}$$

2. **Parallel currents:** When a current I_{tot} reaches a node where it can divide among two or more branches, the current will split, with each branch current inversely proportional to the resistance of the branch. For example, if one branch has a resistance of 10 Ω and the other has a resistance of 20 Ω, the current will split with $(20/30)\,I_{\text{tot}}$ going through the $10-\Omega$ branch, and $(10/30)\,I_{\text{tot}}$ going through the $20-\Omega$ branch.

3. **Kirchhoff's laws:**

    a. Remember that each loop equation must come from a different loop. (Summing the potential changes around a previously used loop, but in a different direction, doesn't give any new information.)

    b. The + and − signs drawn on the ends of each resistance are determined by the (assumed) direction of the current, *not* by whether a

resistor is connected to the positive or negative terminal of the nearest battery.

    c. If after solving for an unknown current, you find a negative value, be sure to use that negative value in all other equations as well.

4. **Resistors vs. capacitors:** Don't get confused between the similar formulas for resistors and capacitors when in series and parallel:

	RESISTORS	CAPACITORS
PARALLEL	$\frac{1}{R_P} = \frac{1}{R_1} + \frac{1}{R_2} + \frac{1}{R_3}$	$C_P = C_1 + C_2 + C_3$
SERIES	$R_S = R_1 + R_2 + R_3$	$\frac{1}{C_S} = \frac{1}{C_1} + \frac{1}{C_2} + \frac{1}{C_3}$

(I keep these straight by remembering that adding resistors in parallel makes it easier for current to flow, thereby *reducing* the parallel *resistance*. However, adding capacitors in parallel just increases the plate area, thereby *increasing* the parallel *capacitance*.)

5. **Meters:** Since an ammeter must be placed in series with the circuit through which the current is needed, its resistance should be as small as possible to avoid disturbing the circuit. A voltmeter, on the other hand, is placed in parallel with the two points whose potential difference is to be measured, so its resistance should be as high as possible. In fact, an ideal ammeter has *zero* resistance, and an ideal voltmeter has *infinite* resistance.

 Connections to *ActivPhysics*

Figure 28-1 shows some of the common symbols used to represent elements in circuits. All of the activities of Unit 12 on DC Circuits employ simulations of circuit diagrams like those shown in the figures throughout the chapter. The symbols for a capacitor, emf source, switch, ground, ammeter, and voltmeter shown in Figure 28-1 are the same symbols employed in the Unit 12 activities. However, a resistor is shown as a rectangle labeled with the value of the resistance instead of as a sawtoothed line, and *ActivPhysics* also includes circles that can change their yellow shading to represent lightbulbs.

I recommend starting with Activity 12.1 *DC Series Circuits: Qualitative* in order to see how to construct your own circuits. Then I recommend completing the short Activity 12.4 *Using Ammeters and Voltmeters* to see how to correctly place these symbols in a circuit to get accurate readings of current and voltage. The rest of the activities on resistor combinations in circuits, Kirchhoff's laws, and capacitance can be viewed when each icon is encountered in the chapter.

Whenever an emf source is added to a circuit, the simulation allows you to choose a value for the voltage ranging from −10 V to +10 V. In the same way, whenever a resistor is added to a circuit, its value may be set to any number between 1 and 10 ohms. In this way, many of the circuit diagrams found in the chapter figures and word problems may be re-created by *ActivPhysics*. This should be very helpful when you are checking the results of a calculation, even if voltages and currents can't be reproduced exactly.

One final comment concerning Unit 12 of *ActivPhysics*: Many of the DC circuit simulations employ lightbulbs instead of resistors when first discussing many of these topics. Many of the ques-tions ask whether a lightbulb will light when the circuit loop is closed, or how their brightness will compare, or if its brightness will change when the configuration of a circuit changes. These types of questions reflect the basic philosophy of *ActivPhysics*, that understanding physics is more than just being able to calculate numerical answers from equations for word problems. This point of view is one that is shared by the vast majority of college physics teachers. Our assumption is that if students understand the basic concepts of physics, then the numerical problem solving will be easier for them and they will also remember physics principles for a longer period of time after the course is over.

CHAPTER 29 THE MAGNETIC FIELD

In this chapter, we define the magnetic field and study how a given magnetic field will affect magnets, electric charges, and currents. We conclude by examining the torque exerted on a current loop in a magnetic field.

DEFINITIONS

You should know the definition of each of these terms. (The number in parentheses is the text chapter and section in which the term is introduced.)

(29-2) We associate a *magnetic field* with every point in the space surrounding a magnet. This can be operationally defined in either of two equivalent ways: (1) in terms of the magnetic force experienced by a tiny N pole at any given point or (2) in terms of the magnetic force acting on an electric charge moving through that point.

The direction of the magnetic field is chosen as the direction of the force acting on a N pole located at that point, which turns out to be the same as the direction of a moving charge that experiences *no* magnetic force.

(29-2) The magnitude of the magnetic field, however, is defined (in SI units) as the ratio of the magnetic force to the product of charge and velocity, *when the charge is moving at right angles to the field:* $B = F_B/qv$. Thus, 1 tesla = 1 T = 1 N/C · m/s = 1 N/A · m. (Note: An older name for the tesla is the weber/meter² [Wb/m²].)

(29-2) A commonly used (though non-SI) unit of magnetic field strength is the *gauss* (G), defined by 1 G = 10^{-4} T.

(29-3) When a charged particle moves freely in a uniform magnetic field, it follow a circular or helical path. The number of revolutions completed per second is known as the *cyclotron frequency*.

(29-5) A *magnetic dipole* contains two equal magnetic poles of opposite polarity. Most permanent magnets are dipoles, with equally strong N and S poles, and most subatomic particles (neutrons, electrons, etc.) are also magnetic dipoles.

(29-5) Many expressions involving current loops and magnetic fields are conveniently expressed in terms of the *magnetic dipole moment*, defined (for a plane loop) as the product of the current and the vector representing the area of the loop: $\boldsymbol{\mu} = I\,\mathbf{A}$.

SUMMARY OF EQUATIONS

1. Magnetic force on a moving charge:

$$\mathbf{F} = q\mathbf{v} \times \mathbf{B} \qquad \text{(Text Eq. 29-1a)}$$

This can be considered the modern definition of magnetic field, and it defines the units in which **B** is to be measured: In the SI system of units, [F] = newtons, [q] = coulombs, [v] = meters/second, and [B] = tesla (T). Thus, a 1 coulomb charge, moving with a 1 m/s velocity at right angles to a magnetic field of 1 tesla, will experience a force of 1 newton. Note that the cross-product implies that the magnetic force is *always* perpendicular to the direction of **B** and **v**.

The magnitude of this force is given by

$$F = qvB \sin\theta, \qquad \text{(Text Eq. 29-1b)}$$

where θ is the angle between **v** and **B**.

2. Electromagnetic force on a charge:

$$\mathbf{F} = q\mathbf{E} + q\mathbf{v} \times \mathbf{B} \qquad \text{(Text Eq. 29-2)}$$

When an electric charge is in a region where both electric and magnetic fields are present, the net electromagnetic force is the sum of the electric and magnetic forces. (This is sometimes called the *Lorentz force*.)

3. Circular trajectory of a charged particle in a magnetic field:

$$\text{radius: } r = \frac{mv}{qB} \qquad \text{(Text Eq. 29-3)}$$

$$\text{frequency: } f = \frac{qB}{2\pi m} \qquad \text{(Text Eq. 29-5)}$$

When a particle (charge = q, mass = m) moves freely through a uniform magnetic field **B**, it describes a circular (if $\mathbf{v} \perp \mathbf{B}$) or helical path. The radius of this path equals the particle's momentum divided by the product qB. The number of revolutions completed per second is known as the cyclotron frequency, and is given by Text Eq. 29-5.

4. Magnetic force on a short segment of current:

$$d\mathbf{F} = I\,d\boldsymbol{\ell} \times \mathbf{B} \qquad \text{(Text Sect. 29-4)}$$

If the current follows a straight-line path of length ℓ through a uniform magnetic field, then the total force is simply

$$\mathbf{F} = I\boldsymbol{\ell} \times \mathbf{B}. \qquad \text{(Text Eq. 29-6)}$$

If not, then one can integrate to find the total force:

$$\mathbf{F} = \int I\,d\boldsymbol{\ell} \times \mathbf{B}. \qquad \text{(Text Eq. 29-8)}$$

5. Magnetic torque on a current-carrying loop:

$$\boldsymbol{\tau} = I\,\mathbf{A} \times \mathbf{B} \qquad \text{(Text Eq. 29-9)}$$

A is a vector whose magnitude equals the area of the (plane) loop, and that lies normal to the plane of the loop. The direction of **A** is given by a right-hand rule: Curl the fingers of your right hand in the direction of the current around the loop, and your right thumb points in the direction of **A**.

6. Magnetic moment of a current-carrying loop:

$$\boldsymbol{\mu} \equiv I\,\mathbf{A}$$

We define the product of current and area *vector* (remember, **A** is normal to the plane of the loop) to be the "magnetic dipole moment" of the loop. If there are N identical turns of wire forming a coil, the net dipole moment of the N-turn coil is

$$\boldsymbol{\mu} = NI\,\mathbf{A}. \qquad \text{(Text Eq. 29-9)}$$

Then the net torque on the coil is given by

$$\boldsymbol{\tau} = \boldsymbol{\mu} \times \mathbf{B}. \qquad \text{(Text Eq. 29-11)}$$

7. Potential energy of a magnetic dipole in a magnetic field:

$$U_B = -\,\boldsymbol{\mu} \cdot \mathbf{B} \qquad \text{(Text Eq. 29-12)}$$

This equation (similar to the potential energy of an electric dipole in an electric field, $U_E = -\mathbf{p} \cdot \mathbf{E}$) is also based on the choice of $U_B = 0$ when the dipole moment is perpendicular to the field. Parallel orientations are lower in energy, and antiparallel orientations are higher in energy.

AVOIDING PITFALLS

1. **Magnetic field units:** There are two different units for magnetic field intensity in common use: the tesla (T) and the gauss (G). However, all the equations we have derived involving magnetic fields require the SI unit of magnetic fields, the tesla (T). Thus the first step in any of these problems is to convert gauss to teslas, using the conversion $1\,\text{T} = 10^4\,\text{G}$.

2. **Direction of magnetic forces:**

   a. Historically, magnetic fields were first investigated using permanent magnets, and the direction of the magnetic field at any point in space was (and is) defined as the direction of the magnetic force acting on a tiny *north* pole located at that point. Then a south pole at that same location would experience a force in the *opposite* direction. (In this *sense*, N poles correspond to + charges, and S poles correspond to − charges.)

   b. When we look at the magnetic force on a moving charge (or current), the situation becomes more complicated, and we have to use the right-hand rule to figure out the direction of the force.

   c. One basic fact is that the magnetic force on a moving charge is *always* perpendicular to both the magnetic field and to the charge's velocity. Because the magnetic force is always perpendicular to a particle's velocity, a magnetic field *cannot* change the kinetic energy (or speed) of a charged particle. (Magnetic fields are very useful for changing the *direction* of a moving charge, however.)

   d. Remember, the magnetic force on any charge is zero if the charge is moving parallel (or antiparallel) to the magnetic field.

3. **Electric vs. magnetic forces:** Both the electric force and the magnetic force experienced by a charge are proportional to the charge q. However, the electric force is independent of the charge's velocity, while the magnetic force is a velocity- (and direction-) dependent force.

4. **Magnetic dipole moment:** In the two equations describing the interaction between a magnetic dipole moment and a magnetic field ($\boldsymbol{\tau} = \boldsymbol{\mu} \times \mathbf{B}$ and $U = -\boldsymbol{\mu} \cdot \mathbf{B}$), the angle θ that appears in the dot or cross product is the angle between $\boldsymbol{\mu}$, which is *perpendicular* to the plane of the loop, and the magnetic field. (θ is *not* the angle between **B** and the *plane* of the loop!)

5. **Speed and accelerating potential:** In many practical applications, electric charges are accelerated by a known electrostatic potential (V). To find the magnetic deflection, however, we need the speed of the particle. This can be easily found by setting the kinetic energy change of the particle equal to its potential energy loss ($\frac{1}{2}mv^2 = qV$) and solving for the speed v.

 Connections to *ActivPhysics*

The ten activities of *ActivPhysics* Unit 13 on Magnetism have applications in all three chapters of the text dealing with magnetism and magnetic effects: Chapter 29, The Magnetic Field, Chapter 30, Sources of the Magnetic Field, and Chapter 31, Electromagnetic Induction. However, the authors of the text and the authors of *ActivPhysics* have very different perspectives on how to organize and present the material to students. The text begins by examining some important applications of the magnetic field, such as the mass spectrometer or the velocity selector in Chapter 29, and then considers the more abstract construction of magnetic field lines in Chapter 30 before presenting the links between electricity and magnetism in Chapter 31. Unit 13 of *ActivPhysics*, on the other hand, begins by visualizing magnetic fields for three simple objects in the first three activities, then explores the forces and torques caused by magnetic fields in different contexts in the next three activities, and concludes with the mass spectrometer and velocity selector applications and two activities on electromagnetic induction.

If you have found the *ActivPhysics* simulations to be helpful in previous chapters, then my advice is to follow its format. I recommend exploring the first three activities first, showing the magnetic fields of a straight wire, a loop, and a solenoid. I suggest concentrating on a basic conceptual understanding of magnetic fields and noting the similarities and differences between electric and magnetic fields, but I don't recommend completing all the questions of the text bar at this time; that can be done for Chapter 30.

The next three activities, 13.4 *Magnetic Force on a Particle*, 13.5 *Magnetic Force on a Wire*, and 13.6 *Magnetic Torque on a Loop,* have a direct application to the discussion of this chapter. Activity 13.4 allows you to re-create the spiral shown in Figure 29-16. Activity 13.5 parallels the discussion found on page 754, and Activity 13.5 animates Figures 29-32 and 29-34. Once the basic relationship between magnetic field and magnetic force is understood, then it is possible to understand the theory and operation of the mass spectrometer (Activity 13.7) and velocity selector (Activity 13.8), which are discussed in the first three sections of the chapter.

CHAPTER 30 SOURCES OF THE MAGNETIC FIELD

In Chapter 29, we studied the forces exerted by a known magnetic field on moving charges, currents, and current loops. Now we learn how to predict the characteristics of the magnetic field produced by a given current distribution. Reminiscent of our development of electric fields, we develop two distinct approaches to the problem of computing the magnetic field strength at a given point. The Biot-Savart law will always allow us to compute the magnetic field from an arbitrary current distribution, but for those situations where there is a high degree of symmetry, we have an easier, more elegant method—Ampère's law. Finally, we discuss qualitatively the three types of magnetic materials: ferromagnetic, paramagnetic, and diamagnetic.

DEFINITIONS

You should know the definition of each of these terms. (The number in parentheses is the text chapter and section in which the term is introduced.)

(30-1) The *Biot-Savart law* states that the magnetic field produced by a tiny segment $d\ell$ carrying a steady current I is given by

$$d\mathbf{B} = \frac{\mu_0}{4\pi} \frac{I \, d\ell \times \hat{\mathbf{r}}}{r^2}$$

(30-2) The *ampere* is the SI unit of electric current, and is defined as "the unvarying current which, if present in two conductors of infinite length, one meter apart in empty space, will produce a magnetic force of precisely 2×10^{-7} newton per meter of length."

(30-3) *Ampère's law* states that the line integral of the magnetic field around any closed path is proportional to the net current encircled by that path:

$$\oint \mathbf{B} \cdot d\ell = \mu_0 I_{\text{encircled}} \, .$$

(30-6) In *ferromagnetic* materials, a very strong cooperation among neighboring atoms causes nearly perfect alignment of their magnetic moments. This alignment causes a dramatic increase in the net magnetic field within the sample.

(30-6) In ferromagnetic materials, all the atoms in a microscopic region known as a *ferromagnetic domain* will have their magnetic moments aligned in the same direction. In an unmagnetized sample, the various domains are oriented randomly, so the net magnetization is zero. When the sample is placed in an external field, however, the domains that are parallel to the applied field grow at the expense of those in other orientations, and the entire sample becomes magnetized.

(30-6) The cooperation between neighboring atoms in ferromagnetic materials will disappear if the sample is heated above a characteristic temperature, known as the *Curie temperature*.

(30-6) If a *paramagnetic* substance, whose atoms each have a net magnetic moment, is placed within a magnetic field, the resulting partial alignment of the atoms will produce a *slight increase* in the net magnetic field within the sample.

(30-6) *Diamagnetism* is a separate and very weak phenomenon, present in all atoms. An external magnetic field will induce a small magnetic moment that opposes the applied magnetic field, resulting in a *slight decrease* in the net magnetic field.

(30-6) Consider a region of space in which a magnetic field B_{applied} exists. When a sample of some material is placed within this field, the net magnetic field inside the sample changes to a value B_{net}. The *relative permeability* (κ_M) is defined as the ratio of these two field intensities:

$$\kappa_M \equiv \frac{B_{\text{net}}}{B_{\text{applied}}} \, .$$

(30-6) Since, for all but ferromagnetic materials, the relative permeability is a number very close to 1, it is often more convenient to use the *magnetic susceptibility* (χ_M), defined as the difference between a material's relative permeability and the number one:

$$\chi_M \equiv \kappa_M - 1 \, .$$

(30-7) A *magnetic monopole* contains a single magnetic pole, either N or S. While their existence has been predicted by several theories and they have been actively sought for several decades, none has been definitively observed to date.

(30-7) *Gauss's law for magnetism* states that the magnetic flux through any closed surface is equal to the net magnetic "charge" encircled by the surface. Since we have never observed isolated magnetic monopoles, the net magnetic charge is always zero, so Gauss's law for magnetism becomes

$$\oint \mathbf{B} \cdot d\mathbf{A} = 0 \, .$$

SUMMARY OF EQUATIONS

1. The Biot-Savart law:

$$d\mathbf{B} = \frac{\mu_0}{4\pi} \frac{I d\boldsymbol{\ell} \times \hat{\mathbf{r}}}{r^2} \quad \text{(Text Eq. 30-1)}$$

This expression gives the magnitude and direction of the magnetic field produced by a short segment $d\boldsymbol{\ell}$ carrying a steady current I. In this equation, $\hat{\mathbf{r}}$ is a unit vector pointing from $d\boldsymbol{\ell}$ to the location of the point at which the field is needed, a distance r away ($\mu_0 = 4\pi \times 10^{-7}\,\text{T} \cdot \text{m/A}$).

For any finite-length current, the net magnetic field is found by integrating the contributions from the infinitesimal lengths that make up the current:

$$\mathbf{B} = \int d\mathbf{B} = \int \frac{\mu_0}{4\pi} \frac{I d\boldsymbol{\ell} \times \hat{\mathbf{r}}}{r^2} \quad \text{(Text Eq. 30-2)}$$

2. Ampère's law:

$$\oint \mathbf{B} \cdot d\boldsymbol{\ell} = \mu_0 I_{\text{encircled}} \quad \text{(Text Eq. 30-7)}$$

While Gauss's law relates the surface integral of the field to the net charge enclosed by the surface, Ampère's law relates the *line* integral of the magnetic field to the net *current* encircled by the path of integration. The magnetic field $\mathbf{B}$ appearing in the integrand is the *net* magnetic field from all sources, whether encircled by the path of integration or not. The right-hand side, however, includes only the current that passes through the area bounded by the path of integration.

3. Magnetic fields of wires, loops, and solenoids:

The equations listed below are not fundamental, as are the above three, but are the result of applying Ampère's law or the law of Biot and Savart to specific cases. However, these particular arrangements are so often encountered, it is useful to become familiar with the expressions for their magnetic field.

- Magnetic field at a distance r from an infinitely long straight wire:

$$B = \frac{\mu_0 I}{2\pi r} \quad \text{(Text Eq. 30-8)}$$

This follows immediately from Ampère's law, using a circular path of integration. Note the $1/r$ dependence, shared with the electric field of an infinitely long line of charge.

- Magnetic field at the center of a current loop of radius R:

$$B_0 = \frac{\mu_0 I}{2R}.$$

A special case of Equation 30-3, this turns out to be very similar to the field of the long straight wire, except for the missing factor of π.

- Magnetic field of a long solenoid with n ($= N/L$) turns per unit length:

$$B_{\text{in}} = \mu_0 n I \quad \text{(Text Eq. 30-11)}$$

$$B_{\text{out}} \approx 0$$

Note that this uniform field does not depend on the radius or total length of the solenoid, but only on n, the number of turns *per unit length*.

- Magnetic field of a toroidal solenoid with N total turns:

$$B_{\text{in}} = \frac{\mu_0 N I}{2\pi r} \quad \text{(Text Eq. 30-12)}$$

$$B_{\text{out}} \approx 0$$

In Eq. 30-12, r represents the distance from the center of the solenoid to the field point.

4. Definition of relative permeability and susceptibility:

$$(\text{permeability}) \quad \kappa_M \equiv \frac{B_{\text{int}}}{B_{\text{applied}}} \quad \text{(Text Eq. 30-13)}$$

$$(\text{susceptibility}) \quad \chi_M \equiv \kappa_M - 1$$

In these equations, B_{int} is the net magnetic field within a substance when it is immersed in an applied magnetic field B_{applied}. Paramagnetic substances slightly increase the net field ($\kappa_M > 1$), diamagnetic substances slightly reduce the net field ($\kappa_M < 1$), and ferromagnetic materials greatly increase the net field ($\kappa_M \gg 1$).

5. Gauss's law for magnetism:

$$\oint_{\text{surface}} \mathbf{B} \cdot d\mathbf{A} = 0 \quad \text{(Text Eq. 30-14)}$$

In essence, this says exactly what Gauss's law for electric fields says: The total flux through any closed surface ($\int \mathbf{E} \cdot d\mathbf{A}$ for electric fields; $\int \mathbf{B} \cdot d\mathbf{A}$ for magnetic fields) is proportional to the net charge enclosed by the surface. In the case of electric fields, the net charge is the algebraic sum of all the electric charge within the surface. For magnetic fields, the net "charge" is proportional to the net number of magnetic poles enclosed by the surface. Since we have never definitively observed an isolated magnetic monopole, every closed surface will enclose a precisely equal number of N poles and S poles, so the net "magnetic charge" within any closed surface is always zero.

AVOIDING PITFALLS

1. **Direction of magnetic fields:** Unlike electric fields, which point radially away from (or toward) a charge, magnetic fields are more complex. Magnetic lines of force are endless loops that generally curl around the currents that produce them in a direction given by the right-hand rule: thumb = current, fingers = lines of force.

2. **Magnetic field in line with a straight current segment:** Occasionally you will encounter the magnetic field produced by a straight segment of wire of finite length. One fact that could save you some work is that the magnetic field is zero at all points along the *extended axis* of the wire.

3. **The Biot-Savart law:** The magnetic field involves a cross-product between $d\ell$ (a vector that points in the direction of the current) and $\hat{r}$ (a unit vector pointing toward the field point.) The magnetic field is, therefore, perpendicular to *both* of these vectors.

4. **Ampère's law:** Ampère's law is useful only in those few situations where the source of the field is symmetric enough that you can invent a path of integration which allows you to pull **B** out of the integral. That is, you must know that **B** will be constant in magnitude and maintain a constant direction relative to the path (constant θ). Alternatively, if **B** is perpendicular to the path, then $\mathbf{B} \cdot d\ell = 0$ along that path.

5. **Encircled currents:** Remember to include the proper sign when computing $I_{encircled}$. For *uniform* current densities, you can find the encircled current by multiplying the total current by the ratio of the encircled area to the total current-carrying area:

$$I_{encircled} = \frac{A_{encircled}}{A_{total}} I_{total}$$

 Connections to *ActivPhysics*

The Connections to *ActivPhysics* for the previous chapter recommended briefly exploring the first three activities of Unit 13 on Magnetism in order to understand the basic character and properties of magnetic fields. Now is the time to complete all of the questions in these activities. Activity 13.1 *Magnetic Field of a Wire* includes two applications of the Biot-Savart law, which is explained in Section 30-1, and reproduces Figures 30-10 and 30-32 with a variable current flow. In the same way, Activity 13.5 *Magnetic Force on a Wire* reproduces Figure 13-13 and explores the effects of different current magnitudes traveling in the same and opposite directions. Activity 13.2 *Magnetic Field of a Loop* corresponds to Figure 30-40, while Activity 13.3 *Magnetic Field of a Solenoid* corresponds to Figure 30-30. All four of these activities should make the nature of the magnetic field for different current configurations much more understandable.

CHAPTER 31 ELECTROMAGNETIC INDUCTION

The magnetic phenomena studied thus far have all depended on the *strength* of the magnetic field. In this chapter, we encounter several new phenomena (induced emfs, electric fields, and currents) that depend not on the strength of the magnetic field, but on its *time rate of change*. The fundamental law describing the relationship between a changing magnetic field and the resulting emf is known as Faraday's law of induction. A qualitative, but very useful corollary to Faraday's law is known as Lenz's law, and we will use this law whenever we need the direction of an induced emf or current.

DEFINITIONS

You should know the definition of each of these terms. (The number in parentheses is the text chapter and section in which the term is introduced.)

(31-1) *Electromagnetic induction* is the phenomenon in which a changing magnetic field gives rise to an induced electric field.

(31-2) The work per unit charge done by an induced electric field as a charge is moved along some specified path is known as the *induced emf*: $\mathscr{E} = W/q = \int \mathbf{E} \cdot d\boldsymbol{\ell}$.

(31-2) The *magnetic flux* through a given surface is defined as the surface integral of the magnetic field, integrated over that surface area: $\phi = \int \mathbf{B} \cdot d\mathbf{A}$. (Note: The surface need not be closed.)

(31-2) *Faraday's law of induction* states that the emf around any closed path is the negative time rate of change of magnetic flux through any surface bounded by that closed path:

$$\mathscr{E} = -\frac{d\phi_B}{dt}$$

Note: The emf can itself be expressed as the line integral of the induced electric field around the path, and the magnetic flux is the surface integral of the magnetic field over any surface bounded by that path, so Faraday's law can be stated more explicitly as

$$\oint \mathbf{E} \cdot d\boldsymbol{\ell} = -\frac{d}{dt} \int \mathbf{B} \cdot d\mathbf{A} \,.$$

(31-3) *Lenz's law* is a handy rule for determining the direction of induced emfs and currents, and it can be stated in several versions, all equivalent to "The direction of the induced current is such as to oppose the change giving rise to it."

(31-3) *Eddy currents* are currents that flow in the interior of a conducting solid in response to the induced emf produced by a changing magnetic flux.

(31-5) *Diamagnetism* is a small effect, present in all atoms, in which a changing magnetic field has the effect of changing the orbital magnetic moments of the electrons. The result is to slightly decrease the moment of electrons whose orbital moments point in the direction of the change in the applied field, and to increase the moment of those electrons that point opposite the change in the applied field. The macroscopic effect is to reduce the net magnetic field within the sample, resulting in a small net force that pulls the sample toward regions of stronger magnetic field.

SUMMARY OF EQUATIONS

1. Definition of magnetic flux:

$$\phi_B \equiv \int \mathbf{B} \cdot d\mathbf{A} \qquad \text{(Text Eq. 31-1)}$$

We first encountered magnetic flux in Chapter 30, when discussing Gauss's law for magnetism. In Gauss's law, we were considering the flux through a *closed* surface, and we found the total magnetic flux to be zero in all cases. Here, however, the surface need not be closed, and we will frequently find the flux to be nonzero.

2. Faraday's law of induced emfs:

$$\mathscr{E} = -\frac{d\phi_B}{dt} \qquad \text{(Text Eq. 31-2)}$$

This fundamentally important law states that an emf ($\mathscr{E}$) is created around any closed path whenever the magnetic flux (through the surface bounded by that path) changes with time, and that the emf is directly proportional to the time rate of change of flux.

3. Faraday's law of electromagnetic induction:

$$\oint \mathbf{E} \cdot d\boldsymbol{\ell} = -\frac{d}{dt} \int \mathbf{B} \cdot d\mathbf{A} \quad \text{(Text Eq. 31-3)}$$

This is identical to Eq. 31-2, except that we have explicitly written out the definitions of emf and magnetic flux: The emf along any path is defined to be the work per unit charge done by the electric field. Expressing work as a line integral of force, the emf along any path becomes the line integral of the electric field along that path: $\mathscr{E} = \int \mathbf{E} \cdot d\boldsymbol{\ell}$. In Ampère's law, the path is a closed path, and the surface through which the magnetic flux is to be calculated may be *any* surface bounded by that path.

AVOIDING PITFALLS

1. **Magnetic flux:** The magnetic flux of a uniform field through a plane surface of area A has a magnitude given by $\phi = \mathbf{B} \cdot \mathbf{A} = B\,A\,\cos\theta$. Remember that the angle θ is the angle between the magnetic field $\mathbf{B}$ and the *vector* $\mathbf{A}$, which is perpendicular to the surface itself. $\mathbf{A}$ is defined to point outward for a closed surface, but open surfaces do not allow this definition. Thus, we make an arbitrary choice of a direction in which to follow around the perimeter of the surface. Once this is done, the right-hand rule gives the direction of $\mathbf{A}$.

2. **Changing magnetic fields:** Remember that when a field is increasing, $\Delta\mathbf{B}$ is parallel to $\mathbf{B}$. But when a field is decreasing, $\Delta\mathbf{B}$ is *opposite* $\mathbf{B}$. Further, Faraday's law tells us that the emf is determined by the time *rate* of change of flux—that is, the *faster* the flux is changing, the greater the emf. (This does not necessarily require strong magnetic fields, just rapidly changing ones.)

3. **Lenz's law:** It may be easier for you to remember Lenz's law in this form: If the applied magnetic field is increasing, the induced magnetic field will try to cancel the increase by pointing in the opposite direction; if the applied magnetic field is decreasing, the induced magnetic field will try to cancel the decrease by *replacing* the disappearing field (*i.e.*, by pointing in the same direction.) Lenz's law most directly gives you the direction of the induced magnetic field. From this, you can deduce the direction of the induced current that would produce the induced field. Finally, the direction of positive emf is the direction of the induced current.

4. **Induced emfs, currents, and fields:** Keep in mind that *whenever a magnetic field changes*, an induced electric field will be created. This induced electric field will give rise to an emf along any path you choose. *If there is a conductor present*, then induced currents will result, along with their own magnetic fields. (The induced *electric* fields always exist, even in empty space.)

5. **emfs:** The emfs in this chapter can be confusing if you think of them as the potential difference between two points. While this was a perfectly good interpretation of the emf caused by a conservative (electrostatic) field, with the nonconservative (induced) electric fields in this chapter, you should always think of emf as the work done per unit charge *along a specific path*.

6. **Rotating loops:** A plane loop rotating within a uniform magnetic field will produce a sinusoidally varying emf. An increase in angular velocity of the loop will, of course, increase the frequency of the induced emf, but it will also increase the *magnitude* of the emf. Finally, remember that angular velocity (ω) must be in *radians* per second. (And don't forget to switch your calculator to the radians mode.)

 Connections to *ActivPhysics*

Electromagnetic induction links the electric and the magnetic field. The first step in understanding the connection is through the definition of magnetic flux, which is the subject of Activity 13.9 *Electromagnetic Induction*. The activity shows the effect of changing flux through an animation of a rotating loop in a constant magnetic field (Figures 31-15 and 31-16). The simulation allows you to plot both the flux and also the induced electromotive force (emf). Activity 13.10 *Motional EMF* reproduces Figure 31-8 and Example 31-4, demonstrating that there is more than one way to vary the area that the B field is passing through and, therefore, the flux.

CHAPTER 32 INDUCTANCE AND MAGNETIC ENERGY

This chapter builds on the concept of electromagnetic induction and examines the induced emfs created by changing currents in a circuit. Mutual and self-inductance are defined, and from these we can compute the energy stored in a magnetic field.

DEFINITIONS

You should know the definition of each of these terms. (The number in parentheses is the text chapter and section in which the term is introduced.)

(32-1) If a current through one coil produces a magnetic flux through another coil, their *mutual inductance (M)* is defined as the ratio of the flux through one to the current through the other:

$$M = \frac{\phi_1}{I_2}.$$

The units of M are $T \cdot m^2 / A$, or henrys (H).

(32-2) The *self-inductance (L)* of a conductor is defined as the ratio of the magnetic flux through the conductor to the current through that conductor:

$$L = \frac{\phi}{I}.$$

The units of self-inductance are the same as for mutual inductance, the henry (H).

(32-2) When the current in an inductive circuit changes, an *induced emf* (known as a "back emf") appears, and its polarity is such as to oppose the change that is occurring.

(32-3) The *inductive time constant* (τ) is the ratio of inductance to resistance in an inductive circuit:

$$\tau = \frac{L}{R}.$$

This ratio has the dimensions of time (with $[L] = $ henrys, $[R] = $ ohms, then $[\tau] = $ seconds), and is a measure of how slowly the current in an inductive circuit will change. Specifically, when a constant emf $\mathscr{E}_0$ is suddenly applied to an inductor and resistor in series, the current will gradually increase toward a final value of $\mathscr{E}_0 / R$ according to the equation $I(t) = (E_0/R)(1 - e^{-t/\tau})$. The time constant τ, then, represents the elapsed time until the current reaches $(1 - 1/e)$ of its final value.

(32-4) Just as it takes energy to create an electric field, energy is also required to create a magnetic field. The energy per unit volume (*magnetic energy density*) stored in a magnetic field is given by

$$u_B = \frac{B^2}{2\mu_0}.$$

(With $[B] = $ teslas, then $[u_B] = $ joules/meter^3.)

SUMMARY OF EQUATIONS

1. Definition of mutual inductance:

$$M \equiv \frac{\phi_2}{I_1} \qquad \text{(Text Eq. 32-1)}$$

The mutual inductance (M) between two circuits (usually involving some arrangements of coils) is defined as the proportionality constant between the *flux* through one circuit and the *current* through the other. I_1 represents the current flowing through one of the circuits, and ϕ_2 represents the total magnetic flux through the *other* circuit caused by the magnetic field of I_1. From this definition, we can see that the units of inductance are $[M] = T \cdot m^2/A = $ henry (H). Remarkably, the mutual inductance between any two circuits is the same no matter which of the two acts as the current-carrying source.

2. Emf caused by a mutual inductance:

$$\mathscr{E}_2 = -M\frac{dI_1}{dt} \qquad \text{(Text Eq. 32-2)}$$

This follows immediately from Eq. 32-1 by taking the time derivative and identifying the induced emf ($\mathscr{E}$) with the negative time rate of change of magnetic flux ($-d\phi/dt$). In this form, we see that an alternative definition of the unit of inductance is 1 henry = 1 volt $\cdot$ second/amp.

3. Definition of self inductance:

$$L \equiv \frac{\phi}{I} \qquad \text{(Text Eq. 32-3)}$$

The self-inductance of any circuit (L) is defined as the ratio of the total magnetic flux through the circuit to the current through the *same* circuit. (Note that the units are the same as for mutual inductance: 1 H = 1 T $\cdot$ m^2/A = 1 V $\cdot$ s/A.)

4. Emf caused by self-inductance:

$$\mathscr{E} = -L\frac{dI}{dt} \qquad \text{(Text Eq. 32-5)}$$

When the current through a circuit element with self-inductance changes, an emf is produced, and the emf is proportional to the time rate of change of current.

5. Current and voltage in an L-R circuit:

a. *Closing the switch: rising current:*

$$\mathscr{E}_L = -\mathscr{E}_0 e^{-Rt/L} \qquad \text{(Text Eq. 32-7)}$$

$$I = \frac{\mathscr{E}_0}{R}(1 - e^{-Rt/L}) \qquad \text{(Text Eq. 32-8)}$$

For a series circuit containing a switch, a total circuit resistance R, an inductance L, and a battery of emf $\mathscr{E}_0$, the emf in the inductor (measured in the direction of current flow) is given by Eq. 32-7, and the current in the circuit is described by Eq. 32-8. We assume that the switch, initially open, is closed at $t = 0$.

b. *Opening the switch: decaying current:*

$$I = I_0 e^{-Rt/L} \qquad \text{(Text Eq. 32-9)}$$

For the same circuit, we now assume that a current I_0 is flowing at time $t = 0$, at which time the battery is shorted out of the circuit.

6. Inductive time constant:

$$\tau = \frac{L}{R}$$

This ratio is known as the "inductive time constant." The greater this ratio, the longer it will take the current to reach any fraction, say 90%, of its final value, and the smaller this ratio, the more quickly will the current approach the final value.

When a switch in an inductive circuit is closed, τ gives the time for the current to reach $(1 - 1/e)$ = 63% of its *final* value. When the switch in an inductive circuit is opened, τ gives the time for the current to drop to $(1/e)$ = 37% of its *initial* value.

7. Total energy in the magnetic field of an inductor:

$$U = \tfrac{1}{2}LI^2 \qquad \text{(Text Eq. 32-10)}$$

By considering the power (VI) delivered to an inductor, we find that there is energy stored in the magnetic field of an inductor, and the total energy is proportional to the square of the current.

8. Energy density of any magnetic field:

$$u_B = \frac{B^2}{2\mu_0} \qquad \text{(Text Eq. 32-11)}$$

By considering the total energy stored in the magnetic field of a solenoid, we find that the magnetic field energy per unit volume (u, in J/m^3) is proportional to the square of the magnetic field amplitude. More advanced calculations show that this is a general result, valid for *any* magnetic field. (Compare this to the very similar expression for the energy density in an electric field: $u_E = \dfrac{\varepsilon_0 \mathscr{E}^2}{2}$.)

AVOIDING PITFALLS

1. **Mutual inductance:** The mutual inductance M between two coils is the same regardless of which coil carries the current and which coil experiences the flux. Thus, if you have to compute the mutual inductance, put the current through the one that produces the simpler magnetic field.

2. **Induced emfs:** Once again, remember that induced emfs (like $\mathscr{E}_L$) appear only when the current is *changing*; so a large, steady current won't produce any induction effects.

3. **"Current inertia":** The *current* through an inductor cannot change instantaneously. Thus, if you know the current in an inductor at any given instant, you know that the current will be nearly the same a short time later. It's almost as if the presence of an inductance in a circuit gives the current a sluggishness or "inertia." (However, knowing the emf in an inductor at one instant doesn't tell you anything about the emf at the next instant, since it can change discontinuously.)

4. **Polarity of emf's in inductive circuits:** There are three different elements in the inductive circuits we encounter in this chapter: batteries, resistors, and inductors. The voltage change each produces follows its own set of rules:

   a. *Batteries:* In moving from the $-$ to the $+$ terminal of a battery, the change in voltage is positive: $\Delta V_B = \mathscr{E}_B$.

   b. *Resistors:* In moving through a resistor in the direction of the current, the change in voltage is negative: $\Delta V_R = -IR$.

   c. *Inductors:* In moving through an inductor in the direction of the current, the change in voltage is given by $\Delta V_L = \mathscr{E}_L = -L\,dI/dt$. (Thus, ΔV_L is positive when the current is decreasing, negative when the current is increasing, and zero when the current is steady.)

5. **Solenoid turns:** When using the solenoid equations, be sure to distinguish between N (the *total* number of turns) and n (the number of turns *per unit length*).

 Connections to *ActivPhysics*

An inductor is an electronic device that exploits Faraday's law of induction to alter the current and voltage of a circuit. Sections 32-1 and 32-2 develop the concept of an inductor and describe its characteristics, while Section 32-3 shows a simple application of an inductor placed in series with a resistor. The RL circuit of Figures 32-8 through 32-12 is animated in Activity 14.1 *The RL Circuit*. Combining this simulation with Section 32-3 may help you understand both the activity and the text discussion more, and will definitely assist you if Problems 24, 25, 27, 28, 30, or 31 have been assigned. For many of these problems, the values suggested in the word problem can be set as the initial values, so the correct answer can be obtained directly by running the simulation. The more complicated circuit problems in the rest of the word problems will be easier to solve if you have a clear understanding of the time constant and its relationship to the measured resistance and inductance in an RL circuit.

CHAPTER 33 ALTERNATING-CURRENT CIRCUITS

In this chapter, we study circuits containing resistance, capacitance, and inductance. We first look at these elements separately and then combine two or three of them in a single circuit. By defining the reactance and impedance of these circuits, we can more easily determine the amplitude of these time-varying voltages and currents. When both capacitance and inductance are present in a circuit, oscillations can be set up. Finally, when a sinusoidal voltage is applied to a series *RLC* circuit, resonance occurs if the driving frequency matches the natural frequency of oscillation of the circuit.

DEFINITIONS

You should know the definition of each of these terms. (The number in parentheses is the text chapter and section in which the term is introduced.)

(33-1) The *root-mean-square* value of a periodic function is defined as the square root of the mean of the square of the function. If *T* is the period of a function *f(t)*, then

$$f_{\mathrm{rms}} = \left[\frac{1}{T} \int_0^T f^2\,(t)\,dt \right]^{\frac{1}{2}}$$

(33-2) The *reactance (X)* is defined as the ratio of voltage amplitude to current amplitude:

$$X \equiv \frac{V}{I}$$

For a capacitor, the capacitive reactance is $X_C = 1/\omega C$, and for an inductor, the inductive reactance is $X_L = \omega L$.

(33-2) The relationship between voltage amplitudes is most easily visualized by the use of *phasors*, vectorlike quantities representing AC voltages. The vertical component of each phasor gives the instantaneous voltage. (This assumes that the sine function is used: if the cosine is used, one would use the horizontal components.)

(33-3) When a charged capacitor is discharged through a resistor and an inductor, the amplitude of the oscillations decreases exponentially because of the energy loss in the resistor. If *R*, *L*, and *C* happen to be related by $R = 2\sqrt{L/C}$, then the circuit is *critically damped*: no oscillations occur, and the charge (and current) decrease monotonically toward zero most rapidly.

(33-3) If the resistance exceeds critical damping ($R > 2\sqrt{L/C}$), then the circuit is *overdamped*: charge and current again decay monotonically toward zero, but more slowly than with critical damping.

(33-3) If the resistance is less than critical damping ($R < 2\sqrt{L/C}$), then the circuit is *underdamped*: the charge and current will oscillate with an exponentially decreasing amplitude.

(33-4) When an oscillatory system is driven at its natural frequency by a driving force, the amplitude of the oscillations is at a maximum and the system is said to be in *resonance*. For series *RLC* circuits, resonance occurs when $X_C = X_L$, which occurs at $\omega_0 = 1/\sqrt{LC}$.

(33-4) Defined as the ratio of applied voltage amplitude to current amplitude in an AC circuit ($Z \equiv V_{\mathrm{app}}/I$), the *impedance* of a series *RLC* circuit turns out to be

$$Z = \sqrt{R^2 + (X_L - X_C)^2}$$

(33-4) The *phase constant* (ϕ) is defined as the angle by which the current leads the applied voltage in an AC circuit. (If the current trails the applied voltage, then ϕ has a negative value.)

(33-5) The *power factor* is defined as the ratio of average power $\langle P \rangle$ to the product of rms current and voltage ($I_{\mathrm{rms}} V_{\mathrm{rms}}$):

$$power\ factor \equiv \frac{\langle P \rangle}{I_{\mathrm{rms}} V_{\mathrm{rms}}}$$

This turns out simply to be the cosine of the phase constant:

$$power\ factor = \cos \phi.$$

(33-6) A *transformer* is a device that is designed to produce an AC voltage output that is proportional to an input AC voltage. This is accomplished by magnetically linking the secondary windings to the alternating flux of the current in the primary windings. (If the output voltage is greater than the input voltage, it is called a "step-up" transformer; if the output voltage is less than the input voltage, it is known as a "step-down" transformer.)

(33-6) The *"ripple factor,"* or "per cent ripple" in a filtered, rectified signal is defined as the ratio of the peak-to-peak fluctuations to the mean DC voltage.

SUMMARY OF EQUATIONS

1. Mathematical description of a sinusoidal voltage:

$$V(t) = V_0 \sin(\omega t + \phi_V) \quad \text{(Text Eq. 33-3)}$$

This expression describes any sinusoidal voltage with a peak voltage (or amplitude) V_0 and angular frequency ω. If the voltage happens to be zero and increasing at $t = 0$, then the voltage is following the sine function, so $\phi_V = 0$. If any other initial condition is present, then the phase angle ϕ_V will have some nonzero value. A similar equation describes a sinusoidal current:

$$I(t) = I_0 \sin(\omega t + \phi_I).$$

2. Relationship between peak and rms values for sinusoidal signals:

$$V_{\text{rms}} = \frac{V_p}{\sqrt{2}} \; ; \; I_{\text{rms}} = \frac{I_p}{\sqrt{2}} \quad \text{(Text Eq. 33-1)}$$

For a *sinusoidal* voltage or current, the root-mean-square (rms) value is just the peak value divided by $\sqrt{2}$. (Note that $1/\sqrt{2} = 0.707$.)

3. Instantaneous current and voltage for a resistor:
   If a sinusoidal voltage $V(t) = V_R \sin(\omega t)$ is applied to a resistor, the current through the resistor is given by

$$I_R(t) = (V_R / R) \sin(\omega t).$$

This shows that the current and voltage applied to a resistor are exactly in phase with each other, and that their amplitudes are related by $I_R = V_R/R$. (Unlike capacitors and inductors, this also holds for the *instantaneous* values in a resistor, since $I_R(t) = V(t)/R$.)

4. Instantaneous current and voltage for a capacitor:

$$I_C(t) = \omega C V_C \sin(\omega t + \pi/2) = \omega C V_C \cos(\omega t)$$
$$\text{(Text Eq. 33-4)}$$

These *equivalent expressions* give the instantaneous value of the current through a circuit containing a capacitor when the voltage applied to the capacitor follows $V(t) = V_C \sin(\omega t)$. Both expressions show that the current reaches its peak one-fourth cycle ($\pi/2$ radians or 90°) *before* the voltage applied to a capacitor.

5. Definition of capacitive reactance:
   The *amplitudes* of the current and voltage applied to a capacitor are related by $I_C = \omega C V_C = V_C/(1/\omega C)$. Since we are used to writing Ohm's law as $V = IR$, we define the capacitive reactance

$$X_c \equiv \frac{1}{\text{w} C}$$

so we can write $V_C = I_C X_C$. (Keep in mind that this only relates the *amplitudes* of these quantities, not the instantaneous values of current and voltage.)

6. Instantaneous current and voltage for an inductance:

$$I_L(t) = \frac{V_L}{\text{w} L} \sin(\text{w} t - \pi/2) = -\frac{V_L}{\text{w} L} \cos \text{w} t$$

$$\text{(Text Eq. 33-6)}$$

These *equivalent expressions* give the instantaneous value of the current through an induc-

tance, given that the voltage applied to the inductor is described by $V(t) = V_L \sin(\omega t)$. Both expressions show that the current reaches its peak one-fourth cycle ($\pi/2$ radians) *later* than the voltage applied to an inductor.

7. Definition of inductive reactance:
   As we did for capacitors, we note that the amplitudes of the current and voltage for an inductor are related by $I_L = V_L/\omega L$. Again, using Ohm's law as a model, defining the inductive reactance as

$$X_L \equiv \omega L$$

allows us to write, for the current and voltage *amplitudes* in an inductor,

$$V_L = I_L X_L.$$

8. Natural frequency of oscillation in a series *RLC* circuit:

$$\text{w} = \frac{1}{\sqrt{LC}} \quad \text{(Text. Eq. 33-11)}$$

When an inductor and capacitor are both present in a circuit, there is the possibility of electromagnetic oscillations. This expression gives the angular frequency (in radians per second) of these oscillations in a series circuit containing a capacitor and an inductor.
   (This is also the frequency that produces the greatest current amplitude in a driven *RLC* circuit.)

9. Definition of impedance:

$$Z \equiv \frac{V_p}{I_p}$$

We define the impedance of a circuit as the ratio of applied voltage amplitude to current amplitude.

10. Phasor diagrams:
    Analyzing a series *RLC* circuit is much easier if you use the phasor model. We consider a circuit like that shown in Figure 33.1, in which a sinusoidal voltage is applied to a resistor, an inductor, and a capacitor.

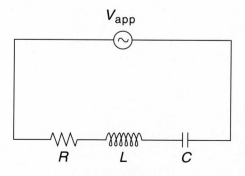

Figure 33.1
A series *RLC* circuit

If we are primarily interested in the amplitudes (rather than the instantaneous values) of the voltages or currents in the circuit, the phasor diagrams are easier to construct and interpret if we let the x-axis be the "current axis." Any voltage that is in phase with the current (e.g., the voltage across a resistor) is drawn as a horizontal arrow, any voltage that reaches its peak one-fourth cycle (90°) *ahead* of the current (e.g., the voltage across an inductor) is drawn as an upward-pointing arrow, and any voltage that reaches its peak one-fourth cycle *after* the current (e.g., the voltage across a capacitor) is drawn as a downward-pointing arrow. Finally, in this model, we set

$$\mathbf{V}_{app} = \mathbf{V}_R + \mathbf{V}_L + \mathbf{V}_C.$$

See Figure 33.2.

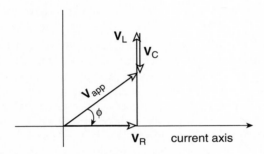

Figure 33.2
Phasor diagram for voltage amplitudes in a series *RLC* circuit. Note that the phase constant ϕ is measured from V_{app} toward the current axis.

Since $V_p = I_p Z$, $V_R = I_p R$, $V_L = I_p X_L$, and $V_C = I_p X_C$, we can also construct a phasor diagram in terms of the reactances and impedance, as shown in Figure 33.3.

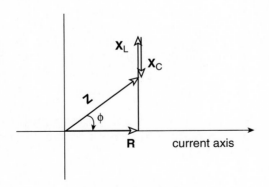

Figure 33.3
Impedence diagram for a series *RLC* circuit.

11. Impedance of series *RLC* circuit:

$$Z = \sqrt{R^2 + (X_C - X_L)^2} = \sqrt{R^2 + \left(\frac{1}{wC} - wL\right)^2}$$

(Text Eq. 33-15)

The impedance, defined as the ratio of applied voltage amplitude to current amplitude, behaves like the "total AC resistance" of the circuit, in that small impedances allow large currents for a given applied voltage, and large impedances produce small currents.

12. Phase constant in an *RLC* circuit:

$$\tan \phi = \frac{X_C - X_L}{R} = \frac{1/wC - wL}{R} \qquad \text{(Text Eq. 33-16)}$$

The "phase constant" ϕ is defined as the angle by which the current *leads* the applied voltage in an *RLC* circuit. (If the current lags behind the applied voltage, then ϕ will have a negative value, as shown in Figures 33.2 and 33.3.) Note: If each term in the right-hand side of this equation is multiplied by the current, we can write

$$\tan \phi = (V_C - V_L)/V_R.$$

13. Average power used by an *RLC* circuit:

$$\langle P \rangle = \tfrac{1}{2} I_P V_P \cos \phi$$

$$\langle P \rangle = I_{rms} V_{rms} \cos \phi \quad \text{(Text Eq. 33-17)}$$

For an *RLC* circuit that is powered by a sinusoidal voltage, the average power drawn from the power supply is proportional to the product of the peak (or rms) voltage and current. The proportionality constant ($\cos \phi$) depends on the phase angle between the applied voltage and current.

14. Power factor:

$$\cos \phi = \frac{R}{Z} \qquad \text{(Text Eq. 33-17)}$$

The "power factor," which turns out to be R/Z (see Figure 33.3), is defined as the ratio of the average power to the product of V_{rms} and I_{rms}:

$$\text{"power factor"} \equiv \frac{\langle P \rangle}{I_{rms} V_{rms}}$$

15. Transformer voltages:

$$\frac{V_1}{V_2} = \frac{N_1}{N_2} \qquad \text{(Text Eq. 33-19)}$$

The voltage ratio in an ideal transformer is the same as the ratio of the number of turns in the windings.

AVOIDING PITFALLS

1. **Linear vs. angular frequency:** Be certain to notice whether you need (or are given) the *linear* frequency f, measured in hertz (Hz or s^{-1}), or the *angular* frequency ω, measured in radians per second (also written as s^{-1}). Also, when working these problems, be sure you set your calculator to the proper (degree or radian) mode!

2. **Phase difference in sinusoidal graphs:** When you see a graph of two sinusoidal voltages like Figure 33.4, if you (incorrectly) think of this as a snapshot of two waves having a race, you will pick the one in front (A) as the leading signal.

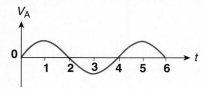

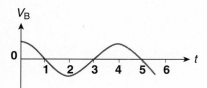

Figure 33.4
Wave A (upper picture) reaches its peak *later* than Wave B (lower picture).

In fact, this is *not* a snapshot of a race but a plot of two functions' time dependence. The proper way to see which of the two leads the other is to ask the question "When does each signal reach its maximum?" Then you will see that V_A reached its peaks at $t = 1$ s and 5 s, whereas V_B reached its peaks one second earlier, at $t = 0$ s and 4 s. Since V_B reached its peak *earlier* than V_A, we say that V_B leads V_A (by one-quarter of a cycle).

3. **Phase angles:** There are at least three different phase angles used in this chapter. In the description of a sinusoidal voltage and current,

$$V(t) = V_p \sin(\omega t + \phi_V),$$

$$I(t) = I_p \sin(\omega t + \phi_I)$$

each expression contains a phase angle (ϕ_V and ϕ_I, respectively) that describes the initial ($t = 0$) appearance of the function.

The more important phase angle (written with no subscript)

$$\phi = \tan^{-1}\left(\frac{X_C - X_L}{R}\right).$$

describes the phase between the voltage applied to a circuit and the current flowing in the circuit. It is ϕ that determines the "power factor" for average power.

4. **Reactance:** The reactance of a capacitor or inductor is like a resistance to an AC current, in that it is defined to be the ratio of voltage to current: $X = V/I$, similar to the definition of resistance ($R = V/I$). The reactance even has the same units as resistance (ohms), but there are several important differences:

a. $X = V/I$ is true for voltage and current amplitudes or for rms values but *not* for the instantaneous values $V(t)$ and $I(t)$:

$$X \neq V(t)/I(t).$$

Ohm's law, however, is true for instantaneous values as well as for average values of I and V:

$$R = \frac{V_R}{I} = \frac{V_r(t)}{I(t)}$$

b. While the resistance of an element is independent of frequency, the reactances both depend on frequency: $X_C = 1/\omega C$, and $X_L = \omega L$.

c. The resistance determines the rate of conversion of electrical energy into heat (a power loss to the circuit) by $P = I^2 R$. For capacitance and inductance, there are *no* power losses—only transfers of electrical energy from electric fields to magnetic fields.

5. **"ELI the ICE man":** This little phrase is a useful mnemonic for remembering whether the voltage or current is leading in a capacitor or inductor. While you can always reason an answer out from fundamental principles, it's nice to have a quick way to check your results. The interpretation of this phrase is as follows: Across a capacitor (C), the current (I) leads the voltage (E): hence, we see I before E in ICE. Across an inductor (L), the voltage (E) leads the current (I): hence, we see E before I in ELI. Remember "ELI the ICE man."

6. **Kirchhoff's loop rule for instantaneous voltages:** If we have a series RLC circuit with an applied voltage V_{app}, at any point in time the instantaneous values of the voltages add algebraically:

$$V_{app}(t) = V_R(t) + V_C(t) + V_L(t)$$

However, these four voltages will, in general, reach their respective maxima at different times, so we cannot simply add their amplitudes:

$$V_{app} \neq V_R + V_C + V_L$$

7. **Kirchhoff's loop rule for voltage amplitudes:** Since voltage amplitudes are easier to measure than the instantaneous values, it would be nice to have a relation similar to Kirchhoff's loop rule for voltage amplitudes. If we treat these as vectorlike phasors, with $\mathbf{V}_R$ drawn in phase with the current, $\mathbf{V}_C$ drawn 90° behind the current, and $\mathbf{V}_L$ drawn 90° ahead of the current, we can write a kind of vector equation:

$$\mathbf{V}_{app} = \mathbf{V}_R + \mathbf{V}_C + \mathbf{V}_L.$$

This is illustrated in a phasor diagram like Figure 33.2.

(Notice that we set $\mathbf{V}_{app} = \mathbf{V}_R + \mathbf{V}_C + \mathbf{V}_L$, not $\mathbf{V}_{app} + \mathbf{V}_R + \mathbf{V}_C + \mathbf{V}_L = 0$. This is a time-honored approach to these problems, similar to the "heat gain = heat loss" approach to calorimetry. In this approach, we measure $\mathbf{V}_{app}$ and $(\mathbf{V}_R + \mathbf{V}_C + \mathbf{V}_L)$ as parallel voltages and then set them equal to each other. See Figure 33.2.)

8. **Resonance:** There are several important facts about resonance you should realize. *At resonance,*

   a. $X_L = X_C$. (This condition produces the smallest impedance Z and the largest current amplitude I. It's easy to show that $X_L = X_C$ when $\omega_0 = 1/\sqrt{LC}$. Note that the resonant frequency depends only on L and C, not on R.)

   b. $Z = R$. (This follows immediately from $X_L = X_C$ but tells you that the circuit is behaving as if the inductor and capacitor were not even present—only the resistor remains. Thus, the current in the circuit at resonance is determined by R, not by L or C.)

   c. $\phi = 0$. (The current is in phase with the applied voltage. Again, this is consistent with the "vanishing" of the inductance and capacitance at resonance, because the circuit is now purely resistive.)

   d. At frequencies below ω_0, the current decreases because the capacitor is becoming "opaque" (*i.e.,* $X_C = 1/\omega C$ is growing); at frequencies above ω_0, the current decreases because the inductor is becoming "opaque" to the current (*i.e.,* $X_L = \omega L$ is growing).

9. **Power:** At any instant, the power delivered to a circuit is given by $P(t) = V_{app}(t) I(t)$. However, since the voltage and current do not generally reach their maxima at the same time, the peak power is *not* the product of the voltage amplitude and the current amplitude: $P_{max} \neq V_{max} I_{max}$; nor is the average power the product of rms voltage and rms current: $P_{av} \neq V_{rms} I_{rms}$. However, one can obtain the average power from the dot product of rms applied voltage and rms current:

   $$P_{av} = \mathbf{V}_{rms} \cdot \mathbf{I}_{rms} = (V_{rms})(I_{rms})(\cos \phi).$$

10. **Phasor diagrams:** If you need to determine instantaneous values for voltage or current, then you will have to construct a phasor diagram with the proper angular orientation, so that $V_{app}(t) = V \sin(\omega t + \phi_V)$. Usually, we will use phasor diagrams to determine voltage amplitudes or the phase angle between V_{app} and I. In this case, I find it easier to orient the phasors so that the $+x$ axis becomes the "current axis." Then $\mathbf{V}_R$ points horizontally to the right, $\mathbf{V}_L$ points vertically upward, and $\mathbf{V}_C$ points vertically downward.

Also note that we can construct a phasor diagram with reactances from $\mathbf{Z} = \mathbf{R} + \mathbf{X}_L + \mathbf{X}_C$, or we can construct a phasor diagram with voltages from $\mathbf{V}_{app} = \mathbf{V}_R + \mathbf{V}_L + \mathbf{V}_C$. The two diagrams are equivalent, since $\mathbf{V}_{app} = I\,\mathbf{Z}$, $\mathbf{V}_R = I\,\mathbf{R}$, $\mathbf{V}_L = I\,\mathbf{X}_L$, and $\mathbf{V}_C = I\,\mathbf{X}_C$.

Connections to *ActivPhysics*

Activity 13.9 *Electromagnetic Induction* is a model showing how the mechanical motion of a loop in a magnetic field can result in a sinusoidal voltage (Figure 33-1). Section 33-2 explains how the behavior of a single resistor, capacitor, or inductor in a circuit powered by an alternating sinusoidal voltage results in an alternating sinusoidal current or AC circuit. As mentioned on page 864 of the text, the LC circuit examined in Section 33-3 can be reproduced and animated by Activity 14.2 *The RLC Oscillator* by setting the value of the resistance in the simulation to zero, and the relationships between inductance, capacitance, energy and frequency summarized in Table 33-1 can be verified by running the simulation. Furthermore, the damping effects shown in Figure 33-14 can be reproduced and the correct time constant verified for the RLC circuit of the latter part of Section 33-3 by choosing a nonzero resistance for the circuit.

The driven RLC circuit is simulated in Activity 14.3 *The Driven Oscillator*. This activity is very helpful for understanding phasor diagrams (Figure 33-17) and exploring the effects of inductance, resistance, and capacitance on resonant frequency by varying these quantities separately in the simulation (Figure 33-18). These two activities should also be helpful when completing Problems 27–29, 31, 32, 35, 40, 41, and 42–47 for Sections 33-3 and 33-4, and also Problems 65–70, 76, and 77.

CHAPTER 34 MAXWELL'S EQUATIONS AND ELECTROMAGNETIC WAVES

This chapter culminates our study of electricity and magnetism, as we bring together the four fundamental equations of electricity and magnetism—Gauss's law for electric fields, Gauss's law for magnetic fields, Ampère's law, and Faraday's law—and then introduce Maxwell's correction to Faraday's law. As Maxwell realized, these four equations imply the existence of self-propagating electromagnetic waves. We conclude by examining various properties of these waves, including their speed of propagation, the rate at which they carry energy and momentum, and the phenomenon of polarization.

DEFINITIONS

You should know the definition of each of these terms. (The number in parentheses is the text chapter and section in which the term is introduced.)

(34-2) *Displacement current* is the name given by James Clerk Maxwell to the term in Ampère's law due to changing electric flux; specifically,

$$I_D \equiv \varepsilon_0 \frac{d\phi_E}{dt}$$

(34-3) The four fundamental equations of electrodynamics, consisting of (1) Gauss's law for electric fields, (2) Gauss's law for magnetic fields, (3) Faraday's law for magnetic induction, and (4) Ampère's law with Maxwell's "displacement current," are collectively known as *Maxwell's equations.*

(34-4) When charges are accelerated, they emit energy in the form of *electromagnetic waves*, which consist of transverse waves in the electric and magnetic fields of these charges. These electric and magnetic fields are perpendicular to each other and to the direction of propagation of the wave, which travels through empty space with a speed $c = 1/\sqrt{\varepsilon_0 \mu_0} = 3.00 \times 10^8$ m/s.

(34-8) If the electric field vectors in an electromagnetic wave all lie in a single plane, the wave is said to be *"polarized."* (Note: The magnetic field vectors will then also be polarized, lying in a plane perpendicular to the electric field plane. The orientation of the electric field plane is chosen to be the "direction of polarization.")

(34-8) Malus's law describes the intensity of a plane-polarized wave after it has passed through a polarizer. Specifically, Malus's law states that the intensity of the transmitted wave is proportional to the square of the cosine of the angle between the plane of polarization of the incident wave and the transmission axis of the polarizer: $S = S_0 \cos^2\theta$.

(34-10) The *intensity* of a wave is defined as the energy per unit time, per unit area, that crosses a small area oriented perpendicular to the wave's direction of propagation. The units of intensity are $[S] = W/m^2$.

(34-10) The *Poynting vector* is defined as $\mathbf{S} = \mathbf{E} \times \mathbf{B}/\mu_0$. The direction of $\mathbf{S}$ gives the direction of energy flux (the direction of propagation for electromagnetic waves), and its magnitude gives the intensity of the energy flow.

(34-11) The momentum carried by electromagnetic waves gives rise to a force exerted upon any surface that absorbs or reflects these waves. The force per unit area is the *radiation pressure.*

SUMMARY OF EQUATIONS

1. Maxwell's equations:

    a. Gauss's law for electric fields:

    $$\oint \mathbf{E} \cdot d\mathbf{A} = \frac{q}{\varepsilon_0} \qquad \text{(Text Eq. 34-2)}$$

    b. Gauss's law for magnetic fields:

    $$\oint \mathbf{B} \cdot d\mathbf{A} = 0 \qquad \text{(Text Eq. 34-3)}$$

    c. Faraday's law for magnetic induction:

    $$\oint \mathbf{E} \cdot d\boldsymbol{\ell} = -\frac{d\phi_B}{dt} \qquad \text{(Text Eq. 34-4)}$$

    d. Ampère's law, with Maxwell's correction:

    $$\oint \mathbf{B} \cdot d\boldsymbol{\ell} = \mu_0 \left(I + \varepsilon_0 \frac{d\phi_E}{dt} \right). \quad \text{(Text Eq. 34-5)}$$

    These four equations should be familiar to you since we have studied each of them in the preceding chapters. The one new term is Maxwell's correction ($\varepsilon_0 \, d\phi_E/dt$) to Ampère's law. If there is no change in electric flux (as with perfectly steady currents), then Maxwell's correction is zero, and we regain the familiar form of Ampère's law. Maxwell's correction predicts that magnetic fields are produced not only by a steady current but also by a changing electric flux.

2. Sinusoidal electromagnetic plane wave:

    $$\mathbf{E}(x,t) = E_p \sin(kx - \omega t)\hat{\mathbf{j}} \quad \text{(Text Eq. 34-10)}$$

    $$\mathbf{B}(x, t) = B_p \sin(kx - wt)\hat{\mathbf{k}} \quad \text{(Text Eq. 34-11)}$$

These equations describe a particular type of electromagnetic wave—a plane wave, traveling in the +x-direction. The electric field points in the y-direction, and the magnetic field points in the z-direction. The wavelength is related to the wave number k by $\lambda = 2\pi/k$, and the period is related to the angular frequency by $\omega = 2\pi/T$.

3. Speed of electromagnetic waves:

$$c = \frac{w}{k} = \frac{1}{\sqrt{\varepsilon_0 \mu_0}} \quad \text{(Text Eq. 34-16)}$$

The speed of any wave is given by $v = \lambda/T$. Expressed in terms of angular frequency $\omega = 2\pi/T$ and wave number $k = 2\pi/\lambda$, $v = \omega/k$. Maxwell's equations predict that all electromagnetic waves travel with the speed given by Eq. 34-16.

4. Electric and magnetic field magnitudes in EM waves:

$$E(x,t) = c\, B(x,t) \quad \text{(Text Eq. 34-18)}$$

At any point in an electromagnetic wave, the electric and magnetic fields have instantaneous magnitudes that are simply related by a factor of c, the speed of light in vacuum. (Note: Eq. 34-18 could also be expressed in terms of the field *amplitudes*: $E_p = cB_p$.)

5. Malus's law for polarized waves:

$$S = S_0 \cos^2\theta \quad \text{(Text Eq. 34-19)}$$

If a plane-polarized electromagnetic wave (of average intensity S_0) is incident upon an ideal polarizer, the resulting average intensity is reduced to $S = S_0 \cos^2\theta$. In this expression, θ represents the angle between the incident electric-field vector and the transmission axis of the polarizer.

6. Poynting vector for arbitrary electric and magnetic fields:

$$\mathbf{S} = \frac{\mathbf{E} \times \mathbf{B}}{\mu_0} \quad \text{(Text Eq. 34-20b)}$$

When electric and magnetic fields are both present in a region, there is a flow of energy in the direction of the vector $\mathbf{S}$. The magnitude of this vector gives the energy per unit area passing through an area normal to $\mathbf{S}$, per unit time.

7. Average intensity of sinusoidal electromagnetic waves:

$$\bar{S} = \frac{E_p B_p}{2\mu_0} \quad \text{(Text Eq. 34-21a)}$$

In electromagnetic waves, $\mathbf{E}$ and $\mathbf{B}$ are perpendicular, so at any instant, $S(t) = E(t)\,B(t)/\mu_0$. This quantity then gives the instantaneous value of the intensity (*i.e.*, power per unit area) of the

radiation. The time average of this expression is found from $\bar{S} = E_{rms} B_{rms}/\mu_0$. If the electric and magnetic fields are sinusoidal, then each rms value is $(1/\sqrt{2})$ times the peak value, and we obtain Eq. 34-21a.

Further, in electromagnetic waves, the electric and magnetic fields at any point are directly proportional ($E = cB$), so we also can write

$$\bar{S} = \frac{E_p^2}{2\mu_0 c} = \frac{cB_p^2}{2\mu_0} \quad \text{(Text Eqs. 34-21b, c)}$$

8. Intensity of a point source of radiation:

$$S = \frac{P}{4\pi r^2} \quad \text{(Text Eq. 34-22)}$$

The intensity of radiation at a distance r from a point (or spherically symmetric) source of radiation of total power P decreases as the square of the distance.

9. Momentum of electromagnetic waves:

$$p = \frac{U}{c} \quad \text{(Text Eq. 34-23)}$$

If the electromagnetic waves in a region of space contain a total electromagnetic energy U, then they also carry a total linear momentum $\mathbf{p}$, where the direction of $\mathbf{p}$ is the direction of propagation of the waves, and the magnitude of the momentum is given by U/c. (This is primarily useful in conjunction with Newton's second law, $\mathbf{F} = d\mathbf{p}/dt$, to deduce the force exerted by an electromagnetic wave on an absorber or reflector.)

10. Radiation pressure:

$$P_{rad} = \frac{\bar{S}}{c} \quad \text{(Text Eq. 34-24)}$$

If an electromagnetic wave has an average intensity $\bar{S}$, it will exert an average force per unit area (*i.e.*, pressure P_{rad}) on a perfect absorber. Note that if the radiation is reflected rather than absorbed, the pressure will be different and will have to be computed from the rate of momentum transfer.

AVOIDING PITFALLS

1. **Displacement current:** Maxwell coined the phrase "displacement current" for the term $\varepsilon_0(d\phi_E/dt)$, which must be added to $I_{encircled}$ in Ampère's law. The idea was brilliant, but it was an unfortunate choice of terminology, since the word "displacement" referred to a no-longer-accepted ether theory of electromagnetism. Furthermore, "displacement current" is not even a current (even though it happens to have units of C/s, or A.) If you simply accept the fact that a

magnetic field can be produced by a current ($I_{encircled}$) or by a changing electric flux $\varepsilon_0(d\phi_E/dt)$ you shouldn't have any problems with this concept.

2. **Poynting vector:** The Poynting vector ($\mathbf{S} = \mathbf{E} \times \mathbf{B}/\mu_0$) gives the energy flux (time rate of energy flow per unit area) for the electric and magnetic fields of an arbitrary distribution of charges and currents, not just for electromagnetic waves. (Because it involves the cross product, there is no energy flux associated with *parallel* electric and magnetic fields, since $|\mathbf{E} + \mathbf{B}| = EB \sin 0° = 0$.)

3. **Cross product:** The direction of propagation of electromagnetic waves is given by the direction of $\mathbf{S} = \mathbf{E} \times \mathbf{B}/\mu_0$. Since $\mathbf{E} \times \mathbf{B} = -\mathbf{B} \times \mathbf{E}$, it's important not to interchange the order of $\mathbf{E}$ and $\mathbf{B}$ in the cross product.

4. **Instantaneous vs. average values:** It is essential to note whether you are dealing with the instantaneous value or the time-averaged value of a quantity. Specifically,

   - The instantaneous Poynting vector $\mathbf{S}(t) = \mathbf{E}(t) \times \mathbf{B}(t)/\mu_0$ gives the *instantaneous* value of energy flux, if $\mathbf{E}(t)$ and $\mathbf{B}(t)$ represent their instantaneous values.

   - The peak Poynting vector ($\mathbf{S}_p = \mathbf{E}_p \times \mathbf{B}_p/\mu0$) gives the *maximum* value of energy flux, if $\mathbf{E}_p$ and $\mathbf{B}_p$ represent their amplitudes.

   - The average Poynting vector ($\bar{\mathbf{S}} = \mathbf{E}_{rms} \times \mathbf{B}_{rms}/\mu_0$) gives the *time-averaged* value of energy flux, if $\mathbf{E}_{rms}$ and $\mathbf{B}_{rms}$ represent their root-mean-square values. (Note: For *sinusoidal* waves, $E_{rms} = E_p/\sqrt{2}$, and $B_{rms} = B_p/\sqrt{2}$. Then $\bar{\mathbf{S}} = \mathbf{S}_p/2$.

5. **Electromagnetic pressure:** The force exerted by an electromagnetic wave is given by (-1) times the time rate of change of its momentum ($\mathbf{F} = -d\mathbf{p}/dt$). When a wave is absorbed, its momentum decreases from $\mathbf{p}$ to zero, but when it is reflected at normal incidence, its momentum changes from $\mathbf{p}$ to $-\mathbf{p}$, so the change in its momentum is $\Delta\mathbf{p} = -2\mathbf{p}$. In any case, the *pressure* exerted by the wave is the force *per unit area*.

6. **Intensity vs. distance:** The geometry of the source determines how rapidly the intensity (defined as power/area) of electromagnetic radiation falls off with distance:

   - Point source: $S \propto 1/r^2$. (This includes any point source or spherically symmetric source of radiation.)

   - Line source: $S \propto 1/r$. (This includes any cylindrically symmetric source of radiation, as long as its ends are much farther away than the distance to the field point.)

   - Plane source: $S = $ constant. (This describes the intensity of a uniform wall of light, as long as the wall's edges are much farther away than the distance to the field point.)

7. **Malus's law:** The intensity of initially *plane-polarized* light after it has passed through a polarizer is given by $S = S_0 \cos^2\theta$. Initially unpolarized light, however, simply has its intensity reduced by one-half.

ActivPhysics **Connections to *ActivPhysics***

Chapter 34 demonstrates how it is possible to create oscillating electromagnetic waves from the four laws governing electric and magnetic fields. There are no *ActivPhysics* activities simulating the production of electromagnetic waves; however, Activity 11.8 *Gauss's Law* and Activity 13.9 *Electromagnetic Induction* visualize some of the key concepts of Maxwell's equations and may be useful to review while completing this chapter. (Activity 11.8 was a recommended investigation for Chapter 24, and Activity 13.9 was a recommended activity for Chapter 31.) Activity 16.9 *Polarization* animates Figure 34-21 in Section 34-8 on the same topic and simulates the behavior of light following Malus's law, Equation 34-19. This activity should be helpful if any of Problems 29–33, 63, or 64 have been assigned.

CHAPTER 35   REFLECTION AND REFRACTION

In the previous chapter, we found that Maxwell's equations predicted the existence of electromagnetic waves. When the frequency and wavelength of these waves fall in the rather narrow range that our eyes can detect, we call the waves "light." The next few chapters investigate optical phenomena in more detail. This introductory chapter addresses four fundamental processes that occur with light: reflection, refraction, dispersion, and polarization.

DEFINITIONS

You should know the definition of each of these terms. (The number in parentheses is the text chapter and section in which the term is introduced.)

(35-Intr) A line (perpendicular to a wavefront) that points in the direction of wave propagation is known as a *ray*. (You may think of a ray as an extremely narrow beam of light.)

(35-2) *Specular reflection* is the mirrorlike reflection from a surface whose irregularities are smaller than the wavelength of the waves striking it.

(35-2) When the surface irregularities are larger than the wavelength of the waves striking it, the reflected wavefronts are scattered in random directions, producing *diffuse reflection*.

(35-3) *Refraction* is the change in the direction of propagation of a wave when it crosses a boundary between two media with different speeds of propagation.

(35-3) The *index of refraction* is the ratio of the speed of light in vacuum (c) to the speed of light in a given material (v): $n = c/v$.

(35-3) *Snell's law* states that the product of index of refraction and the sine of the angle between the normal to a surface and the direction of propagation is constant across any boundary:

$$n_1 \sin \theta_1 = n_2 \sin \theta_2.$$

(35-4) The minimum angle of incidence that will allow total internal reflection is known as the *critical angle*.

(35-5) A substance whose index of refraction depends on the frequency (or wavelength) of the waves is said to show *dispersion*. A result of this behavior is that different wavelengths are refracted through different angles.

(35-6) When unpolarized light reflects from a dielectric surface at a particular angle ("Brewster's angle"), the reflected light is totally polarized. This occurs when the reflected ray is perpendicular to the refracted ray.

SUMMARY OF EQUATIONS

1. Law of reflection:

$$\theta'_1 = \theta_1 \qquad \text{(Text. Eq. 35-1)}$$

This very simple equation states that the angle of incidence (θ_1, measured between a ray of light and the normal to the surface) equals the angle of reflection θ'_1 (also measured between the reflected ray and the normal to the surface).

2. Definition of index of refraction:

$$n \equiv \frac{c}{v} \qquad \text{(Text Eq. 35-2)}$$

The "index of refraction" (n) of a substance is defined as the ratio of the speed of light in vacuum (c) to the speed of light traveling through the medium (v). Because the speed of light through *all* materials is less than c, it follows that the index of refraction of all materials is greater than 1.

3. Snell's law:

$$n_1 \sin \theta_1 = n_2 \sin \theta_2 \quad \text{(Text Eq. 35-3)}$$

If a ray of light passes from one medium with an index of refraction n_1 to another medium with an index of refraction n_2, Snell's law describes the refraction that occurs at the boundary. In this equation, θ_1 is the angle between the ray while in medium 1 and the *normal* to the boundary, and θ_2 is the angle between the ray while in medium 2 and the normal to the boundary. (This equation works for light passing in either direction, and there is no restriction as to which index of refraction is greater.)

4. Wave frequency and wavelength at the boundary between two media:

$$f_1 = f_2$$

$$n_1\lambda_1 = n_2\lambda_2 \qquad \text{(Text Eq. 35-4)}$$

Because each wave propagating through medium 2 is the result of a wave emerging from medium 1, the number of waves per second emerging from medium 1 will produce the same number of waves per second in medium 2. In other words, the waves don't pile up at the boundary, so the frequencies are identical.

In each medium $f = v/\lambda$, so $v_1/\lambda_1 = v_2/\lambda_2$. Using $v = c/n$, we find Text Eq. 35-4, which states that the wavelength is inversely proportional to the index of refraction.

5. Critical angle:

$$\sin \theta_c = \frac{n_2}{n_1} \qquad \text{(Text Eq. 35-5)}$$

When light approaches a boundary where the index of refraction *decreases* (*i.e.*, the wave speed increases), the possibility of total internal reflection exists. If the angle of incidence exceeds the "critical angle," then all the light will be reflected back into the medium from which it came. When light traveling through a medium with index of refraction n_1 encounters a boundary with a material whose index n_2 is *lower* than n_1, total internal reflection occurs if $\theta_1 \geq \theta_c$.

6. Polarization angle:

$$\tan \theta_p = \frac{n_2}{n_1} \qquad \text{(Text Eq. 35-6)}$$

If unpolarized light (traveling through medium 1) falls on the boundary with medium 2 at an angle of θ_p, the reflected light will be totally polarized, with its plane of polarization perpendicular to the plane containing the incident and reflected rays. (This angle is also known as Brewster's angle.) This is the angle that makes the reflected and *refracted* rays perpendicular.

AVOIDING PITFALLS

1. **Index of refraction:** If you forget whether *n* was defined as *c/v* (it is) or as *v/c* (it's not!), remember that the index of refraction of all materials is greater than unity, and that all materials slow light below its vacuum speed (that is, $v < c$). Also note that a high index of refraction means a low speed of propagation.

2. **Changes in a wave upon refraction:** If a wave moves across a boundary where the speed of propagation (and index of refraction) changes, the *frequency* of the wave is unchanged. (The waves don't pile up at the boundary, so the number of waves per second arriving at the boundary matches the number per second leaving the boundary.) Since $v = f\lambda$, a change in speed implies a proportional change in wavelength as well.

3. **Definition of angles:** All the equations of optics (*e.g.*, the laws of reflection, refraction, and polarization) are written for angles measured between the light ray and the *normal* to the surface, not the surface itself.

4. **Angle of refraction:** When a wave moves into a medium with a lower speed of propagation (higher index of refraction), it bends toward the normal; if it moves into a medium with a higher wave speed (lower index), it bends away from the normal, unless the light happens to come in at normal incidence ($\theta = 0°$). (This all follows directly from Snell's law, but it's a good check on your calculations and diagrams.)

5. **Critical angle:** Total internal reflection can occur only when light reaches a boundary where the wave speed *increases* (*i.e.*, the index of refraction decreases). The critical angle occurs when the *refraction* angle reaches 90°.

(ActivPhysics) **Connections to *ActivPhysics***

An animated version of Figure 35-6 is incorporated into the first three activities of Unit 15 of *ActivPhysics* on geometric optics. I recommend completing Activities 15.1 *Reflection and Refraction*, 15.2 *Total Internal Reflection*, and 15.3 *Refraction Applications* before reading Chapter 35. These *ActivPhysics* investigations are concerned with just the basic principles necessary to understand reflection and refraction, whereas the book focuses more on the connections to the electromagnetic theory of light. The three activities will also immediately introduce you to simple applications of Snell's law of refraction, so if you already have a clear understanding of reflection and refraction, then these investigations can be completed quickly; if Snell's law is unfamiliar to you, then completing these activities will be time well spent.

Figure 35-14 can also be animated by the *Reflection and Refraction* simulation. Example 35-5 *Whale Watch* is similar to Question 4 of Activity 15.3 and is almost exactly the same as Problem 18. Question 6 of Activity 15.2 is related to the discussion of fiber optics on page 926. Completing these activities will be of benefit when attempting most of Problems 8–33 of the text.

CHAPTER 36 IMAGE FORMATION AND OPTICAL INSTRUMENTS

In this chapter, we study how reflecting and refracting surfaces (mirrors and lenses) can form images by affecting the propagation of light. In doing so, we will encounter fiber optics, prisms, rainbows, cameras, microscopes, telescopes, and the human eye.

DEFINITIONS

You should know the definition of each of these terms. (The number in parentheses is the text chapter and section in which the term is introduced.)

(36-Intr) An image of an object formed by diverging rays of light that appear to emerge from a particular point but that are not physically present at the image's location is known as a *virtual image*. (A virtual image cannot be projected on a screen.)

(36-Intr) A *real image* of an object is formed by rays of light physically converging at that point. (Thus, a real image can be projected on a screen.)

(36-2) When parallel rays of light pass through a converging lens, they converge to a more or less well-defined point, called the *focal point*. When parallel rays pass through a diverging lens, they appear to diverge from a point called the (*virtual*) *focal point*. Note that nonparallel rays may also be brought to a focus, but the term *focal point* refers to the point of convergence (or divergence) for *parallel* rays.

(36-2) The *focal length* is the distance from the center of a lens or mirror to the focal point.

(36-3) The *thin-lens* approximation, used in deriving most of the equations in this chapter, assumes that the thickness of the lenses is negligible in comparison with any focal length, object distance, or image distance.

(36-4) The *lensmaker's formula* relates the focal length of a lens to the index of refraction and the radii of curvature:

$$\frac{1}{f} = (n-1)\left(\frac{1}{R_1} - \frac{1}{R_2}\right)$$

(36-5) The power of a lens in *diopters* is defined as the reciprocal of its focal length in meters.

SUMMARY OF EQUATIONS

1. Linear magnification of a mirror:

$$M \equiv \frac{h'}{h} = -\frac{\ell'}{\ell} \qquad \text{(Text Eq. 36-1)}$$

The linear magnification is defined as the ratio of image size (h') to object size (h), and this is very nearly the ratio of image distance ℓ' to object distance ℓ. In this equation, ℓ represents the distance from the mirror to the object, and ℓ' the distance from the mirror to the image. Since each of the variables can be positive or negative, careful attention must be paid to a sign convention. A real object (on the shiny side of the mirror) has a positive object distance ℓ, and a real image (also on the shiny side of the mirror) has a positive image distance ℓ'. A positive M implies an erect image, whereas a negative value of M implies an inverted image.

2. The mirror equation:

$$\frac{1}{\ell} + \frac{1}{\ell'} = \frac{1}{f} \qquad \text{(Text Eq. 36-2)}$$

This equation relates the positions of an object and its image to the focal length of a mirror. In this equation, the focal length f of a *converging* (concave) mirror is defined to be positive.

3. Mirror focal length and curvature:

$$f = \frac{R}{2} \qquad \text{(Text Eq. 36-3)}$$

For a spherical mirror, its focal length is very nearly one-half its radius of curvature. (Note that R and f are both positive for a *concave* mirror.)

4. The thin-lens equation:

$$\frac{1}{\ell} + \frac{1}{\ell'} = \frac{1}{f} \qquad \text{(Text Eq. 36-5)}$$

The focal length of a thin lens is related to the positions of an object and its image in exactly the same way as a mirror. For lenses, we again define the focal length of converging lenses to be positive, but a converging lens is convex, not concave. The object distance ℓ for a real object is again positive, and a real image (one formed on the opposite side of the lens from the object) has a positive value of ℓ'.

5. Lensmaker's formula:

$$\frac{1}{f} = (n-1)\left(\frac{1}{R_1} - \frac{1}{R_2}\right) \qquad \text{(Text Eq. 36-8)}$$

This equation relates the focal length of a spherical lens to its index of refraction n and radii of curvature R_1 and R_2. Surface 1 is the first (front) surface encountered by the light; surface 2 is the second (back) surface of the lens. R_1 and R_2 are considered positive if the center of curvature lies on the *back* side of the lens.

6. Angular magnification:

$$m \equiv \frac{\theta'}{\theta}$$

When you are using a magnifier or telescope, the perceived size of the image is determined by the angle subtended by the image, rather than its linear size. In such cases, it is usually more informative to refer to the angular magnification of the system, defined as the ratio of the angular size of the image (θ') to the angular size of the object (θ). The angular magnifications of three common optical instruments are listed below:

- Simple magnifier: $m = \dfrac{25\text{ cm}}{f}$ (Text Eq. 36-9)

    f is the focal length of a simple magnifier (a convex lens).

- Microscope: $m = -\dfrac{L}{f_0}\left(\dfrac{25\text{ cm}}{f_e}\right)$ (Text Eq. 36-10)

    f_o = focal length of the objective lens; f_e = focal length of the eyepiece. L is the distance between the two lenses, approximately the image distance for the objective lens.

- Telescope: $m = \dfrac{f_o}{f_e}$ (Text Eq. 36-11)

    f_o = focal length of the objective lens or mirror; f_e = focal length of the eyepiece.

AVOIDING PITFALLS

1. **Real or virtual image:** If the rays of light actually *converge* and pass through the image location, it is a *real* image—it can be projected on a screen held at that location. If, however, the rays of light only appear to be emerging from the image's location, it is a *virtual* image.

2. **Focal length:** Remember that the focal length (f) of a mirror or lens is defined to be the distance from the lens to the point where *parallel* rays of light are converged. Nonparallel rays will converge at some other point (the "image" distance, ℓ').

3. **Focal length of a mirror:** The focal length of a spherical mirror is *one-half* its radius of curvature. Concave mirrors have positive values of f and R; convex mirrors have negative f and R.

4. **Ray diagrams:** In making a ray diagram of a thin-lens problem, we assume that all the refraction occurs at the midplane of the lens, and that we can draw the lens as large as we need to in order to intercept the needed rays.

5. **Reciprocals:** Many of the optics equations are expressed in terms of the *reciprocal* of a variable (e.g., $1/f = (n - 1)(1/R_1 + 1/R_2)$; $P = 1/f$; $1/f = 1/\ell' + 1/\ell$.) Don't forget to use the **[1/x]** key to find the variable you need.

6. **Sign conventions:** Most errors in using these equations involve the signs associated with the various distances (ℓ, ℓ', f, R). Following is a verbal description of the cases that produce *positive* values, as used in the text and study guide:

    - *Mirrors:* converging (*i.e.*, concave) mirror ($+f$); object and image both on the reflecting side of the mirror ($+\ell$, $+\ell'$).

    - *Lenses:* converging (*i.e.*, convex) lens ($+f$); object on the side of the lens from which the light is coming ($+\ell$); image on the side of the lens toward which the light is heading ($+\ell'$).

    - *Lensmaker's equation:* If a refracting surface has its center of curvature on the back side (the side of the lens from which the light emerges), the radius of curvature R is positive.

7. **Magnification:** A positive value of m or M indicates an *erect* image; a negative magnification indicates an inverted image. (Also, remember that "erect" means that the image has the same orientation as the object.) If $|M| > 1$, then the image is enlarged; if $|M| < 1$, then the image is reduced.

8. **Power:** The power of a lens (in diopters) is the reciprocal of the focal length in *meters*. Since many optical measurements are given in cm, it's easy to forget that f must be expressed in meters when working with diopters.

 Connections to *ActivPhysics*

Section 36-1 discusses image formation in plane mirrors, and Figure 36-1a is reproduced in the simulation of Activity 15.4 *Plane Mirrors*. One advantage of the activity is that the object may be moved in both the x- and y-directions, with the simulation showing the effects on the ray diagram and the image location. The four activities investigating the function of spherical mirrors—15.5 *Spherical Mirrors: Ray Diagrams*, 15.6 *Spherical Mirror: Mirror Equation*, 15.7 *Spherical Mirror: Linear Magnification*, and 15.8 *Spherical Mirror: Problems*—all employ the same simulation. As with the previous "matched set" of simulations in this unit, Activities 15.1–15.3, it is a good idea to complete these four sequentially. In this case, it is also a good idea to read the textbook first. Some of the questions in the activities expect you to deduce general principles and specific relationships (such as the relationship between focal length and the radius of curvature or Eq. 36-1) based on data observed in the simulation. That approach is very effective at insuring that you actually understand those relationships, but it could be helpful to have some sense of the final result in advance.

A similar correspondence is found between the matched Activities 15.9 *Thin-Lens Ray Diagrams*, 15.10 *Converging Lens Problems*, and 15.11 *Diverging Lens Problems* and Section 36-3 *Lenses*. Once again, all three activities employ the same simulation, the three activities build sequentially, and the same advice of reading the text first applies. Even if you choose not to complete all of the spherical mirror and lens activities, I still strongly recommend exploring both of these key simulations; they will definitely help you understand the basic characteristics and properties of images formed from curved surfaces.

Activities 15.14 *The Eye* and 15.15 *Eyeglasses* share a simulation that explains the nature of nearsightedness, farsightedness, and corrective eyeglasses. These two activities complement the first part of Section 36-5 *Optical Instruments* quite nicely. The general nature of cameras and magnifiers is considered in Activities 15.9 and 15.10. The theory of two-lens systems such as the telescope and the microscope are clarified in Activities 15.12 *Two-Lens Optical Systems* and 15.13 *The Telescope and Angular Magnification*. It should be worthwhile to at least skim through these two simulations in order to understand the basic principles behind these common optical instruments. You should also discover that setting parameters for the *Spherical Mirror*, *Thin-Lens*, or *Multiple-Lens* simulations should help you answer many of the chapter word problems corresponding to the appropriate sections of the text.

CHAPTER 37   INTERFERENCE AND DIFFRACTION

When light interacts with slits, films, mirrors, etc., whose dimensions approach the wavelength of light, the phenomena of diffraction and interference become important. All of the phenomena studied in this chapter are consequences of the wave nature of light.

DEFINITIONS

You should know the definition of each of these terms. (The number in parentheses is the text chapter and section in which the term is introduced.)

(37-1) When a wave is *coherent*, there is a definite, long-lasting, phase relationship that exists between different points in a wave.

(37-1) *Constructive interference* is the process whereby two or more waves arrive at a given point in phase with each other, their amplitudes adding arithmetically to produce a maximum amplitude for the composite wave.

(37-1) In *destructive interference*, two waves arrive at the same point 180° out of phase with each other so that their amplitudes subtract, thereby producing a minimum amplitude composite wave. (When three or more waves arrive at the same point, their phase relationships are more complex, but "destructive interference" still refers to the condition that produces the minimum amplitude composite wave.)

(37-3) A *diffraction grating* is a smooth surface with many closely spaced parallel grooves.

(37-3) The *resolving power* of a grating is a measure of its ability to separate two nearly equal wavelengths. If $\Delta\lambda$ is the minimum wavelength difference that can be resolved at an average wavelength λ, the resolving power of the grating is defined as the ratio $\lambda/\Delta\lambda$. (This turns out to equal the product mN, where N is the total number of illuminated slits in the grating, and m is the order of the spectrum being viewed.)

(37-3) *Bragg diffraction* refers to the interference between electromagnetic waves (usually X-rays) diffracted from successively deeper layers of atoms in a crystal.

(37-4) *Thin-film interference* refers to the interference between light waves reflected from the front and back surfaces of a thin transparent film.

(37-4) An *interferometer* is a device that splits a beam of light into two separate beams heading in different directions, and then recombines the two into one beam to display interference effects. (If the wavelength of the light is known, an interferometer can be used for precise measurements of lengths, or if the distance traveled by its movable mirror is known, the interferometer can determine the wavelength of light.)

(37-5) *Huygens's principle* is a geometric model for predicting the propagation of wavefronts. Specifically, Huygens's principle states that every point on a given wavefront may be thought of as radiating a spherical wavelet (in the forward direction), and the envelope of all the wavelets defines the wavefront for the next wave.

(37-5) When part of a wavefront is obstructed by a barrier, the waves tend to spread out into the "shadow" region around the edge. This spreading is known as *diffraction*.

(37-7) *Rayleigh's criterion* is an arbitrary (though reasonable) criterion for determining whether the images of two points are resolved or not. Specifically, Rayleigh stated that if the center of one diffraction peak gets no closer than the first diffraction minimum of the other, then the two points can be resolved; if the centers move closer than this, they cannot be resolved.

SUMMARY OF EQUATIONS

1. Double-slit interference:

    a. *Angular position of maxima, minima:*

    (maxima) $d \sin\theta = m\lambda$ \qquad (Text Eq. 37-1a)

    (minima) $d \sin\theta = (m + \frac{1}{2})\lambda$ \quad (Text Eq. 37-1b)

    (for both, $m = 0, \pm1, \pm2, \ldots$)

    When light of wavelength λ falls on a pair of narrow, parallel slits whose separation is d, the light emerging from the two slits at a given angle θ will produce constructive or destructive interference if the phase difference ($d \sin\theta$) is an integer or odd half-integer number of wavelengths.

    b. *Approximate screen position of maxima, minima:*

    (maxima) $y \approx m\dfrac{\lambda L}{d}$ \qquad (Text Eq. 37-2a)

    (minima) $y \approx (m + \frac{1}{2})\dfrac{\lambda L}{d}$ \quad (Text Eq. 37-2b)

    (for both, $m = 0, \pm1, \pm2, \ldots$)

    When the light from two parallel slits falls on a screen a distance L from the slits, the maxima (bright fringes) and minima (dark fringes) will appear at a distance y from the center of the pattern. These (simpler) expressions can be used whenever θ is small enough that $\sin\theta \approx \tan\theta \approx y/L$.

    c. *Intensity at a given angular position:*

    $$\bar{S} = 4\bar{S}_0 \cos^2\left(\frac{\pi d \sin\theta}{\lambda}\right).$$ \qquad (Text Eq. 37-3)

$\bar{S}$ is the (time-averaged) intensity at an angle θ from the center of a double-slit interference pattern. $\bar{S}_0$ is the intensity that would be observed at the center with only one slit open.

d. *Intensity at a given screen position:*

$$\bar{S} \approx 4\bar{S}_0 \cos^2\left(\frac{\pi d}{\lambda}\frac{y}{L}\right) \quad \text{(Text Eq. 37-4)}$$

$\bar{S}$ is the (time-averaged) intensity at a distance y from the center of a double-slit interference pattern seen on a screen that lies at a distance L from the slits. $\bar{S}_0$ is the intensity that would be observed at the center with only one slit open. Again, this simpler expression can be used whenever θ is small enough that $\sin\theta \approx \tan\theta = y/L$.

2. Interference from N parallel slits:

(maxima) $\quad d \sin\theta = m\lambda \quad$ (Text Eq. 37-1a)

$$(m = 0, \pm 1, \pm 2, \dots)$$

When this condition is satisfied, the light from all N equally spaced slits will produce constructive interference on a distant screen.

(minima) $\quad d \sin\theta = \dfrac{m}{N}\lambda$ (Text Eq. 37-5)

Destructive interference results when $m = $ (integer), but $(m/N) \neq$ (integer).

3. Resolving power of a grating:

$$\frac{\lambda}{\Delta\lambda} = mN \quad \text{(Text Eq. 37-6)}$$

A grating with N slits will barely be able to resolve two lines (of wavelength $\lambda 1 \approx \lambda 2 \approx \lambda$) in the mth-order spectrum if their wavelengths differ by $\Delta\lambda$.

4. Interference in light reflected from a thin film:

(constructive) $2nd = (m + \frac{1}{2})\lambda \quad$ (Text. Eq. 37-8a)

(destructive) $2nd = m\lambda \quad$ (Text Eq. 37-8b)

When light (at nearly normal incidence) falls on a thin film whose index of refraction is greater than that of the medium on either side, interference will occur in both the reflected and transmitted beams. Eqs. 37-8 describe conditions for constructive and destructive interference in the *reflected* beam. In these equations, n is the index of refraction of the film, d is the thickness of the film, and λ is the wavelength of the light *in air*. For both equations, m is an integer: $m = 0, 1, 2, \dots$.

5. Single-slit diffraction:

a. *Angular position of minima:*

(minima) $\quad a \sin\theta = m\lambda \quad$ (Text Eq. 37-9)

$$(m = 0, \pm 1, \pm 2, \dots)$$

When coherent light of wavelength λ passes through a single slit of width a, *destructive* interference will be observed at the angle θ described above. (Note carefully the similarity to the location of multiple-slit *maxima!*)

The maxima in a single-slit diffraction pattern lie *approximately* midway between adjacent minima, but the exact position of the maxima cannot be expressed in a closed-form expression.

b. *Intensity at a given angular position:*

$$\bar{S} = \bar{S}_0\left[\frac{\sin(\text{w}/2)}{\text{w}/2}\right]^2, \text{ where} \quad \text{(Text Eq. 37-12)}$$

$$\text{w} = \frac{2\pi}{\lambda} a \sin\theta \quad \text{(Text Eq. 37-11)}$$

The intensity at an angle θ from the central maximum is given by Eq. 37-12. $\bar{S}_0$ represents the intensity at the central peak of the pattern.

6. Rayleigh's criteria for resolution:

(slit) $\quad \theta_{\min} = \dfrac{\lambda}{a} \quad$ (Text Eq. 37-13a)

(circular aperture) $\theta_{\min} = \dfrac{1.22\lambda}{D} \quad$ (Text Eq. 37-13b)

These equations describe the minimum angular separation of two point sources of light that can barely be resolved according to Rayleigh's criterion: The central maximum of one diffraction pattern can be no closer than the first minimum of the other pattern.

The angular spread of the diffraction pattern is slightly larger for light passing through a circular aperture than for a single slit with the same width.

AVOIDING PITFALLS

1. **Young's (double-slit) experiment:** The small-angle approximation ($\sin\theta \approx \tan\theta \approx \theta$) is often convenient in this situation, but be sure it's justified ($\theta \approx 10°$ or less, depending on the precision needed).

2. **N-slit grating:**

   • *Location of maxima:* The principal maxima in the interference pattern of any N-slit aperture ($N \geq 2$) are located by the double-slit formula: $m\lambda = d \sin\theta$. (Don't forget that d is the *distance* between adjacent slits, not the number of slits per centimeter.)

   • *Location of minima:* Between any adjacent pair of principal maxima will lie $(N-1)$ minima and $(N-2)$ much fainter secondary maxima.

   • *Resolving power:* The resolving power of a grating is determined by the *total* number of grooves in the grating and the *order* of the spectrum being used. (A grating with a narrow slit separation will move any two maxima farther apart, but it will also make them broader, so the resolution isn't improved.)

3. **Interferometer:** The basic point to remember is that the interference seen on the viewing screen is due to differences in the optical path lengths *after* the beam has been split. Also, in the Michelson interferometer, a movement of the mirror through a distance D changes the optical path length of that beam by $2D$.

4. **Thin films:**

   • *Path difference*: The phase relationship is, in part, determined by the extra distance traveled by one beam, measured from the point where the two beams split. For reflected light, this occurs at the *front* surface of the film; for transmitted light, this occurs at the *back* surface of the film.

   • *Phase reversals*: Whenever a wave is reflected from a boundary where the index of refraction *increases*, the phase of the wave shifts by 180°. If the index of refraction *decreases*, the phase is unchanged.

   • *"Wet wavelengths"*: When counting wavelengths as the beam travels through the film (twice), don't forget that the "wet wavelength" of light is reduced by the index of refraction of the film: $\lambda' = \lambda_{air}/n$.

   • *Reflected vs. transmitted beams*: Interference occurs between front and back-surface reflections in *both* the reflected and transmitted beams. Because of the half-cycle phase shift at reflection from one of the surfaces, conditions that produce *constructive* interference in the reflected beam will produce *destructive* interference in the transmitted beam, and vice versa.

5. **Diffraction:** The location of the *minima* in the single-slit diffraction pattern,

$$m\lambda = a\sin\theta, \qquad \text{(minima)}$$

is so similar to the location of the *maxima* in the multiple-slit interference pattern,

$$m\lambda = d\sin\theta \qquad \text{(maxima)}$$

that it is *easy* to forget that one locates dark fringes and the other locates bright fringes.

Also, the first minimum from a *slit* occurs with $m = 1$, but the first minimum of a *circular* diffraction pattern occurs with $m = 1.22$.

 **Connections to *ActivPhysics***

Unit 16 of *ActivPhysics* is an excellent supplement to this chapter on interference and diffraction. Read Sections 37-1 and 37-2 first, then complete the *Two-Source Interference* activities, 16.1 *Introduction*, 16.2 *Qualitative Questions*, and 16.3 *Problems*. All three activities employ the same simulation, which should help you visualize interference phenomena and better understand the effects of wavelength and source separation on the interference pattern. In fact, the "Got It!" question on page 976 is one that is asked in Activity 16.2.

Similar advice can be given for Activities 16.4 and 16.5 on *The Grating* and Section 37-3, Activity 16.6 *Single-Slit Diffraction* and Section 37-6 of the same name, and Activity 16.8 *Resolving Power* and the discussion and figures found on page 996 of the text. In all of these cases, your ability to visualize interference and diffraction effects makes both the concepts and the equations describing the behavior much more understandable.

CHAPTER 38   THE THEORY OF RELATIVITY

From some apparent ambiguities in Maxwell's laws of electrodynamics, Albert Einstein was led to propose that the principle of relativity (previously thought to apply only to mechanical phenomena) is a truly fundamental principle, applying to *all* physical phenomena. This principle, which implies the universality of the speed of light, forms the basis of all the relativistic phenomena described in this chapter: length contraction, time dilation, the equivalence of mass and energy, and the relativity of simultaneity.

DEFINITIONS

You should know the definition of each of these terms. (The number in parentheses is the text chapter and section in which the term is introduced.)

(38-1) In the late 1800s, it was believed that all waves consisted of vibrations in some medium. The medium proposed for electromagnetic waves (including light) was called the *luminiferous ether*. Since starlight reaches the Earth from distant corners of the universe, the ether evidently permeated all space, and thus constituted a universal, absolute frame of reference.

(38-1) Based on the common sense addition of velocities as ordinary vector quantities, the *principle of Galilean relativity* asserts that the laws of mechanics are the same in all unaccelerated frames of reference.

(38-3) Einstein's *special theory of relativity* states that *all* the laws of physics (including electrodynamics) are the same in all unaccelerated frames of reference.

(38-4) One of the manifestations of the Lorentz transformations is that time will pass more slowly in any frame of reference that is moving relative to your own, a phenomenon known as *time dilation*.

(38-4) The time interval between two events, as measured in a reference frame in which the two events occur at the same location, is known as the *proper time interval* between the two events.

(38-4) The *Lorentz contraction* refers to the reduction in the length of an object when it moves parallel to its length.

(38-4) For the speed of light to have the same value in all inertial frames of reference, space and time coordinates of an event must be related through a set of four equations known as the *Lorentz (or Einstein-Lorentz) transformations*.

(38-6) A *relativistic invariant* is any quantity that has the same value in all frames of reference. (Examples include electric charge, the speed of light, and the spacetime interval defined below.)

(38-6) The *space-time interval* between two events is defined as

$$(\Delta s)^2 = c^2(\Delta t)^2 - [\,(\Delta x)^2 + (\Delta y)^2 + (\Delta z)^2\,].$$

(38-8) Einstein's *general theory of relativity* extended the ideas of special relativity to noninertial reference frames. The cornerstone idea is that gravitational effects are indistinguishable from accelerations.

SUMMARY OF EQUATIONS

1. Time dilation:

$$\Delta t = \frac{\Delta t'}{\sqrt{1 - v^2/c^2}} \qquad \text{(Text Eq. 38-4)}$$

In this equation, $\Delta t'$ represents the time interval between two events, as measured in a frame of reference in which the two events occurred at the same location. (This time interval can, therefore, be measured with a *single* clock and is known as the "proper time.") Δt represents the time interval between the same two events, but measured in a frame of reference that is moving with a speed v relative to the first. In this frame, the events occurred at different locations, so *two* synchronized clocks are needed (one at the location of the first event, the other at the location of the second event). Note that this equation shows that $\Delta t' \le \Delta t$ in all cases.

2. Length contraction:

$$\Delta x' = \Delta x\sqrt{1 - v^2/c^2} \quad \text{(Text Eq. 38-5)}$$

In this equation, Δx represents the separation of two events *that occur simultaneously* in frame S. $\Delta x'$ represents the separation between the same two events, as measured in a frame (S') that is moving with a speed v with respect to S. (Note: These two events will not be simultaneous in S'.) If we interpret Δx as a measurement of the length L_0 of an object, we find that $L' = L_0\sqrt{1 - v^2/c^2}$.

3. Lorentz transformation of space and time coordinates:

$x' = \gamma\,(x - vt)$	$x = \gamma\,(x' + vt')$
$y' = y$	$y = y'$
$z' = z$	$z = z'$
$t' = \gamma\,(t - vx/c^2)$	$t = \gamma\,(t' - vx'/c^2)$

$$\left(\gamma = \frac{1}{\sqrt{1 - v^2/c^2}}\right) \qquad \text{(Table 38-1)}$$

These equations are the basis for all of special relativity. They relate the space-time coordinates of an event as measured in one frame of reference S to its coordinates in a second frame of reference S'. These equations assume that S' is moving with a speed v in the $+x$ direction relative to S, and their clocks have been set so that $t = t' = 0$ when their origins coincide.

Note that the inverse transformations, giving unprimed coordinates in terms of the primed coordinates, can be found by exchanging the prime and unprime coordinates *and* replacing v with -v.

4. Relativistic transformation of velocities:

$$u = \frac{u' + v}{1 + u'v/c^2} \quad \text{(Text Eq. 38-11)}$$

$$u' = \frac{u - v}{1 - uv/c^2} \quad \text{(Text Eq. 38-12)}$$

In these equations, frame S' is moving in the x direction with a speed v relative to S. An object is moving with a constant velocity, also in the x direction. Its velocity relative to frame S is u, and its velocity relative to S' is u'. (If any of these velocities is pointing to the left, then we use a negative value for that velocity.) Again, the inverse transformation can be found by exchanging u and u', and by replacing v with $-v$.

5. Relativistic momentum:

$$\mathbf{p} = \gamma m \mathbf{v} \quad \text{(Text Eq. 33-13)}$$

By defining this quantity as "relativistic momentum," we are able to retain the law of conservation of momentum for isolated systems.

6. Mass-energy equivalence:

$$E = \frac{mc^2}{\sqrt{1 - u^2/c^2}} = \gamma mc^2 \text{(Text Eq. 38-15)}$$

This states that the mass of a system is directly proportional to its total energy E. That is, when energy is added to a system, its mass increases; when energy is removed from a system, its mass decreases; and if its energy is constant, its mass will be constant. Note that the energy of an isolated particle at rest is not zero, but there is a "rest energy" given by $E_0 = mc^2$.

7. Energy-momentum relation:

$$E^2 = p^2c^2 + (mc^2)^2 \quad \text{(Text Eq. 38-16)}$$

Analogous to the classical expression $K = p^2/2m$, the total energy of a particle can be expressed in terms of its mass m and momentum p.

8. Space-time interval:

$$(\Delta s)^2 = c^2(\Delta t)^2 - [\,(\Delta x)^2 + (\Delta y)^2 + (\Delta z)^2\,]$$

$$\text{(Text Eq. 38-18)}$$

We consider two events, E_1 and E_2, as observed in any single frame of reference. We define $\Delta x = x_2 - x_1$, $\Delta y = y_2 - y_1$, $\Delta z = z_2 - z_1$, and $\Delta t = t_2 - t_1$. Then the term $[\,(\Delta x)^2 + (\Delta y)^2 + (\Delta z)^2\,]$ represents the (square of the) spatial distance between the two events, and the term $c^2(\Delta t)^2$ represents the (square of the) distance that light would travel during the elapsed time between the two events. The significant aspect of this "space-time interval" is that it will have exactly the same value (for a given pair of events) *in all reference systems.* Thus, this quantity is often called the "invariant interval."

AVOIDING PITFALLS

1. **Gamma:** Don't forget that γ in all the relativity expressions is the *reciprocal* of the square-root factor: $\gamma = 1/\sqrt{1 - v^2/c^2}$. Also, note that γ increases from $\gamma = 1$ (for $v = 0$) to $\gamma \to \infty$ (as $v \to c$).

2. **Speed of light:** The most fundamental fact in all of relativity is that *all* observers will observe light to travel at the same speed c, regardless of their own motion.

   When working a problem with distances given in light-years (or light-minutes, etc.), the speed of light becomes very simple:

   $c = 1\ \text{lt} \cdot \text{yr}/\text{yr} = 1\ \text{lt} \cdot \text{hr}/\text{hr} = 1\ \text{lt} \cdot \text{min}/\text{min} = \dots$

3. **Length contraction:** The length of any object will always be *reduced* when measured in any frame relative to which the object is moving. Thus, the rest length (also called "proper length") is always its *greatest* length. Also, this contraction occurs only in the dimension of an object that is measured *parallel* to its observed motion. The other dimensions do not change. Finally, this is a *true* contraction, not just an illusion: any phenomenon that depends on the length of that object will find its length to be contracted.

4. **Time dilation:** The tricky part of this effect is to decide which clock is running slower than the other. These problems fall into two types: (1) comparison of clocks in two reference frames that move with constant velocity, and (2) comparison of two clocks that start together in space and then return to the same point.

   The first type is a bit harder to visualize but is less ambiguous. In this (constant velocity) case, two clocks in relative motion can coincide in position only once, so we must visualize a whole system of clocks in each frame of reference, where all the clocks in a given frame are synchronized with each other. The "proper time interval" ($\Delta t'$) between two events is the time interval recorded in a frame (S') in which the two events occur *at the same point* in space. Then Δt is the time interval between the same two events, as recorded in S. Since the events occur at different locations in S, Δt is the difference between the readings on *two* clocks, one of which was present at the first event, the other of which was present at the second event. As Eq. 38-4 shows, $\Delta t > \Delta t'$, so the proper time interval is always the shortest.

The second type of problem, where one or both clocks move and eventually come back together, is not rigorously answerable within special relativity. For certain cases, however, we can use Eq. 38-4 to compare the readings on two clocks if we let Δt be the unaccelerated clock, and $\Delta t'$ the accelerated clock. (Thus, in the "twin paradox," Δt is the age of the twin left behind, and $\Delta t'$ is the age of the twin who goes on the round-trip voyage.) Again, note that $\Delta t' < \Delta t$.

5. **Inverse Lorentz transformations:** Don't forget to change v to $-v$ (while replacing x with x', etc.) in obtaining the inverse transformations.

6. **u vs. v:** We use two different symbols to distinguish between the velocity of a particle as measured in a given reference frame (**u** or **u'**), and **v**, the velocity of one reference frame (S') relative to another frame (S).

7. **Kinetic energy:** Even though we defined the relativistic momentum to be $\mathbf{p} = \gamma m\mathbf{u}$, we do *not* define the kinetic energy of a relativistic particle to be $K = \gamma\left(\frac{1}{2}mu^2\right)$. We *do* define (as in classical mechanics) the kinetic energy as the energy associated with its motion. In other words, the kinetic energy is the energy possessed by an object when in motion that it wouldn't have if it were at rest. Since the total energy of an object is simply $E = \gamma mc^2$ and its rest energy is $E_0 = mc^2$, we see that $K = E - E_0 = \gamma mc^2 - mc^2$.

8. **E = mc²:** This, probably the most famous equation in all of physics, does *not* describe "the conversion of matter into energy." Rather, it says that whenever the energy content of a system (in the form of gravitational potential energy, thermal energy, electrical potential energy, kinetic energy, or whatever) is increased, then its mass increases as well. Energy and mass are added to a system together, since they are, in effect, the same thing: matter-energy. The higher-energy system has a greater inertia, and it weighs more as well.

The energy released in a nuclear reaction comes about from a conversion of nuclear potential energy into electromagnetic energy and the kinetic energy of the decay products. The total mass of the system does not change: the change is a conversion of the nuclear potential energy, a form of energy that normally remains localized within the nucleus, into other forms of energy (typically gamma rays and kinetic energy), which then leave the nucleus.

 Connections to *ActivPhysics*

Chapter 38 explores Einstein's theory of relativity, and two activities from Unit 17 of *ActivPhysics* should aid in your understanding of this abstract subject. Activity 17.1 *Relativity of Time* illustrates the discussion of time dilation on pages 1014–1017; the simulation is an animated version of Figure 38-8. Activity 17.2 *Relativity of Length* uses the same concept of a "light clock" from the previous activity to demonstrate the necessity of the length contraction described on pages 1020–1021 of the text.

If you are using the Standard Version of the text, which ends with Chapter 39, you should follow this brief Study Guide chapter. If you are using the Extended Version, which continues to Chapter 45, you should skip to the following Study Guide chapter (39–Extended Version).

We conclude with a brief look at the behavior of matter on the atomic and nuclear level. Just as we had to adjust our "common sense" when we studied the physics of the very fast (special relativity), we will also be confronted with a profoundly different behavior when we study the physics of the very small. As we trace the development of our understanding of the structure of the atom, the nucleus, and the subnuclear particles, we will, surprisingly, come face-to-face with phenomena that relate to the big bang and the structure of the universe itself. Today, high-energy particle physicists and cosmologists find themselves asking many of the same questions and waiting for many of the same answers.

DEFINITIONS

You should know the definition of each of these terms. (The number in parentheses is the text chapter and section in which the term is introduced.)

(39-Intr) When used in this context, *classical physics* refers to the laws that describe the behavior of matter on an everyday, macroscopic scale. The fundamental characteristics are that most physical quantities (*e.g.*, energy, mass, momentum, etc.) are presumed to have a continuum of values, and that there is no *theoretical* limit to the precision with which we may measure any physical quantity.

(39-Intr) *Quantum mechanics* describes the behavior of matter on the atomic and nuclear scale. Quantum mechanics is characterized by the fact that many physical quantities can take on values only from a discrete set, and that the wave nature of matter places a *fundamental* lower limit on the uncertainty with which we can ever measure certain pairs of variables.

(39-1) When an object is heated to incandescence, it emits light with a characteristic, continuous spectrum. In general, this spectrum depends on the material and surface finish of the object. However, objects that are perfectly absorbing (black) at normal temperatures turn out to be the most efficient radiators when incandescent, and the spectrum is the same for all black bodies at a given temperature. The detailed shape of this *blackbody* spectrum led Max Planck to the quantum hypothesis.

(39-1) Electromagnetic energy is quantized, and one of these single packages of electromagnetic energy is known as a *photon*. (The photon carries not only energy but also linear and angular momentum.)

(39-1) In the *photoelectric effect*, when light shines on a clean metal surface, electrons can be given enough energy to be ejected from the surface of the metal.

(39-1) *de Broglie's hypothesis:* Led by the wave-particle duality of electromagnetic radiation, Louis de Broglie proposed that matter also possesses a wave nature, and that its inherent wavelength is inversely proportional to its linear momentum.

(39-2) The *Schrödinger equation* is a second-order partial differential equation that determines, for a given potential, the exact wave behavior of a particle. The solutions of the Schrödinger equation, known as "wave functions," are closely related to the probability of the particle's being located at any given point in space, and other dynamical properties of the system (energy, momentum, etc.) can also be deduced from the wave functions.

(39-2) Heisenberg's *uncertainty principle* states that the product of the uncertainties in simultaneous measurements of certain pairs of variables (*e.g.*, position and momentum or energy and time) can never be less than a certain minimum value $(h/2\pi)$.

(39-2) Experiments performed in the 1920s demonstrated that electrons possess a magnetic moment that results from an internal angular momentum. This *spin* magnetic moment is quantized, and can take on only one or the other of two values, corresponding to an "up-spin" state and a "down-spin" state.

(39-2) The wave functions for any particle are characterized by a set of *quantum numbers*, usually integers. The state of any electron in a single-electron atom, for example, is specified by three quantum numbers that identify the particular wave function (n, ℓ, and m), plus one extra number (s) that identifies the spin state of the electron.

(39-2) The *Pauli exclusion principle* states that no two electrons in a given atom may occupy the same state, as labeled by the four quantum numbers n, ℓ, m, and s.

(39-2) *Antimatter:* First verified by the discovery of the positron in 1932, Dirac's equation predicts that, for every kind of "normal" particle, there exists a kind of mirror-image "antiparticle." The two are identical in mass, but the antiparticle will have the opposite sign of electric charge.

(39-2) *Quantum electrodynamics* is a description of electromagnetic interactions in terms of virtual photon exchanges between charged particles.

(39-3) Because of the very strong attractive forces holding the nucleons together, a large amount of work is needed to separate them from each other. The work we do in disassembling a nucleus increases the energy of the system, and this additional energy equals the *"binding energy"* of the nucleus.

(39-3) Many nuclei are unstable, and these *radioactive* nuclei can transform to a more stable configuration by emitting various particles. (Beta particles, alpha particles, and gamma-ray photons are the most common.)

(39-3) The *half-life* of a radioactive sample is the time required for one-half of the nuclei to decay.

(39-3) *Fission*: Many large nuclei decay to more stable configurations by splitting into two pieces (called "daughter nuclei"), frequently releasing one or more neutrons in the process. (If the fission occurs naturally, it is known as "spontaneous fission"; if the fission occurs because an otherwise stable nucleus has been injected with an extra particle (usually a neutron), it is called "induced fission.")

(39-4) Subnuclear particles that *experience the strong nuclear force* (including the proton and neutron) are today thought to be composite systems of *quarks* (and/or antiquarks). Quarks are characterized by carrying electric charges of $(2/3)e$ or $(-1/3)e$, and by the fact that they are so tightly bound to each other that we can never observe a free quark—only triplets of quarks, or quark-antiquark pairs.

(39-4) The other major class of fundamental particles, *leptons* are particles that do not experience the strong nuclear force.

SUMMARY OF EQUATIONS

1. Energy of a photon:

$$E = hf \qquad \text{(Text Eq. 39-1)}$$

According to the photon model of electromagnetic radiation, electromagnetic energy is radiated or absorbed in discrete "quanta," each of which has an energy E that is directly proportional to the frequency f of the wave we would associate with the radiation. The constant of proportionality h is known as Planck's constant, and has the very tiny value $h = 6.626 \times 10^{-34}$ J · s.

2. Wavelengths in hydrogenlike spectra:

$$\frac{1}{\lambda} = R\left(\frac{1}{n_2^2} - \frac{1}{n_1^2}\right) \qquad \text{(Text Eq. 39-3)}$$

This expression gives the wavelengths emitted or absorbed by single-electron atoms (neutral hydrogen, singly ionized helium, doubly ionized lithium, etc.). In this expression, R is a constant that is a characteristic of the atom (for hydrogen, $R_H = 1.097 \times 10^7$ m^{-1}), and n_2 and n_1 are integers that identify the upper (high-energy) and lower (low-energy) states of the atom.

3. Wavelength of matter waves:

$$\lambda = \frac{h}{P} \qquad \text{(Text Eq. 39-4)}$$

de Broglie predicted that matter should exhibit wave behavior, and that the wavelength of a particle is inversely proportional to its momentum.

4. Heisenberg's uncertainty principle:

$$\Delta x \cdot \Delta p_x \geq \frac{h}{2\pi} \qquad \text{(Text Eq. 39-5)}$$

$$\Delta t \cdot \Delta E \geq \frac{h}{2\pi} \qquad \text{(Text Eq. 39-6)}$$

These are two equivalent statements of what is probably the most profound difference between classical physics and quantum physics. The uncertainty principle states that the product of the uncertainties in, say, the x-coordinate of position and the x-component of momentum of *any* particle can *never* be less than $h/2\pi$. The same principle also states that the product of the uncertainty in any particle's energy and the uncertainty in the time at which the particle had that energy is also greater than $h/2\pi$.

AVOIDING PITFALLS

1. **Photoelectric effect:** Although we haven't treated the photoelectric effect quantitatively, it's important to realize that the kinetic energy of the electrons ejected from the illuminated metal surface is determined by the *frequency* of the light, not its intensity. Thus, higher-frequency light, not brighter bulbs, produces higher-energy electrons.

2. **Energy of a photon:** The energy of a photon is determined strictly by its frequency, according to $E = hf$. (Note: The frequency does determine the wavelength, so we could equally well write $E = hc/\lambda$.) Thus, short-wavelength (high-frequency) photons have high energies.

3. **The uncertainty principle:**
   a. Heisenberg's uncertainty principle places a minimum value on the uncertainties of *simultaneous* measurements of x and p_x, or of E and t.
   b. The uncertainty principle relates measurements of x and p_x or y and p_y, but it says nothing about simultaneous measurements of x and p_y, for example.

c. Δp_x is determined by Δx alone, regardless of the mass of the object.

d. Generally speaking, the limits imposed by the uncertainty principle are immeasurably small for macroscopic systems, but as the size of the system gets smaller, the effects become more important.

4. **Fundamental particles:** Of the electron, proton, and neutron, only the electron is today considered a "fundamental particle." The proton and neutron, like other hadrons, are composed of various combinations of quarks.

The fundamental constituent particles of matter fall into two categories:

a. *Leptons:* e^-, μ^-, τ^-, ν_e, ν_μ, ν_τ.

b. *Quarks: u, d, c, s, t, b.*

There is also an antiparticle corresponding to each of these twelve particles. Further, each force (electromagnetic, color, weak) is transmitted through the exchange of *bosons* (spin-zero particles): *photons* mediate the electromagnetic force, *gluons* mediate the strong force, and the *W* and *Z* particles mediate the weak nuclear force.

 Connections to *ActivPhysics*

Quantum theory evolved as a response to experimental observations that either contradicted the current theories of mechanics and electromagnetism or couldn't be explained by them. Many of the key experiments of modern physics or the models developed to explain their results discussed in Chapter 39 are illustrated by *ActivPhysics* activities.

The photoelectric effect is one of the important experiments that led to the development of quantum theory. The experiment is discussed on pages 1047–1049 and simulated in Activity 17.3 *Photoelectric Effect*. This activity, like most of the activities found in the last four units of *ActivPhysics*, should help you visualize the concepts and principles relating to the physical behavior of atomic and subatomic particles.

One of the first models of quantum theory is described on pages 1049–1051 and simulated by Activity 18.1 *The Bohr Model*. Figures 39-5 and 39-7 are included in the simulation, and "seeing" the motion of the electron in its quantum orbits and the transitions it makes between orbits that Bohr envisioned should help make this model more understandable. In the same way, Activity 18.3 *Standing Electron Waves* animates and explains Figure 39-11, and Activity 17.5 *Electron Interference* relates to Figure 39-10.

The final sections of the chapter survey some of the ideas that will be explored in greater detail in later chapters. The uncertainty principle is explained in the text on pages 1055–1056 and illustrated in Activity 17.6 *Uncertainty Principle*. Activity 17.7 *Wave Packets* demonstrates how it is possible to unify the contradictory concepts of a wave and a particle into a single model. Although nuclear physics is covered in great detail in Chapters 43–45, a survey of the topic is included in Section 39-3; Activities 19.2 *Nuclear Binding Energy* and 19.4 *Radioactivity* have a direct bearing on these topics. They can be studied here if nuclear physics will be included on an exam covering this chapter, or they could be saved for a later time when these subjects are covered in greater detail.

CHAPTER 39   LIGHT AND MATTER: WAVES OR PARTICLES?   (EXTENDED VERSION)

We now begin our look into the atomic, molecular, and nuclear structure of matter. Two fundamental, radical, and interconnected concepts are developed in this chapter: the quantization of physical systems, and the wave-particle duality of nature.

We begin by studying the electromagnetic spectrum emitted by a blackbody. Classical thermodynamics and electromagnetism predict a spectrum that not only differs from the observed spectrum but is also physical nonsense. The resolution of this dilemma was provided in 1900 by Max Planck's quantum hypothesis: The energy of a vibrating particle can take on values only from a discrete set.

Five years after Planck's quantum hypothesis, Einstein explained the photoelectric effect by proposing that light consists of individual "photons," each carrying a well-defined energy and momentum. That is, electromagnetic radiation has not only a wave nature, but also a *particle* nature.

Building on Planck's quantum hypothesis, Neils Bohr successfully explained the line spectrum, ionization potential, and the size of hydrogen atoms by proposing that electron orbits were also quantized. Specifically, Bohr assumed that the angular momentum of the orbiting electron could have only integer multiples of Planck's constant (divided by 2π).

Within the next several years, it became evident that matter itself also had a wave nature, so that both electromagnetic radiation and matter possessed wave *and* particle properties. The wave nature of matter was first proposed by Louis de Broglie in 1923, and electron diffraction was observed less than 5 years later.

An important consequence of the wave nature of matter is stated by Heisenberg's uncertainty principle, which holds that certain pairs of related properties (*e.g.*, position and momentum, or energy and time) cannot be measured with unlimited precision, but an irreducible indeterminacy exists in such pairs of quantities.

DEFINITIONS

You should know the definition of each of these terms. (The number in parentheses is the text chapter and section in which the term is introduced.)

(39-Intr) When used in this context, *classical physics* refers to the laws that describe the behavior of matter on an everyday, macroscopic scale. The fundamental characteristics are that all physical quantities are presumed to have a continuum of values, and that there is no *theoretical* limit to the precision with which we may measure any physical quantity.

(39-Intr) *Quantum mechanics* describes the behavior of matter on the atomic and nuclear scale. Quantum mechanics is characterized by the fact that many physical quantities can take on values only from a discrete set, and that the wave nature of matter places a *fundamental* lower limit on the uncertainty with which we can ever measure certain pairs of variables.

(39-2) When an object is heated to incandescence, it emits light with a characteristic, continuous spectrum. In general, this spectrum depends on the material and surface finish of the object. However, objects that are perfectly absorbing (black) at normal temperatures turn out to be the most efficient radiators when incandescent, and their spectrum is the same for all black bodies at a given temperature. The detailed shape of this *blackbody* spectrum led Max Planck to the quantum hypothesis.

(39-2) The *radiance* is defined to be the power (energy per time) radiated per unit area, per unit wavelength range.

(39-2) Classical physics (thermodynamics and Maxwell's equations of electrodynamics) predicts the radiance of a blackbody to be inversely proportional to the fourth power of the wavelength ($R \propto \lambda^{-4}$). Thus, any object above absolute zero should be emitting unlimited amounts of short wavelength radiation (ultraviolet and beyond). This unphysical prediction is known as the *ultraviolet catastrophe*.

(39-3)   Electromagnetic energy is emitted and absorbed in discrete packages of energy called *photons*. Each photon travels at precisely the speed of light, carries energy $E = hf$, and has momentum $p = E/c$.

(39-3) In the *photoelectric effect*, light shining on a clean metal surface can give electrons enough energy to be ejected from the surface of the metal.

(39-3) In the *Compton effect*, a photon collides with a particle and scatters through some angle, emerging with less energy (and hence, longer wavelength) than before the collision.

(39-3) *Wave-particle duality* refers to the fact that both matter and radiation have a dual nature, behaving like particles under certain circumstances, and behaving like waves at other times.

(39-4) The *ground state* of an atom is the state with lowest total energy.

(39-4) The *ionization energy* of an atom is the energy needed to remove an electron from the atom.

(39-5) *de Broglie's hypothesis:* Led by the wave-particle duality of electromagnetic radiation, Louis de Broglie proposed that matter also possesses a wave nature, and that its inherent wavelength is inversely proportional to its linear momentum.

(39-6) Heisenberg's *uncertainty principle* states that the product of the uncertainties in simultaneous measurements of certain pairs of variables (*e.g.*, position and momentum or energy and time) can never be less than a certain minimum value ($h/2\pi$).

(39-7) The *complementarity principle* states that the wave and particle natures of matter and radiation are complementary aspects. At any given moment, we will either observe the wave nature *or* the particle nature, but not both.

(39-8) The *correspondence principle,* first stated by Neils Bohr, states that any new physical theory must agree with older, well-established laws in the situation(s) in which the old laws are known to be valid.

SUMMARY OF EQUATIONS

1. Stefan-Boltzmann law of radiation:

$$P_{\text{blackbody}} = \sigma A T^4 \qquad \text{(Text Eq. 39-1)}$$

First encountered in Chapter 19 while discussing radiation as one of the three methods of thermal transport, this law is one of two empirical descriptions of the electromagnetic energy radiated by a (black) incandescent object. The Stefan-Boltzmann law states that the total power radiated by an object at kelvin temperature T is proportional to the surface area A and the *fourth* power of the temperature. The proportionality constant is known as the Stefan-Boltzmann constant, and has the (SI) value $\sigma = 5.67 \times 10^{-8}$ W/m²·K⁴.

2. Wien's displacement law:

$$\lambda_{\text{max}}T = 2.898 \times 10^{-3} \text{ m} \cdot \text{K} \qquad \text{(Text Eq. 39-2)}$$

This is the quantitative description of the observation that the color of an incandescent object shifts from a dull red through orange and yellow to a brilliant white as the temperature increases. The wavelength of the most intense radiation emitted by an object at kelvin temperature T is inversely proportional to the temperature.

3. Rayleigh-Jeans law of thermal radiation:

$$R(\lambda, T) = \frac{2\pi c k T}{\lambda^4} \qquad \text{(Text Eq. 39-5)}$$

Consider the electromagnetic energy radiated by a black (perfectly absorbing) object at a kelvin temperature T. The power radiated per unit area per unit wavelength is called the radiance, R. The Rayleigh-Jeans law, derived rigorously from classical electromagnetic theory and thermodynamics, predicts a radiance that increases without limit as the wavelength goes to zero. (Thus, any object above absolute zero would be a deadly source of lethal gamma rays!) This prediction is nonsense, of course. However, the Rayleigh-Jeans formula remains a useful long-wavelength approximation for the exact (but more complicated) Planck radiation law. In this expression, $c = 3.0 \times 10^8$ m/s (the speed of light), and $k = 1.38 \times 10^{-23}$ J/K (Boltzmann's constant).

4. Planck's radiation law:

$$R(\lambda, T) = \frac{2\pi hc^2}{\lambda^5(e^{hc/\lambda kT} - 1)} \qquad \text{(Text Eq. 39-3)}$$

This rather complicated-looking equation accurately describes the spectrum of thermal radiation from a blackbody at a kelvin temperature T. It embodies both the Stefan-Boltzmann law (by integrating the radiance over all wavelengths, we obtain the total radiated power) and Wien's displacement law (obtained by solving for the wavelength that maximizes R).

5. Planck's quantum hypothesis:

$$E = nhf/(n = 1, 2, 3, \dots) \qquad \text{(Text Eq. 39-4)}$$

To obtain his radiation law, Planck had to assume that the energy of the oscillating molecules in the radiating surface was quantized—that is, the energy could only take on values from a discrete set. The proposed energies were integer multiples of hf, where f is the frequency of oscillation (in Hz), and h, now known as Planck's constant, has the value $h = 6.626 \times 10^{-34}$ J·s.

6. Energy of a photon:

$$E = hf \qquad \text{(Text Eq. 39-6)}$$

To explain the photoelectric effect, Einstein proposed that light is emitted or absorbed in discrete quanta of energy, which we now call "photons." Each photon has an energy E that is directly proportional to the frequency f of the wave we would associate with the radiation. The constant of proportionality h is Planck's constant.

7. Photoelectron kinetic energy:

$$K_{\text{max}} = hf - \phi \qquad \text{(Text Eq. 39-7)}$$

A certain amount of energy (ϕ) is required to remove an electron from the surface of a metal. When a photon of light strikes a metal surface, an electron can be ejected from the metal if the photon energy (hf) exceeds the "work function" (ϕ) of the metal. The kinetic energy of the ejected electron is the photon energy minus the work function. (Values of ϕ for several different metals are given in Table 39-1, on page 1051 of the text.)

8. Compton wavelength shift:

$$\Delta\lambda = \frac{h}{mc}(1 - \cos\theta) \quad \text{(Text Eq. 39-8)}$$

A photon of light scatters from a particle of mass m. The scattered photon has a longer wavelength than the incident photon. The increase in wavelength ($\Delta\lambda = \lambda_f - \lambda_i$) is inversely proportional to the mass of the target particle. $\Delta\lambda$ also depends on the scattering angle θ, reaching a maximum shift for a scattering angle $\theta = 180°$. Note that the change in wavelength is independent of the actual photon wavelength.

9. Wavelengths in hydrogenlike spectra:

$$\frac{1}{\lambda} = R\left(\frac{1}{n_2^2} - \frac{1}{n_1^2}\right) \quad \text{(Text Eq. 39-9)}$$

This expression gives the wavelengths emitted or absorbed by single-electron atoms (neutral hydrogen, singly ionized helium, doubly ionized lithium, etc.). In this expression, R is a constant that is a characteristic of the atom (for hydrogen, $R_H = 1.097 \times 10^7 \text{ m}^{-1}$), and n_2 and n_1 are integers that identify the upper (high-energy) and lower (low-energy) states of the atom.

10. Energy levels of hydrogen:

$$E = -\frac{k^2e^4m}{2\hbar^2}\frac{1}{n^2} \quad (n = 1, 2, 3, \ldots)$$

In the Bohr model of the hydrogen atom, the atom can only have an energy ($E = K + U$) from a set of discrete values. Because the (negative) electrical potential energy is greater than the (positive) kinetic energy of the electron, the total energy is negative. The SI values of the constants appearing in this equation are as follows:

$$k = 8.988 \times 10^9 \text{ N} \cdot \text{m}^2/\text{C}^2$$

$$e = 1.602 \times 10^{-19} \text{ C}$$

$$m = 9.109 \times 10^{-31} \text{ kg}$$

$$\hbar = h/2\pi = 1.055 \times 10^{-34} \text{ J} \cdot \text{s}$$

It is often more convenient when describing atomic-sized systems to express energies in electron-volts rather than joules (1 eV = 1.602 $\times$ 10^{-19} J). Then the hydrogen energy levels become

$$E = -(13.6\,\text{eV})\frac{1}{n^2} \quad \text{(Text Eq. 39-12b)}$$

11. Radius of Bohr orbits for hydrogen:

$$r = \left(\frac{\hbar^2}{mke^2}\right)n^2 = a_0 n^2 \quad \text{(Text Eq. 39-13)}$$

In the Bohr model of hydrogen, the electron is visualized as orbiting in well-defined circular orbits. The radii of the possible orbits are also quantized, and increase with higher quantum number n. The smallest possible orbit (called the "ground state") has a radius $a_0 = 0.0529$ nm. (Note: We now know that the electrons do *not* move in well-defined circular orbits, but they have a more wavelike behavior. As such, we can only predict the probability of a measurement finding the electron at a given distance from the nucleus. The most probable distance for an electron in the ground state, however, happens to be a_0.)

12. de Broglie's hypothesis:

$$\lambda = \frac{h}{p} \quad \text{(Text Eq. 39-14)}$$

Prompted by the dual (wave and particle) nature of radiation, de Broglie proposed that matter should also have a dual nature. The wavelength of the "matter wave" associated with a particle with momentum p is given by $\lambda = h/p$.

13. Heisenberg's uncertainty principle:

$$\Delta x \cdot \Delta p_x \geq \hbar \quad \text{(Text Eq. 39-15)}$$

$$\Delta t \cdot \Delta E \geq \hbar \quad \text{(Text Eq. 39-16)}$$

These are two complementary statements of what is probably the most profound difference between classical physics and quantum physics. The uncertainty principle states that the product of the uncertainties in, say, the x-coordinate of position and the x-component of momentum of any particle can *never* be less than $\hbar$ ($= h/2\pi$). The same principle also states that the product of the uncertainty in any particle's energy and the uncertainty in the time at which the particle had that energy is also greater than $\hbar$.

AVOIDING PITFALLS

1. **"k":** Two different quantities are represented by the symbol k in this chapter: In the Rayleigh-Jeans and Planck radiation laws, k represents Boltzmann's constant (1.38×10^{-23} J/K). In the Bohr theory of the hydrogen atom, k represents the Coulomb's-law constant (9.0×10^9 N $\cdot$ m^2/C^2). If you encounter an unfamiliar equation with k and you aren't sure which k is used, you can be sure that when you see kT, it's a thermodynamic quantity of energy, and you need Boltzmann's constant. However, when k is multiplied by e^2, it's an electrical quantity, and you need the Coulomb's law constant.

2. **h and $\hbar$**: Because Planck's constant ($h = 6.626 \times 10^{-34}$ J·s) often appears in an equation divided by 2π, it's convenient to define $\hbar = h/2\pi = 1.055 \times 10^{-34}$ J·s. Both h and $\hbar$ appear in this chapter, so take care to notice which is being used.

3. **Intensity of blackbody radiation:** The total power radiated (per unit area) of a blackbody is directly proportional to the *fourth* power of the absolute temperature, so doubling the (kelvin) temperature increases the total power radiated by a factor of 2^4, or 16.

4. **Peak wavelength:** The wavelength at which a blackbody radiates most strongly is *inversely* proportional to the (absolute) temperature. Thus, if the temperature is doubled, the wavelength of the peak is cut in half, moving toward shorter wavelengths.

5. **Harmonic oscillators:** Classically, the energy of a harmonic oscillator ($E = \frac{1}{2}kA^2$) is independent of the vibration frequency, and is determined by the stiffness of the restoring force (k) and the amplitude of the oscillations (A). Since the amplitude can vary continuously, the energy of the oscillator can take on any of a continuum of values. Quantum theory, however, holds the energy of an oscillator is quantized (according to $E_n = nhf$, $n = 1, 2, 3, \ldots$), and the quantum of energy (hf) is determined solely by the *frequency*.

6. **Energy of a photon:** The energy of a photon is determined strictly by its frequency, according to $E = hf$. (Note: The frequency does determine the wavelength, so we could equally well write $E = hc/\lambda$.) Thus, a short-wavelength (high-frequency) photon is a high-energy photon and, since $E = pc$, a high-momentum photon.

7. **Photoelectric effect:** If the photons have an energy ($E = hc/\lambda$) *greater* than the work function ϕ of the metal, electrons will be ejected from the surface with kinetic energies up to $K_{\max} = hc/\lambda - \phi$. If the photons have an energy *less* than the work function of the metal, then *no* photoelectrons will appear. It's important to realize that the kinetic energy of the electrons ejected from the illuminated metal surface is determined by the *frequency* of the light, not its intensity. Thus, higher frequency light, not more intense light, produces higher-energy electrons. (A more intense light source will produce *more* photoelectrons, but their kinetic energy is determined by the light frequency.)

8. **Compton scattering:**
   a. The scattered photon always has a longer wavelength than the incoming photon, because some of the incoming photon's energy is given to the target particle in the form of recoil kinetic energy.

   b. The *increase* in wavelength ($\Delta\lambda$) is independent of the incoming photon's energy (or wavelength), and is determined by the scattering angle and the mass of the target particle:
   $$\Delta\lambda = \frac{h}{mc}(1 - \cos\theta).$$

   c. Because m appears in the denominator of the Compton formula, massive target particles (typically, nuclei or tightly bound inner electrons) produce negligible changes in wavelength, while lighter target particles produce larger wavelength shifts. Even the lightest target particle (a free electron) increases the wavelength by no more than $2h/mc \approx 0.005$ nm, so the Compton shift is significant only for short-wavelength photons.

9. **de Broglie wavelength:** Just as electromagnetic waves have a particle nature, matter possesses wave properties. The wavelength associated with any particle is inversely proportional to its linear momentum ($\lambda = h/p$). As the momentum of a particle increases, its de Broglie wavelength decreases, becoming immeasurably small for macroscopic-sized objects. Note that all particles with the same momentum (regardless of mass) have the same wavelength. Obviously, a massive particle will move more slowly than a lighter particle with the same momentum, but they will have the same wavelength.

10. **Momentum and kinetic energy:** As mentioned above, the de Broglie wavelength is determined by the momentum of a particle. In many problems, however, you are given the particle's energy rather than the momentum. The relationship between kinetic energy and momentum depends on the particle's speed:

    exact: $E^2 = p^2c^2 + E_0^2$, where $E = K + E_0$.

    While this is correct at all speeds, there are two common situations where simpler (approximate) relations can be used:

    nonrelativistic case:

    ($v \ll c$, or $K \ll E_0$, or $pc \ll E_0$): $K \approx p^2/2m$;

    extreme relativistic case:

    ($v \approx c$, or $K \gg E_0$, or $pc \gg E_0$): $K \approx pc$.

11. **Uncertainty principle:**
    a. The uncertainty principle relates indeterminacies in *identical* components of position and momentum:

    $\Delta x \cdot \Delta p_x \geq \hbar$, $\Delta y \cdot \Delta p_y \geq \hbar$, and $\Delta z \cdot \Delta p_z \geq \hbar$.

    There is no restriction on *different* components, so $\Delta x \cdot \Delta p_y \geq 0$, $\Delta y \cdot \Delta p_z \geq 0$, etc.

b. The uncertainty principle also refers only to *simultaneous* measurements. Thus, it is (in principle) possible to measure precisely the *x*-coordinate of a particle at one instant ($\Delta x = 0$), and then, *at some later time*, precisely measure its momentum ($\Delta p_x = 0$).

c. Generally speaking, the limits imposed by the uncertainty principle are immeasurably small for macroscopic systems, but as the size of the system gets smaller, the effects become more important.

 Connections to *ActivPhysics*

Quantum theory evolved as a response to experimental observations that either contradicted the contemporary theories of mechanics and electromagnetism or couldn't be explained by them. Many of the key experiments of modern physics or the models developed to explain their results discussed in Chapter 39 are illustrated by *ActivPhysics* activities.

The photoelectric effect is one of the important experiments that led to the development of quantum theory. The experiment is discussed on pages 1047–1049 and simulated in Activity 17.3 *Photoelectric Effect*. This activity, like most of the activities found in the last four units of *ActivPhysics*, should help you visualize the concepts and principles relating to the physical behavior of atomic and subatomic particles.

One of the first models of quantum theory is described on pages 1049–1051 and simulated by Activity 18.1 *The Bohr Model*. Figures 39-5 and 39-7 are included in the simulation, and "seeing" the motion of the electron in its quantum orbits and the transitions it makes between orbits that Bohr envisioned should help make this model more understandable. In the same way, Activity 18.3 *Standing Electron Waves* animates and explains Figure 39-11, and Activity 17.5 *Electron Interference* relates to Figure 39-10.

The final sections of the chapter survey some of the ideas that will be explored in greater detail in later chapters. The uncertainty principle is explained in the text on pages 1055–1056 and illustrated in Activity 17.6 *Uncertainty Principle*. Activity 17.7 *Wave Packets* demonstrates how it is possible to unify the contradictory concepts of a wave and a particle into a single model. Although nuclear physics is covered in great detail in Chapters 43–45, a survey of the topic is included in Section 39-3; Activities 19.2 *Nuclear Binding Energy* and 19.4 *Radioactivity* have a direct bearing on these topics. They can be studied here if nuclear physics will be included on an exam covering this chapter, or they could be saved for a later time when these subjects are covered in greater detail.

CHAPTER 40 QUANTUM MECHANICS

In this chapter we study the wave nature of matter in greater detail. The wave properties of any particle are described by its wave function, the solution to Schrödinger's equation. In this chapter we will concentrate on the part of the wave function that does not depend on time. The significance of this function (ψ) lies in the fact that its square gives the probability of finding the particle at any point in space. The dynamical properties of the particle (energy, momentum, angular momentum, etc.) can then be derived from its wave function.

Solving Schrödinger's equation can, in general, be a rather formidable task, so we will consider only a few, relatively simple cases: (1) a free particle, absolutely confined to a certain region (the "infinite square well"), (2) a particle oscillating about its equilibrium position in response to a linear restoring force (the "quantum harmonic oscillator"), and (3) a free particle moving near a finite square-well potential.

Finally, Schrödinger's theory is nonrelativistic, appropriate for low-energy ($K \ll E_0$) particles. Paul Dirac developed a fully relativistic theory of quantum mechanics, which we will discuss only qualitatively. Dirac's theory predicts the intrinsic angular momentum ("spin") of the electron, as well as the existence of "antiparticles."

DEFINITIONS

You should know the definition of each of these terms. (The number in parentheses is the text chapter and section in which the term is introduced.)

(40-2)   The Schrödinger equation is a postulated equation that has, as its solutions, functions that describe the wave nature of matter on a microscopic scale. When the potential energy of a system is independent of time, we can separate out the time dependence, and we are left with the *time-independent Schrödinger equation*.

(40-2) The ψ *function*, or *wave function*, of a particle is the part of its full wave function that does not depend on time. ψ determines the probability density as a function of position.

(40-2) The *probability density* gives the probability per unit volume of a measurement finding the particle at a particular point in space. (In one- or two-dimensional situations, the probability density is interpreted as the probability per unit length or probability per unit area, respectively.)

(40-2) When a wave function has been scaled (by multiplying it by an appropriate constant) to make the total probability over all space equal to unity, we say that the wave function has been *normalized*.

(40-3) A particle that moves freely while trapped between impenetrable boundaries is said to be moving in an *"infinite square well."* (The "infinite" refers to the fact that it would take an infinite amount of energy for the particle to escape, not that the width of the well is infinite. (The width is, in fact, a finite value *L*.) "Square" refers to the fact that the potential increases abruptly at the boundaries, so a plot of *U(x)* has a square shape.

(40-3) A particle confined to a finite region of space is never at rest, but always has some minimum kinetic energy, known as its *ground-state energy*.

(40-5) The wave nature of subatomic particles allows them to occasionally pass through barriers that, according to classical physics, should be impenetrable. This phenomenon is known as *barrier penetration* or *quantum tunneling*.

(40-5) A *scanning tunneling microscope* works on the phenomenon of quantum tunneling. An extremely sharp needle is passed very close to the surface whose details are being studied. A small potential difference between the surface and the needle allows electrons to "tunnel" from the surface to the tip of the needle. Variations in the electron current allow a highly magnified topographic profile of the surface to be constructed.

(40-6) Consider a particle in a finite potential well. Its potential energy is zero inside the well, and U_0 outside the well. All states with energy $E < U_0$ are known as *bound states*, since the particle will always return to the well.

(40-6) All states of a particle in a finite well with energy $E > U_0$ are known as *unbound states*, since the particle is free to move away from the well and not return. (It is important to realize that the bound states have quantized energy values, but the unbound states have a continuum of energies.)

(40-7) It sometimes happens that two or more states (differing in probability distributions, momentum, etc.) have exactly the same energy. Different states with the same energy are said to be *degenerate states*.

(40-8) The Schrödinger equation is nonrelativistic. Paul Dirac derived a relativistic description of atomic systems, and the result (a four-component matrix equation) is known as the *Dirac equation*.

(40-8) Dirac's relativistic wave equation predicted the existence of an entire new class of particles in a one-to-one correspondence with "ordinary" matter. Each of these *"antiparticles"* is something like a mirror image of its ordinary partner. For example, an antiproton has the same mass and spin as a proton, but it carries a negative electrical charge. A positron (or antielectron) is just like a positively charged electron.

(40-8) When a high-energy photon interacts with the electromagnetic field of a nucleus, the photon can disappear, creating in its place a matter-antimatter *pair* of particles.

(40-8) A particle's *spin* refers to its internal angular momentum. The spin angular momentum is independent of the particle's motion. It is an intrinsic property of the particle, much like its mass or electrical charge.

SUMMARY OF EQUATIONS

1. Time-independent Schrödinger equation: one dimension:

$$-\frac{\hbar^2}{2m}\frac{d^2 c(x)}{dx^2} + U(x)\,c(x) = E\,c(x) \quad \text{(Text Eq. 40-1)}$$

In this equation, $U(x)$ gives the potential energy of the particle as a function of its position. In general, a set of solutions $\psi_n(x)$ will be found, each corresponding to a different total energy ($E_n = K + U$). Each of the solutions $\psi_n(x)$ of this equation is known as the "wave function" of the particle for that particular state.

If the particle is free to move in two or three dimensions, then the wave function becomes $\psi(x, y)$ or $\psi(x, y, z)$, and the second derivative $(d^2\psi/dx^2)$ in Schrödinger's equation is replaced with $(\delta^2\psi/\delta x^2 + \delta^2\psi/\delta y^2)$ or $(\delta^2\psi/\delta x^2 + \delta^2\psi/\delta y^2 + \delta^2\psi/\delta z^2)$, respectively.

2. Probability:

$$P(dx) = \psi^2(x)\,dx \quad \text{(Text Eq. 40-2)}$$

The probability that any measurement will find a particle within a tiny region dx located at the position x is given by the product of the *square* of the wave function and the width of the region.

It then follows that the probability of finding the particle within a *finite* region (between $x = a$ and $x = b$) is the sum of the probabilities for each part of that region:

$$P(a,b) = \int_a^b \psi^2(x)dx.$$

If the particle is free to move within a two-dimensional region, then its wave function depends on two coordinates (x and y), and the probability of finding the particle within a tiny area $dA = dx\,dy$ is given by

$$P(dA) = \psi^2(x, y)\,dx\,dy.$$

Similarly, the probability of finding the particle within a tiny three-dimensional *volume* is

$$P(dV) = \psi^2(x, y, z)\,dx\,dy\,dz.$$

3. Normalization:

$$P(-\infty, +\infty) = \int_{-\infty}^{+\infty} \psi^2(x)dx = 1 \quad \text{(Text Eq. 40-3)}$$

A particle confined to a one-dimensional region must exist *somewhere* between $x = -\infty$ and $x = +\infty$, so the total probability in that region must be 100%, or 1.

For two- or three-dimensional systems, the normalization conditions are

$$\iint_{-\infty}^{+\infty} \psi^2(x,y)dx\,dy = 1 \qquad \text{(two dimensions)}$$

$$\iiint_{-\infty}^{+\infty} \psi^2(x,y,z)dx\,dy\,dz = 1 \qquad \text{(three dimensions)}$$

4. One-dimensional infinite square-well solutions $U = 0$ for $0 \le x \le L$; $U = \infty$ otherwise:

wave function: $c_n(x) = A \sin\left[\dfrac{n\pi x}{L}\right]$, $n = 1, 2, 3, \ldots$

normalization constant: $A = \sqrt{\dfrac{2}{L}}$. (Text Eq. 40-5, 7)

The wave functions that describe the different states of a particle free to move along the x-axis between $x = 0$ and $x = L$ are given by $\psi(x)$. Note that this particular normalization constant A is independent of the quantum number n.

$$\text{energy: } E_n = \frac{n^2 h^2}{8mL^2} \quad \text{(Text Eq. 40-6)}$$

The energy of the states described above are squared-integer multiples of the minimum, or "ground-state" energy, $E_1 = h^2/8mL^2$.

5. Three-dimensional infinite square-well solutions ($U = (0, 0, 0)$ for $0 \le (x, y, z) \le (L, L, L)$; $U = \infty$, otherwise):

wave function:

$$c(x, y, z) = A \sin\left(\frac{n_x\pi x}{L}\right)\sin\left(\frac{n_y\pi y}{L}\right)\sin\left(\frac{n_z\pi z}{L}\right)$$

$$\text{energy: } E = \frac{h^2}{8mL^2}(n_x^2 + n_y^2 + n_z^2) \quad \text{(Text Eq. 40-12)}$$

(Each of the three quantum numbers is a positive integer.)

6. Harmonic oscillator:

Potential energy:

$$U = \tfrac{1}{2}m\omega^2 x^2. \quad \text{(Text Eq. 40-8)}$$

A harmonic oscillator moves in response to a linear restoring force of the form $F_x = -kx$. Equivalently, we can describe this in terms of the potential energy $U = \tfrac{1}{2}kx^2$. Since $\omega = \sqrt{k/m}$, $U = \tfrac{1}{2}m\omega^2 x^2$.

Total energy:

$$E_n = (n + \tfrac{1}{2})\hbar\omega, \quad n = 0, 1, 2, \ldots \text{(Text Eq. 40-11)}$$

While the kinetic and potential energy both vary with position (and time), the total energy ($E = K + U$) of a harmonic oscillator in a given quantum state remains constant. Note that the minimum energy is *not* zero, but $E_{min} = E_0 = \tfrac{1}{2}\hbar\omega$.

Ground-state wave function:

$$\psi_0(x) = \left(\frac{m\omega}{\pi\hbar}\right)^{\frac{1}{4}} e^{-m\omega x^2/2\hbar} \qquad \text{(Text Eq. 40-10)}$$

Note that the maximum value of ψ (and hence, the maximum probability) occurs at $x = 0$; *i.e.*, at the equilibrium position.

AVOIDING PITFALLS

1. **Nonrelativistic Schrödinger equation:** The Schrödinger equation is based on *nonrelativistic* physics. Thus, in any results derived from the Schrödinger equation, we assume that the kinetic energy is much less than the particle's rest energy. (If this were not the case, we would need to use the more difficult Dirac equation.) Assuming we are indeed working with nonrelativistic energies, then:

   a. Kinetic energy is simply $K = \tfrac{1}{2}mv^2$, and momentum is simply $p = mv$.

   b. The rest energy of a particle is not considered, so E represents the sum of the particle's kinetic and potential energy: $E = K + U$.

2. **Characteristics of wave functions:** ψ, the wave function of a particle, must have the following behavior:

   a. $\psi = 0$ in any region where the particle is *absolutely* forbidden (*e.g.*, in any region where $U = \infty$). However, it is possible for $\psi \neq 0$ in regions where $E < U$.

   b. ψ is consistent with de Broglie's postulate ($\lambda = h/p$), so ψ has a long wavelength where the particle's momentum (and kinetic energy) are small, and ψ has a short wavelength where the momentum is high.

   c. The amplitude of ψ is related to the probability of finding the particle at that point, so ψ has its greatest amplitude where the particle is most likely to be found. For higher-energy states (large quantum number n), the correspondence principle lets us use classical physics as our guide: The particle spends a relatively large amount of time in regions where the particle moves slowly (low kinetic energy). Thus, in places where the kinetic energy is small (because the potential energy is large), the amplitude of ψ will be large. Generally speaking, then,

   large U (small K) $\Rightarrow$ long λ, large ψ;

   small U (large K) $\Rightarrow$ short λ, small ψ.

3. **Ground-state energy:** For any particle confined to a certain region, the energy of the lowest-lying state will *not* be zero. (This is in accord with Heisenberg's uncertainty principle. For any confined particle, $\Delta x \neq \infty$, so $\Delta p > 0$. If a state of zero (kinetic) energy were to exist, we would then know the particle's momentum exactly ($p = 0$), and the uncertainty principle forbids the product $\Delta x\, \Delta p_x$ to be less than $\hbar$.)

4. **Schrödinger vs. Planck harmonic oscillators:** In Chapter 39, we saw that Max Planck hypothesized that the energy of a particle in simple harmonic motion was $E_{Planck} = n(hf) = n(\hbar\omega)$. The Schrödinger equation, however, gives us $E_{Schr} = (n + \tfrac{1}{2})\hbar\omega$. Who's right? *The Schrödinger equation gives the correct energy.* Both theories predict the correct *difference* between adjacent energy levels, but Planck was unaware of the ground-state energy possessed by all confined particles.

5. **Quantum numbers: Square-well vs. harmonic oscillator:** The states (and energies) of both the one-dimensional square well and the harmonic oscillator are labeled by a single quantum number n.

   square well: $E_n = \dfrac{n^2 h^2}{8mL^2}, \ n = 1, 2, 3, \ldots$

   harmonic oscillator:
   $E_n = (n + \tfrac{1}{2})\hbar\omega, \ n = 0, 1, 2, \ldots$

   Note, however, that the square-well energies are proportional to n^2, whereas the harmonic-oscillator energies are proportional to n. Finally, the square-well ground state is labeled by $n = 1$, whereas the harmonic-oscillator ground state is labeled by $n = 0$.

6. **Linear vs. angular frequency:** Most of the harmonic-oscillator equations in this chapter are expressed in terms of the *angular* frequency (ω), measured in radians/second. Don't confuse this with the more common *linear* frequency (f), measured in oscillations/second, or hertz. (They are related by $\omega = 2\pi f$.)

7. **Radian mode:** When integrating and evaluating wave functions that involve trig functions (*e.g.*, $\psi = A \sin kx$), remember that the argument is always expressed in *radians*, not in degrees.

Connections to *ActivPhysics*

The theory of quantum mechanics can be very difficult to understand, but the four activities of Unit 20 should help illustrate some of the key concepts. It may be a good idea to simply work through the unit sequentially as each topic is encountered. Activity 20.1 *Potential Energy Diagrams* begins with a classical look at the behavior of a particle in a two-level potential well. The "strobe" picture it produces looks very similar to Figures 40-1 and 40-3 and is designed to help you understand the "probability" interpretation of quantum mechanics. Activity 17.7 *Wave Packets* should also help here.

Activity 20.2 *Particle in a Box* follows closely the discussion of Section 40-3; Figures 40-9, 40-10, and 40-11 are reproduced in the simulation with adjustable parameters. The finite square well and the harmonic potential function (Section 40-4) are tackled in Activity 20-3 *Potential Wells*. The activity does a very good job of demonstrating why a given potential only supports a discrete set of energy levels: watch carefully what happens to the wave function at the boundaries for nonquantum-state energies. And finally, Activity 20.4 *Potential Barriers* illustrates the principles of potential barriers and quantum tunneling by animating Figures 40-16 and 40-17 with adjustable parameters.

CHAPTER 41   ATOMIC PHYSICS

Having applied Schrödinger's equation to relatively simple systems in the previous chapter, we now use it to further our understanding of atomic structure. We begin with a quantitative look at the simplest atomic system—the hydrogen atom. We find the existence of quantized energy levels, and we compute the size and orbital angular momentum of the various states. A surprising phenomenon known as "space quantization" restricts the orientation of the angular momentum vector to certain positions. After introducing the intrinsic angular momentum (spin) of the electron, we then study how orbital and spin angular momenta combine. Finally, we are led to the Pauli exclusion principle, the foundation of the periodic table. Transitions among outer electrons give rise to the visible spectrum of atoms, while the greater energy of inner-shell transitions produces characteristic X-ray spectra. Finally, the existence of metastable states and the process of stimulated emission give rise to the coherent radiation observed in lasers.

DEFINITIONS

You should know the definition of each of these terms. (The number in parentheses is the text chapter and section in which the term is introduced.)

(41-1)   In *spherical polar coordinates*, a particle's position is specified by giving its radial distance r from the origin, an azimuthal angle θ and a polar angle ϕ.

(41-1) The *radial probability density* is the probability (per unit radial distance) of finding an electron at a given distance r from the nucleus. In terms of ψ, $P(r) = 4\pi r^2 \psi^2$.

(41-1) The *principal quantum number (n)* is the quantum number that primarily determines the size of a given orbital. In single-electron atoms, the energy is primarily determined by the principal quantum number. n can take on positive integer values: $n = \{1, 2, 3, \ldots\}$, where $n = 1$ labels the lowest-energy state.

(41-1) The *orbital angular momentum* of a state is the angular momentum due to the electron's orbital motion around the nucleus. (Admittedly, in the wave-mechanical view of the atom, it's not so easy to visualize the "angular momentum of a wave," but the various states do have a property that behaves in much the same way as classical angular momentum.)

(41-1) The magnitude of the orbital angular momentum (L) is given by the *orbital quantum number*, ℓ, which can take on integer values $\ell = 0, 1, 2, \ldots, n - 1$: $L = \sqrt{\ell(\ell + 1)}\hbar$.

(41-1) The *magnetic orbital quantum number* (m_ℓ), gives (in units of $\hbar$) the z-component of the orbital angular momentum: $L_z = m_\ell \hbar$.

(41-1) *Space quantization* refers to the fact that when any single component of a quantum-mechanical angular momentum (**L**, **S**, or **J**) is measured, that component will take on quantized values that differ by integer multiples of $\hbar$. In effect, the orientation of the angular-momentum vector in space is quantized.

(41-2) The *intrinsic angular momentum (or spin)* of a particle refers to the angular momentum that is carried as an intrinsic part of the particle, irrespective of any orbital motion. (A classical model of this property is that of a tiny particle spinning on its own axis.)

(41-2) The *Stern-Gerlach experiment* directly demonstrated the existence of space quantization, and of electron spin. A beam of neutral atoms is passed through a nonuniform magnetic field. For atoms with $L = 0$, the beam is split into two parts, indicating that the z-component of the (spin) magnetic moment of the atom has two (and only two) values, regardless of the orientation of the magnet's poles.

(41-2) The angular momentum due to the electron's spin (**S**) can add (vectorially) to the orbital angular momentum (**L**), coupling to form a total angular momentum (**J**). Because of the magnetic field produced by the nucleus, this *spin-orbit coupling* causes the up- and down-spin states to differ slightly in energy.

(41-2) The *fine structure* in atomic spectra is a splitting of spectral lines into two or more closely spaced components (visible under high resolution spectroscopy). This is caused by the atom's internal magnetic field separating the up-spin and down-spin states slightly in energy.

(41-2) *Hyperfine splitting* is an even smaller effect, caused (in hydrogen) by the magnetic field due to the electron's orbital motion interacting with the spin magnetic moment of the nucleus.

(41-3) The *Pauli exclusion principle* states that no two fermions in a given system may occupy the same quantum-mechanical state.

(41-3) A *fermion* is a particle whose spin quantum number s has a half-integer value (1/2, 3/2, 5/2, . . .). Electrons, protons, and neutrons are all fermions.

(41-3) *Bosons* are particles whose spin quantum number s has an integer value (0, 1, 2, . . .). Photons, mesons, and alpha particles are all bosons.

(41-4) A *shell* refers to a set of states within a given atom with the same principal quantum number, n.

(41-4) A *subshell* refers to a set of states within a given atom with the same principal and orbital quantum numbers (n and ℓ).

(41-4) An *orbital* is a set of states within a given atom that share the same n, ℓ, and m_ℓ quantum numbers. (They may differ in spin quantum numbers, though.)

(41-5) A *metastable state* is an excited state with an unusually long lifetime (perhaps 10^{-3} s, as compared to a normal 10^{-8} s). Generally, this is caused by selection rules forbidding downward transitions to lower-lying states.

(41-5) The *characteristic X-ray* spectrum of an atom is produced by electrons dropping into inner-shell vacancies. As the electron moves to a lower-energy shell, a photon is emitted. Since the binding energies of inner-shell electrons are typically tens of kilovolts, the photons have wavelengths in the X-ray region.

(41-5) In *stimulated absorption*, a photon is absorbed by an atom, thereby increasing the energy of the atom. (In this context, "stimulated" refers to any process that requires the presence of a photon to initiate the process.)

(41-5) In *spontaneous emission*, an atom in an excited state drops to a lower energy level, emitting a photon in the process. This happens spontaneously, with no external stimulus.

(41-5) In *stimulated emission*, the presence of one photon (of energy E) induces ("stimulates") an atom to make a downward transition (with $|\Delta E| = E$), emitting a second photon in the process. Of particular importance is the fact that these two photons have exactly the same energy and phase.

(41-5) If a system is somehow stimulated to have a significant fraction of its atoms in an excited state, we say that a *population inversion* exists.

SUMMARY OF EQUATIONS

1. Radial time-independent Schrödinger equation:

$$-\frac{\hbar^2}{2mr^2}\frac{d}{dr}\left(r^2\frac{d\mathbf{c}}{dr}\right) - \frac{ke^2}{r}\mathbf{c} = E\mathbf{c} \quad \text{(Text Eq. 41-4)}$$

When the potential energy of a quantum system depends only on the radial coordinate (not on θ or ϕ), the spherically symmetric wave functions $\psi(r)$ obey the radial part of the time-independent Schrödinger equation. (Note that even with a spherically symmetric potential, angular-dependent wave functions $\psi(r, \theta, \phi)$ also exist, and they require the full spherical polar Schrödinger equation.)

2. Hydrogen atom:

ground-state wave function:

$$\psi_1 = Ae^{-r/a_0}, \quad \text{(Text Eq. 41-3)}$$

where: $A = \dfrac{1}{\sqrt{\pi a_0^3}}$, and $a_0 = \dfrac{\hbar^2}{mke^2} = 0.0529$ nm.

ground-state energy: $E_1 = -\dfrac{\hbar^2}{2ma_0^2} = -13.6\text{eV}$

excited-state energy:

$$E_n = \frac{E_1}{n^2} = \frac{-13.6\text{eV}}{n^2} \quad \text{(Text Eq. 41-7)}$$

$$(n = 1, 2, 3, \ldots)$$

A hydrogen atom has an infinite number of bound states (called orbitals), each labeled by three quantum numbers (n, ℓ, m_ℓ). The size of each orbital and its energy are primarily determined by the "principal quantum number" n. (ℓ and m_ℓ are discussed below.)

3. Radial probability density:

$$P(r) = 4\pi r^2 \psi^2 \quad \text{(Text Eq. 41-6)}$$

$P(r)$ gives the probability per unit radius of finding the electron at a radial distance r from the nucleus. (Note: This assumes that the eigenfunction is spherically symmetric; *i.e.*, ψ is independent of θ or ϕ.)

From this, it follows that the probability of finding the electron at any point that lies between r_1 and r_2 is

$$P(r_1, r_2) = \int_{r_1}^{r_2} 4\pi r^2 \psi^2 \, dr$$

4. Energy of a single-electron ion:

$$E_n = Z^2 \frac{E_1}{n^2} = Z^2 \frac{(-13.6\text{eV})}{n^2} \quad \text{(Text Eq. 41-9)}$$

An atom (with Z protons) that has lost all but one of its electrons has a hydrogenlike structure. The energy of the nth state is just Z^2 times the corresponding hydrogen-atom energy.

5. Orbital angular momentum:

magnitude: $L = \sqrt{\ell(\ell + 1)}\,\hbar$ \quad (Text Eq. 41-10)

$$(\ell = 0, 1, 2, \ldots, n - 1)$$

z-component: $L_z = m_\ell \hbar$ \quad (Text Eq. 41-11)

$$(m_\ell = -\ell, -\ell + 1, \ldots, \ell - 1, \ell)$$

An electron in an orbital labeled by the three quantum numbers (n, ℓ, m_ℓ) has an orbital angular momentum $\mathbf{L}$ whose magnitude L is determined by the "orbital quantum number" ℓ. (Note that ℓ is restricted to integer values smaller than n.)

If we measure any component of this angular momentum (usually by applying an external magnetic field), we will find that the component of $\mathbf{L}$ along the field direction will always be an integer multiple of $\hbar$. (By convention, we denote the direction along which we take this measurement the "z-axis.") Because this measurement usually involves a magnetic interaction, m_ℓ is known as the "magnetic orbital quantum number."

6. Spin angular momentum:

   magnitude: $S = \sqrt{s(s + 1)}\hbar$ (Text Eq. 41-12)

   (s = integer or half-integer)

   z-component: $S_z = m_s\hbar$ (Text Eq. 41-13)

   ($m_s = -s, -s + 1, \ldots, s - 1, s$)

   Each particle has an intrinsic angular momentum ("spin") whose magnitude $|\mathbf{S}| = S$ is determined by the "spin quantum number" s. (Electrons, protons, and neutrons always have the single value $s = \frac{1}{2}$, regardless of n, ℓ, or m_ℓ. Other particles, though, may have different values of s.)

   Any measurement of one component of this spin angular momentum will show a quantized value S_z. For spin-$\frac{1}{2}$ particles, the "magnetic spin quantum number" m_s will be either $+\frac{1}{2}$ (the "up-spin" state) or $-\frac{1}{2}$ (the "down-spin" state.)

7. Spin magnetic moment of the electron:

   $$\mathbf{M} = -\frac{e}{m}\mathbf{S} \qquad \text{(Text Eq. 41-14)}$$

   $$M_z = \pm\frac{e\hbar}{2m} \qquad \text{(Text Eq. 41-15)}$$

   The intrinsic magnetic dipole moment of an electron ($\mathbf{M}$) is related to its intrinsic angular momentum ($\mathbf{S}$). Because the z-component of $\mathbf{S}$ is restricted to $\pm\frac{1}{2}\hbar$, the z-component of $\mathbf{M}$ is also quantized.

   Just as it takes work to rotate a compass needle through an external magnetic field, it takes work to flip an electron from a $+M_z$ state to the $-M_z$ state. Hence, up- and down-spin states differ in energy whenever the electron finds itself in a magnetic field.

8. Total angular momentum of a single particle:

   definition: $\mathbf{J} \equiv \mathbf{L} + \mathbf{S}$ (Text Eq. 41-16)

   magnitude: $J = \sqrt{j(j + 1)}\hbar$,   (Text Eq. 41-17)

   where $j = \ell \pm \frac{1}{2}$, (for $\ell \neq 0$),

   $j = \frac{1}{2}$, (for $\ell = 0$).

   z-component: $J_z = m_j\hbar$ (Text Eq. 41-19)

   ($m_j = -j, -j + 1, \ldots, j - 1, j$)

   The total (orbital plus spin) angular momentum of a single electron is given by the quantity $\mathbf{J}$. (For an atom with a single electron in its outer shell, the angular momenta of the inner electrons cancel, and the total angular momentum of the atom is due to the outer electron.)

9. Energy of X-ray transitions:

   $$\Delta E = (13.6\text{eV})Z_{\text{eff}}^2\left(\frac{1}{n_2^2} - \frac{1}{n_1^2}\right). \qquad \text{(Text Eq. 41-20)}$$

   A characteristic X-ray photon (of energy $E = \Delta E$) is emitted when an electron (initially in the n_1 shell) falls down into a vacancy in the n_2 shell. (The vacancy is normally produced by an impact from an external electron.)

   These X-ray processes occur in multi-electron atoms (with nuclear charge Z), so the orbital energies are *not* just $Z^2(-13.6/n^2)$. Because of the electron-electron interactions not present in single-electron atoms, the true nuclear charge (Z) is replaced with an *effective* nuclear charge (Z_{eff}) that takes these interactions into account. For $L \rightarrow K$ transitions, $Z_{\text{eff}} \approx Z - N'$, where N' is the number of electrons in states that lie between n_1 and the nucleus.

AVOIDING PITFALLS

1. **Bohr radius:** Bohr visualized a hydrogen atom in the ground state as an electron orbiting neatly in a circular orbit of radius $a_0 = 0.0529$ nm. In the quantum-mechanical (Schrödinger) picture, the electron behaves more like a wave, spreading out in the region surrounding the nucleus, as shown in Figure 41.1. A measurement is *more likely* to find the electron at a distance a_0 than any other, but other distances are certainly not excluded.

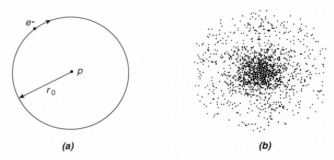

(a)   *(b)*

Figure 41.1
(a) Bohr model of the hydrogen atom, with an electron orbiting the nucleus in a circular orbit. (b) Quantum-mechanical hydrogen atom, with its wavelike electron. The density of shading is proportional to ψ^2, the point probability density.

2. **Negative energies:** The energy ($K + U$) of any atomic *bound* state is a negative number.

   We have defined the Coulomb potential energy to be zero when two charged particles are infinitely far apart. It takes work to separate oppositely charged particles, so the separated (zero-energy) state is higher in energy than the close-together state. (Thus, the closer two oppositely charged particles approach, the more negative their potential energy becomes.) If the kinetic energy exceeds the magnitude of the potential energy, then the electron will escape from the atom. Hence, bound states are those for which $K < |U|$, making the total energy E negative.

3. **ψ^2 vs. most probable distance:** The most probable distance (a_0 for a hydrogen atom in its ground state) is *not* the distance at which ψ^2 (the probability density) has its maximum. In fact, the single point with the greatest probability of finding the electron lies in the exact center of the nucleus. (ψ^2 might be more accurately called the *point* probability density.) The *radial* probability density, $P(r)$, equal to the probability per unit radial distance of finding the electron at a given radial distance r, is itself a product of two factors: the point probability density (ψ^2), and the size of the region in which the electron is sought ($4\pi r^2$). See Figure 41.2.

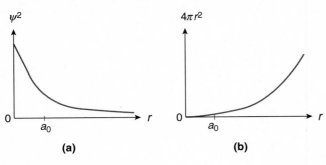

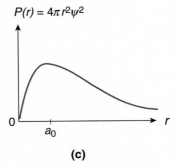

Figure 41.2

(a) Point probability density (ψ^2) for the hydrogen atom in its ground state. (b) Surface area of a sphere, plotted as a function of its radius. (c) The product of (a) and (b) gives the probability (per unit radial distance) of finding the electron at a given distance r from the nucleus.

At the origin ψ^2 has its maximum, but the $4\pi r^2$ factor is zero. As r increases, their product $P(r)$ reaches a maximum at $r = a_0$, but then the exponential decrease of ψ^2 takes over, decreasing the radial probability beyond a_0.

4. **L, S, J vs. ℓ, s, j:** The lowercase letters are quantum numbers that identify the state, and the capital letters denote the magnitude of an angular momentum (orbital, spin, and total, respectively):

$$L = \sqrt{\ell(\ell + 1)}\,\hbar \qquad (\ell = 0, 1, 2, \ldots, n-1)$$

$$S = \sqrt{s(s + 1)}\,\hbar \qquad (s = \tfrac{1}{2})$$

$$J = \sqrt{j(j + 1)}\,\hbar \qquad (j = \ell \pm \tfrac{1}{2}\ \text{for}\ \ell \neq 0);$$

$$(j = \tfrac{1}{2}\ \text{for}\ \ell = 0)$$

5. **Shells and subshells:** It's easy to get confused by all the letters we use to label the shells and subshells. "Shell" refers to a set of orbitals, all of which have the same principal quantum number (n). When a specific orbital is identified, the numerical value of n is usually given: *e.g.*, $3d$ identifies an orbital with $n = 3$. When we only need to distinguish between shells, the shells are labeled by a capital letter:

Shell	K	L	M	N	O	...
$n =$	1	2	3	4	5	...

A "subshell" refers to the orbitals that share the same principal and orbital quantum numbers (n and ℓ). The values of ℓ are also given by a letter code:

Symbol	s	p	d	f	g	..
$\ell =$	0	1	2	3	4	..

Note that the principal quantum number starts at $n = 1$, while the orbital quantum number starts at $\ell = 0$.

6. **Good quantum numbers:** Why have we identified some states with the four quantum numbers (n, ℓ, m_ℓ, m_s), and other states with the set (n, ℓ, j, m_j)? When we label a state with a particular quantum number, we are stating that the corresponding physical quantity has a known, precise value. For example, if a state is labeled by $m_\ell = -2$, we know that the orbital angular momentum has a z-component exactly given by $L_z = m_\ell \hbar$. If a state is labeled by $j = 5/2$, we know that its total (orbital + spin) angular momentum has the exact magnitude $J = \sqrt{j(j + 1)}\,\hbar = \sqrt{35/4}\,\hbar$.

In atomic states with $L = 0$, the spin and orbital angular momentum are independent of each other, and we can definitely state the values of L_z and S_z (by listing the quantum numbers m_ℓ and m_s.) In this case, the total angular momentum is due entirely to the spin, so $j = \tfrac{1}{2}$ and $m_j = m_s$. For these states, the good angular-momentum quantum numbers (those that label a quantity with a precisely known value) are

$$\{\ell, m_\ell, s, m_s, j, m_j\} \qquad (L = 0)$$

(To be honest, with $L = 0$, then $\ell = m_\ell = 0$, and $s = j = \tfrac{1}{2}$, so there isn't much freedom of choice: The only possibilities are $m_s\ (= m_j) = \pm \tfrac{1}{2}$.)

In states with $L \neq 0$, the situation is different because of the interaction between **L** and **S**. In these states, $|\mathbf{L}|$ is known (so ℓ is a good quantum number), but L_z fluctuates (so m_ℓ is meaningless). Similarly, $|\mathbf{S}|$ is known (electrons *always* have $s = \frac{1}{2}$), but the spin-orbit interaction causes S_z to fluctuate. However, **L** and **S** do not fluctuate independently, but in such a way as to give their vector sum $(\mathbf{J} = \mathbf{L} + \mathbf{S})$ a constant magnitude J *and* a constant z-component J_z. Hence, j and m_j become good quantum numbers. Thus, in atoms with $L \neq 0$, the good quantum numbers are

$$\{\ell, s, j, m_j\} \quad (L \neq 0)$$

7. **z-axis**: Perhaps you are curious why it is the z-component of each quantity (L_z, S_z, J_z) that is quantized, and not the x- or y-components. The answer is really very simple: *Any* component of an angular momentum that you measure will be quantized. We have, through tradition, simply become used to calling whatever direction we have selected the "z-axis." (Note: The uncertainty principle prevents us from simultaneously knowing the exact values of more than two of the four quantities (L, L_x, L_y, L_z). Since we know L exactly if we are given the orbital quantum number ℓ, we can then, at best, know the precise value of only *one* of the three components. We arbitrarily call the measured component the "z-component" (identified by the magnetic quantum number m_ℓ), and the other two components remain indeterminate.)

8. **The Pauli exclusion principle:** The Pauli exclusion principle applies *only* to fermion systems—particles with half-integer spin ($s = 1/2, 3/2$, etc.). Particles with integer spin (bosons) do *not* obey the Pauli exclusion principle, so they are free to crowd into the lowest energy state.

ActivPhysics **Connections to *ActivPhysics***

The first four sections of Chapter 41 explore the quantum-mechanical details of the hydrogen atom and extrapolate those results to multi-electron atoms. *ActivPhysics* does not deal with these matters directly; however, it may be useful to review Activity 18.1 showing the simpler model of the Bohr atom. Bohr's explanation of the hydrogen atom may be incomplete, but the basic concepts of that model will still be helpful for understanding the nature of the energy transitions between quantum states, especially with respect to Section 41-5 on transitions and atomic spectra. Activity 18.2 *Spectroscopy* is an opportunity to clearly see the relationship between quantum-state energy levels and the spectra resulting from energy transitions, such as those shown in Figure 41-25, by having you "adjust" quantum-state energies until a theoretical spectrum matches an experimental one. In the same way, Activity 18.4 *The Laser* should clarify the discussion of the laser found on page 1125 and illustrated in Figures 41-32 and 41-33.

When we began our investigations into the wave nature of matter using Schrödinger's equation in Chapter 40, we first studied some simple, rather artificial systems (square wells, one-dimensional harmonic oscillators, etc.). We then tackled the case of a real, live atom in Chapter 41 when we studied the hydrogen atom in some detail. The complexity grew with the addition of more and more electrons in larger atoms. We now investigate the behavior of atoms, not as isolated entities, but as part of a community of interacting atoms—molecules and solids.

Because of the complexity of many-particle systems, the approach now becomes somewhat more descriptive and less computational than before. Nonetheless, we will be able to understand many of the features of molecular bonding and molecular spectra by studying the vibrational and rotational states of molecules.

When we allow 10^{20} atoms or more to form a crystalline solid, we find the single states of isolated atoms merging into energy bands. These bands (and the gaps between them) determine the electrical and thermal properties of crystalline solids. The entire technology of semiconductor devices and integrated circuits owes its existence to our ability to control the size of these gaps with carefully chosen impurities.

Finally, we consider one of the most exciting recent developments in physics—superconductivity. First observed in pure metals at temperatures near absolute zero, the recent discovery of ceramic superconductors has raised the transition temperature much closer to room temperature than ever before.

DEFINITIONS

You should know the definition of each of these terms. (The number in parentheses is the text chapter and section in which the term is introduced.)

(42-1) The *dissociation energy* of a molecule is the energy that must be added to the molecule to completely separate the atoms from each other.

(42-1) In an *ionic bond*, two atoms bond together by transferring an electron from one atom to another, and the resulting electrostatic force between the two ions holds them together.

(42-1) *Covalent bonds* form between two (or more) atoms, each of which lacks a small number of electrons from forming an inert-gas configuration. By sharing one or more pairs of electrons, each atom reduces its energy.

(42-1) *Hydrogen bonds* form between hydrogen atoms in separate molecules that possess a dipole moment.

(42-1) The electric field of a molecule with a dipole moment can induce a dipole moment in a nearby molecule, and the dipole-dipole interaction produces an attractive force. This *Van der Waals* force falls off very rapidly with distance (typically, like r^{-7}), so it is significant only when molecules are rather close together.

(42-1) When the atoms of a metal form a solid, the outermost electron (or two) from each atom wanders away from its parent atom and drifts throughout the entire lattice of metal ions. In *metallic bonding*, the positive metal ions (each of which has lost an electron) are held together by the swarm of free (conduction) electrons.

(42-3) In a *crystalline solid*, the atoms are arranged in a geometric pattern. Because of this, crystals can be cleaved into fragments whose shape follows the geometry of the crystal lattice.

(42-3) The atoms in an *amorphous solid* are sort of clumped together, with no overall symmetry to their arrangement. Amorphous solids (like glass) will fracture into irregular-shaped fragments.

(42-3) In any crystalline solid, one can always identify a particular group of atoms whose arrangement repeats itself over and over. A crystal is comprised of these *unit cells*.

(42-3) The *ionic cohesive energy* is defined as the energy that must be supplied to remove an interior ion from a crystal.

(42-3) When $N = 10^{20}$ or more atoms are brought together to form a crystalline solid, the overlapping orbitals of the atoms spread out into *energy bands*, where each band consists of $N \times$ (the number of states in each orbital) individual electron states.

(42-3) The gap between the top of a completely filled band and the bottom of the next (unoccupied) band is known as the *band gap*.

(42-3) The *Fermi energy* of a solid is defined as the energy of the highest occupied state when all the electrons are in their lowest-energy configuration (*i.e.*, the solid is at absolute zero).

(42-3) The *valence band* is the highest-energy occupied band in a solid.

(42-3) The *conduction band* is the band immediately higher in energy than the valence band.

(42-3) A *semiconductor* is a material whose resistivity is intermediate between that of insulators and conductors, a consequence of the semiconductor's small band gap. Thermal vibrations excite a certain fraction of the most energetic electrons in the valence band across the band gap up into states within the conduction band. Electrical current can then be carried by both the electrons in the conduction band and by electrons moving from vacancy to vacancy in the valence band. (Note: This describes an *intrinsic semiconductor*.)

(42-3) *Doping* refers to the deliberate introduction of "impurity" atoms into a crystalline semiconductor.

(42-3) In an *N-type semiconductor*, the impurity atoms have five valence electrons (a Group V element), so an extra electron is added to the crystalline lattice at each impurity site. These become conduction electrons since their energy lies immediately below that of the (otherwise empty) conduction band.

(42-3) In a *P-type semiconductor*, however, a Group III element is chosen for the impurity. With three valence electrons, the impurity sites have a "missing" electron, and these vacancies ("holes") introduce states for the electrons that lie near the top of the valence band.

(42-4) *Superconductivity* is a state in which the electrical resistivity of a material becomes zero.

(42-4) The *transition temperature* is the temperature at which superconductivity appears in a given material.

(42-4) The *Meissner effect* refers to the fact that the net magnetic field within any superconductor is zero. (There are actually two closely related Meissner effects: In one version, a superconductor is moved into a magnetic field (or a magnetic field is brought to the superconductor); the magnetic field is "repelled" by the superconductor. In the other version, a magnetic field is allowed to permeate a superconductor, initially above its transition temperature (and in its "normal" state); when the temperature is lowered below T_C, the magnetic field is expelled from the interior of the superconductor.)

(42-4) The superconducting behavior disappears when an external magnetic field exceeds the *critical field* strength.

(42-4) In a *type I superconductor*, the superconducting behavior disappears abruptly when $B_{ext} > B_C$.

(42-4) In a *type II superconductor*, the superconducting behavior disappears gradually over a range of external magnetic field strengths. Specifically, magnetic flux penetration begins at a lower value (B_{C1}) and increases gradually with B_{ext}. The resistivity remains zero until a higher field (B_{C2}) is reached.

SUMMARY OF EQUATIONS

1. Molecular rotations:
   a. *Angular momentum: classical definition:*

   $$J = I\omega$$

   An object with a moment of inertia I ($= mr^2$), rotating with an angular velocity ω, has an angular momentum J.

   b. *Angular momentum: quantum values:*

   $$J = \sqrt{j(j + 1)}\,\hbar \qquad \text{(Text Eq. 42-1)}$$

   $$(j = 0, 1, 2, \ldots)$$

   The magnitude of the angular momentum (J) of a molecule is restricted to the values given by integer values of j.

   c. *Rotational kinetic energy: classical values:*

   $$E_{rot} = \tfrac{1}{2}I\mathbf{w}^2 = \frac{J^2}{2I}$$

   (Note the similarity in form to $K = \tfrac{1}{2}mv^2 = p^2/2m$.)

   d. *Rotational kinetic energy: quantum values:*

   $$E_{rot} = \frac{j(j + 1)\hbar^2}{2I} \qquad \text{(Text Eq. 42-2)}$$

   The energy of a rotational state is quantized because of the quantization of J. (Transitions from one rotational state to another follow the selection rule $\Delta j = \pm 1$.)

2. Molecular vibrations:
   Energy of vibrations: quantum:

   $$E_{vib} = (n + \tfrac{1}{2})\hbar\,\omega \qquad \text{(Text Eq. 42-5)}$$

   $$(n = 0, 1, 2, \ldots)$$

   The energy ($E = K + U$) of a vibrational state is quantized by the vibrational quantum number n. Recall that $\omega = \sqrt{k/m}$ when the force is given by $F_x = -kx$ (so the potential energy is $U = \tfrac{1}{2}kx^2$). Finally, transitions from one vibrational state to another follow the selection rule $\Delta n = \pm 1$.

3. Energy of an ionic crystal:
   a. *Electrostatic potential energy of a single ion:*

   $$U_1 = -\alpha\frac{ke^2}{r}$$

   An ion (of charge $\pm e$) is part of an ionic crystal. The potential energy due to its electrostatic interaction with the rest of the crystal is given by U_1, where k is the Coulomb's law constant (8.988×10^9 N$\cdot$m^2/C^2), and r is the distance from the ion to its nearest neighbor. α is known as the Madelung constant, and it accounts for the interactions of the ion with its more distant neighbors. The Madelung constant must be calculated for each different crystal structure.

   b. *Total potential energy of an ion in a crystal:*

   $$U = -\alpha\frac{ke^2}{r_0}\left[\frac{r_0}{r} - \frac{1}{n}\left(\frac{r_0}{r}\right)^n\right]. \qquad \text{(Text Eq. 42-4)}$$

   The first term is just the electrostatic potential energy discussed above. The second term describes the repulsion felt by ions as they crowd close together. (This arises from the Pauli exclusion principle affecting the energy of the electrons' states when they overlap.) r_0 represents the equilibrium value of r, and the parameter n measures the "stiffness" of these repulsive interactions in a given crystal. (Note: The $(r_0/r)^n$ is only one possible form. Other texts may use an exponential term like e^{-r/r_0} to describe the repulsive interaction.) Having defined $U = 0$ when the ion is far from the crystal, $U(r_0)$ then gives the *ionic cohesive energy*–the energy needed to remove a single ion from the crystal.

4. Density of states in a three-dimensional square well:

$$g(E) = \frac{2^{7/2}\pi m^{3/2}}{h^3} E^{1/2} \quad \text{(Text Eq. 42-5)}$$

For a large number of particles, $g(E)$, the number of states (per unit volume) per unit energy range at energy E in a three-dimensional square well is proportional to $\sqrt{E}$.

AVOIDING PITFALLS

1. **Electron affinity:** The "electron affinity" is a *positive* quantity that gives the *decrease* in the atom's energy as it picks up an extra electron. (For example, the electron affinity for Br is 3.36 eV. This means that Br⁻ is 3.36 eV *lower* in energy than a neutral Br atom.)

2. **Frequencies: Rotational, vibrational, and electromagnetic:** When studying molecular spectra, you must keep track of at least three separate frequencies:

   • *Rotational:* The rotational frequency (or angular velocity) is quantized because the angular momentum $L = I\omega$ is quantized:

   $$w_{\text{rot}} = \sqrt{j(j + 1)}\left(\frac{\hbar}{I}\right).$$

   (Since $E_{\text{rot}} = \frac{1}{2}I\omega^2$, higher-energy rotational levels correspond to higher rotational frequencies.)

   • *Vibrational:* The vibrational frequency is determined by the mass and by the stiffness of the restoring force:

   $$w_{\text{vib}} = \sqrt{\frac{k}{m}}.$$

   (The vibrational energy $E_{\text{vib}} = (n+\frac{1}{2})\hbar\omega$. Note that the vibrational frequency is constant for a given system. A transition from one vibrational state to another changes the amplitude, but the frequency remains constant.)

   • *Electromagnetic:* The frequency of the photon involved in any transition is determined solely by the energy of the photon: $\omega_{\text{photon}} = E/\hbar$.

3. **Energy-level spacing:** The spacing between adjacent rotational energy levels increases with j, while the spacing between adjacent vibrational energy levels is uniform. Also, one generally finds that $\Delta E_{\text{rot}} < \Delta E_{\text{vib}}$, and both of these are smaller than the spacing between adjacent molecular orbitals. Figure 42.1 illustrates these points for one molecular orbital.

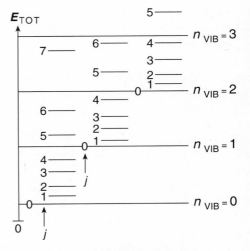

Figure 42.1
Vibrational and rotational energy levels for one molecular orbital. The vibrational levels are labeled by n_{VIB}, and the rotational levels are labeled by j. (Note that the vibrational levels are equally spaced, while the rotational spacing increases with j.) Typical vibrational levels in small molecules differ by a few tenths of an eV. The spacing between rotational levels is only a few meV, and the next molecular orbital may lie several eV above this one.

4. **Center of mass rotations:** The rotations of a molecule are all calculated about the molecule's center of mass. The kinetic energy and angular momentum of a diatomic molecule with bond length r_0, rotating about its center of mass (as shown in Figure 42.2a), are identical to those of a single particle of "reduced mass" $\mu = m_1 m_2/(m_1 + m_2)$ revolving about a fixed point in a circle of radius r_0 with the same angular velocity. (See Figure 42.2b.)

5. **Center of mass vibrations:** Similarly, a diatomic molecule vibrating with a frequency ω_{vib} about its center of mass, as shown in Figure 42.3a, has the same energy as a single particle of mass $\mu = m_1 m_2/(m_1 + m_2)$, vibrating about a fixed point with the same frequency ω_{vib} (see Figure 42.3b).

6. **Density and bond length:** For *cubic* crystals, you can easily compute the density by dividing the mass of a single atom by the volume of a cube whose edge length equals the bond length between adjacent ions.

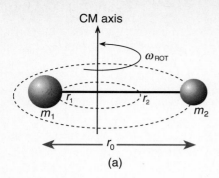

Figure 42.2

(a) A diatomic molecule, rotating around its center of mass with an angular velocity ω_{ROT}. The atoms are treated as point particles, with a fixed separation r_0. (b) The single particle, of "reduced mass" $\mu = m_1 m_2/(m_1 + m_2)$, has the same kinetic energy and angular momentum as the two-particle molecule shown in (a).

7. **Conductors vs. insulators:** The crucial factor that determines many of the electrical, thermal, and optical properties of a crystalline solid is the size (or absence) of the "band gap" between the top of the filled states and the bottom of the unoccupied states. For a solid to absorb a photon, the band gap must be smaller than the photon energy; for a solid to conduct a current, the band gap must be smaller than the drift kinetic energy of a conduction electron. (This is a minuscule amount of energy, so the band gap must be virtually nonexistent for electrical conductivity.) Thus, a good electrical conductor will have its highest occupied band *partially filled* (hence, no band gap), while an insulator will have a *completely filled* band with a relatively large band gap.

8. **hc and $e^2/4\pi\varepsilon_0$:** These two quantities appear so frequently that you may find it useful to keep their "atomic" values handy:

$$hc = 1240 \text{ eV·nm}$$

$$e^2/4\pi\varepsilon_0 = 1.440 \text{ eV·nm}.$$

(These are simply derived by computing their SI values and then converting J to eV and m to nm.)

9. **Angstroms, nanometers, and microns:** Of these three, only the nanometer (1 nm = 10^{-9} m) is an official SI unit, but the Angstrom unit is often used for optical wavelengths, and the micron is commonly used with microwave and infrared wavelengths:

$$1 \text{ Å (Angstrom unit)} = 10^{-10} \text{ m } (= 0.1 \text{ nm})$$

$$1 \text{ } \mu \text{ (micron)} = 1 \text{ } \mu\text{m (micrometer)}$$

$$= 10^{-6} \text{ m } (= 10^3 \text{ nm}).$$

ActivPhysics **Connections to *ActivPhysics***

There are no *ActivPhysics* activities that deal directly with the concepts of Chapter 42 on Molecular and Solid-State Physics.

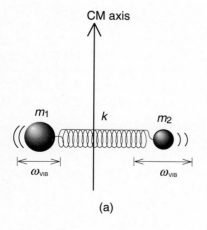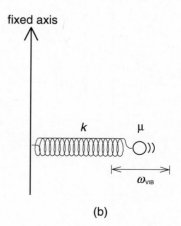

Figure 42.3

(a) The atoms in a diatomic molecule vibrate about their center of mass with a vibrational frequency ω_{VIB} and an instantaneous potential energy $U = 1/2kx^2$, where x is the difference between their instantaneous separation and their equilibrium separation. (b) The single particle, of "reduced mass" $\mu = m_1 m_2/(m_1 + m_2)$, vibrating about a fixed axis, has the same frequency and energy as the diatomic molecule shown in (a).

CHAPTER 43 NUCLEAR PHYSICS

We have thus far treated the nucleus as a positively charged point particle resting at the center of each atom, serving only to hold the electrons in their orbits. We now turn our attention to the structure of the nucleus itself, identifying characteristics of the various nuclides, including their size, shape, binding energy, and radioactive decay modes.

DEFINITIONS

You should know the definition of each of these terms. (The number in parentheses is the text chapter and section in which the term is introduced.)

(43-1) A *nucleon* refers to either a proton or a neutron.

(43-2) The *atomic number (Z)* equals the number of protons in the nucleus of an atom.

(43-2) The *mass number (A)* equals the number of nucleons (protons and neutrons together) in the nucleus of an atom.

(43-2) Atoms of a given element that have different mass numbers are called *isotopes* of the element. (All atoms of a given element have, by definition, the same number of protons, but isotopes differ in the number of neutrons in the nucleus.)

(43-3) 1 *unified atomic mass unit (u)* is defined as one-twelfth of the mass of a neutral ^{12}C atom, exactly.

(43-3) The process known as *nuclear magnetic resonance* depends on the fact that the energy of a nucleus depends on the orientation of its magnetic moment relative to an external magnetic field. Transitions between different states can be induced by irradiating the sample with photons (usually in the radio or microwave range) and observing the energy absorption.

(43-4) The *nuclear binding energy* is the amount of energy required to disassemble a nucleus completely into its constituent protons and neutrons.

(43-4) In the process of *fusion,* two lighter nuclei fuse together, forming a single (more massive) nucleus.

(43-4) In the process of *fission,* a large nucleus splits into two or more smaller nuclei.

(43-5) The *decay constant (λ)* is the probability per unit time that any single nucleus will decay.

(43-5) The *half-life* of a radioactive nuclide is the time required for the population of parent nuclei (or the activity) to decrease by a factor of two.

(43-5) The *activity* of a sample is defined as the number of decays that occur per unit time.

(43-5) In *alpha decay,* an *alpha particle,* consisting of two protons and two neutrons bound together, is ejected from a heavy nucleus.

(43-5) In *beta decay,* an electron is ejected from the nucleus. (It should be noted that the electron, or "beta particle," is created when a neutron decays into a proton, an antineutrino, and a beta particle, which is immediately ejected from the nucleus.)

(43-5) In *gamma decay,* a high-energy photon, called a "gamma ray," is produced when a nucleus makes a downward transition from a high to a low energy level.

(43-5) A *neutrino* is an uncharged, spin-$\frac{1}{2}$ particle that has a nearly zero rest mass and travels at nearly the speed of light. It interacts with matter so weakly that it is extremely hard to detect.

(43-5) Every particle has a corresponding *antiparticle* with the same rest mass and magnitude of spin but the opposite charge.

(43-5) A *Geiger counter* is a device for detecting ionizing radiation (α or β particles, or γ-rays). It consists of a sealed chamber containing a low-pressure gas. Inside the chamber is a wire, held at a high potential. When radiation enters the chamber, it ionizes some of the gas molecules. As these ions accelerate toward the wire, they ionize other gas molecules through collisions, and a momentary avalanche of ions reaches the wire. This brief current pulse is then amplified and counted.

(43-5) In a *scintillation counter,* a photon (or charged particle) strikes a special crystal or plastic, producing a brief flash of light. This light is detected by a photomultiplier tube, which produces a current pulse that can be detected and analyzed.

(43-6) Nuclei that contain *magic numbers* of protons, neutrons, or nucleons have been found to be particularly stable. The generally accepted magic numbers include {2, 8, 20, 28, 50, 82, 126}.

(43-6) In the nuclear *shell model,* one computes the states of each nucleon by using Schrödinger's equation with a central potential representing the cumulative effect of the other (A-1) nucleons. (To obtain realistic values, the potential energy must include a large term that originates in the coupling between the spin and orbital magnetic moments of the nucleons.) With proper finagling, the shell model predicts the existence of particularly stable shells, much like the electron shells in atomic physics. Generally speaking, the shell model works best for medium-to-small nuclei.

(43-6) The *liquid drop model* of the nucleus is a classical model in which the nucleus is treated somewhat like a liquid drop with a surface tension and uniform density. (This model works best for large nuclei, and has had some success in explaining the binding energy curve and certain aspects of fission.)

(43-6) In the *collective model,* one treats the core of the nucleus as a closed shell, and the remaining nucleons orbit around the core. The outer nucleons often pair up in a kind of collective motion.

SUMMARY OF EQUATIONS

1. Nuclear radius:

$$R = R_0 A^{\frac{1}{3}} \qquad \text{(Text Eq. 43-1)}$$

The radius of any given nucleus (in femtometers, 10^{-15} m) is given approximately by this formula, where $R_0 = 1.2$ fm is essentially the radius of a single proton or neutron, and A is the mass number (number of protons plus number of neutrons) of the nuclide. Because $R \propto A^{1/3}$, it follows that $V \propto A$, so the volume is directly proportional to the number of nucleons. Hence, all nuclei have nearly the same density.

2. Nuclear binding energy:

$$m_N c^2 + E_b = Z(m_p c^2) + (A - Z)m_n c^2 \quad \text{(Text Eq. 43-3)}$$

The binding energy of a nucleus (E_b) is defined as the energy needed to disassemble the nucleus into well-separated protons and neutrons. Because the binding energy of the electrons is usually negligible when compared to the binding energy of the nucleons, and published tables usually list the *atomic* masses (rather than nuclear masses), the binding energy is often computed as if the atom were disassembled into Z hydrogen atoms and (A-Z) neutrons:

$$m_{\text{atom}} c^2 + E_b = Z(m_H c^2) + (A - Z)m_n c^2.$$

3. Reaction energy for $a + X \rightarrow y + b + Q$:

$$Q = (M_X + M_a - M_y - M_b)c^2$$

The reaction energy (Q) is defined as the energy transferred from the reaction to the surroundings, so $E_i = E_f + Q$.

If $Q > 0$, then $E_f < E_i$, and energy is released by the system (an "exothermic" reaction).

If $Q < 0$, then $E_f > E_i$, and energy must be supplied to the system (an "endothermic" reaction).

If $Q = 0$, then $E_f = E_i$ (an "elastic" reaction, or scattering).

4. Radioactive decay:

   a. *Activity of a radioactive sample:*

$$R = -\frac{dN}{dt} = \lambda N \qquad \text{(Text Eq. 43-4)}$$

In a radioactive sample with N nuclei, the rate at which this number changes (dN/dt) is directly proportional to the number of atoms remaining. The proportionality constant (λ) is known as the *decay constant* for the nuclide. The decay constant gives the probability per unit time that any given nucleus will decay. (The minus sign in the definition allows λ to be positive, since N is decreasing.)

   b. *Number of parent nuclei remaining in a radioactive sample:*

$$N = N_0 e^{-\lambda t} \qquad \text{(Text Eq. 43-5a)}$$

If at any given time there are N_0 nuclei in a sample, the number (N) found at a time t later will decrease exponentially. (This equation is obtained by integrating the differential equation $dN/N = -\lambda t$.)

   c. *Half-life of a nuclide:*

$$t_{\frac{1}{2}} = \frac{\ln 2}{\lambda} \qquad \text{(Text Eq. 43-6)}$$

One characteristic of an exponential decrease is that the time required for the quantity (*e.g.,* population or activity) to decrease to one-half its present value is always the same, and is inversely proportional to the decay constant.

AVOIDING PITFALLS

1. **Atomic mass vs. atomic number:** Remember that Z (the atomic number) is the number of *protons* only, while A (the atomic mass number) is the total number of protons and neutrons together.

2. **Atomic vs. nuclear mass:** Note carefully whether you are given (or asked for) the *atomic* mass or the *nuclear* mass. (The atomic mass is larger by an amount equal to the mass of the Z electrons.) Most tables list atomic masses.

3. **Unified atomic mass unit:** 1 u is defined as $\frac{1}{12}$ the mass of a neutral ^{12}C *atom,* not the bare ^{12}C nucleus.

4. **e vs. β:** The distinction between "electrons" and "beta particles" is, to a certain extent, a question of semantics. Both refer to a spin-$\frac{1}{2}$ particle with a rest energy of 0.511 MeV that carries an electric charge $-e$. Some scientists reserve the term "beta particle" (symbol: β, or β^-) for electrons that are created during the decay of other particles, and call those particles that reside in atomic orbitals "electrons" (symbol: e, or e^-). This distinction follows the pattern of calling photons emitted by nuclear transitions or particle decays "gamma rays," and photons emitted by electron transitions "X-rays." Others use the

symbols e and $\bar{e}$ (for the electron and positron) when discussing nuclear reactions, while β^- and β^+ are used in radioactive studies. Fortunately, it doesn't matter very much what you call them, as long as you recognize that $\{e, e^-, {}_{-1}^{0}e, \beta, \text{ and } \beta^-\}$ all refer to electrons, whereas $\{e^+, {}_{+1}^{0}e, \bar{\beta}, \text{ and } \beta^+\}$ all refer to positrons.

5. **Population and activity decay:** In any given radioactive sample, the number of parent nuclei (N) and the activity ($R = -dN/dt$) both decay at the same rate: $N = N_0 e^{-\lambda t}$, and $R = R_0 e^{-\lambda t}$. (This is, in fact, the *definition* of the exponential function: the rate of change is proportional to the value of the function.)

6. **Half-life:** Because of the close connection ($R = \lambda N$) between N and R, both the population *and* the activity decrease by a factor of two during one half-life, both decrease by a factor of four in two half-lives, both decrease by a factor of eight in three half-lives, and both decrease by a factor of 2^n in n half-lives.

7. **Q for nuclear reactions:** Remember that Q represents the amount of energy transferred *from* the reaction *to* the surroundings. Since it represents the energy *lost* by the system, $Q = -\Delta E = -(E_f - E_i)$.

8. **Radiation units:** There exist three different types of units for measuring radioactivity:

   - The simplest units just count the number of particles emitted per second: The becquerel (1 Bq = 1 decay/s) is the SI unit, but the curie (1 Ci = 3.7×10^{10} decays/s) is still in common use.

   - The second type of unit looks at the energy absorbed in the form of radiation: The gray (Gy) is the amount of radiation that will deposit 1 J of energy into 1 kg of any particular substance. An older unit is the rad, which is simply 0.01 Gy. (When human tissue absorbs a 1 rad exposure, the dose is known as 1 roentgen.)

   - The third type of unit considers the biological effect of radiation. The sievert (Sv) (or the older rem) is an empirical measure of the biological damage caused by radiation, considering three factors: (1) the energy dose (in Gy); (2) the energy of each particle (a small number of high-energy particles will generally cause more damage than a large number of low-energy particles: I would rather be exposed to 1 joule of visible light than 1 joule of gamma rays); and (3) the sensitivity of the particular tissue that absorbs the radiation (reproductive organs are much more susceptible than bones, for example).

ActivPhysics **Connections to *ActivPhysics***

Unit 19 of *ActivPhysics* on Nuclear Physics is composed of five activities that are relevant to the last three chapters of the text. The first activity, 19.1 *Particle Scattering*, demonstrates how the scattering of particles off a material can help scientists deduce the structure of matter, along the same lines as the discussion of Section 43-1 and Figure 43-2. Section 43-2 explains the concepts of nuclear binding force and stability, placing these ideas on a mathematical footing in Section 43-4; Activity 19.2 *Nuclear Binding Energy* also speaks to both the concept and the measurement of binding energy between protons and neutrons in the nucleus. Completing the activity should increase your understanding of the plot in Figure 43-11. In the same way, Activity 19.4 *Radioactivity* will help you visualize the concept of a half-life, the importance of time scales in radioactivity, and exponential decay curves. Two of the isotopes in Table 43-2 are among the choices given in the simulation. This exercise demonstrates examples of both the alpha and beta decay mechanisms discussed in Section 43-5.

CHAPTER 44 NUCLEAR ENERGY: FISSION AND FUSION

The strength of the nuclear strong interaction allows tremendous amounts of energy to be released in nuclear reactions. Two distinct reactions are considered in this chapter: *fission* (the splitting of large nuclei into smaller fragments) and *fusion* (the fusing of light nuclei into heavier ones).

Fission of heavy nuclei is relatively rare in nature, since most of the easily fissionable nuclei have long ago decayed into more stable elements. However, fusion, which is occurring constantly within the core of every star, is responsible for nearly all the light we see in the universe.

Within the past 50 years or so, we have learned to use the power of fission and fusion for the advancement (and endangerment) of mankind. Fission reactions power all nuclear reactors, and fission bombs caused the destruction of Hiroshima and Nagasaki at the end of WWII. Fusion reactors, using a nearly limitless source of fuel in a nonpolluting reaction, are presently under development (although not yet productive), but the threat of thermonuclear weapons pervades today's society.

Fission reactions usually result from a low-energy neutron being absorbed by a heavy nucleus (^{233}U, ^{235}U, or ^{239}Pu). The now unstable nucleus splits into two fragments, releasing two or three free neutrons. A self-sustaining chain reaction occurs if, on the average, exactly one of these neutrons causes another reaction. If less than one neutron causes another reaction, the chain will die out, but if more than one neutron causes other reactions, the reaction rate increases exponentially.

Fusion reactions can occur only under conditions of high density and temperature. If a fusion reaction is to produce more energy than it requires for the initial heating, the product of particle density (n) and confinement time (τ) of the particles must exceed a certain value (the "Lawson criterion").

In any kind of reaction, the energy released to the surroundings can be calculated from the difference between the initial mass and the final mass of the system.

DEFINITIONS

You should know the definition of each of these terms. (The number in parentheses is the text chapter and section in which the term is introduced.)

(44-2) *Spontaneous fission* refers to the process in which a heavy nucleus spontaneously splits into two comparably sized fragments, usually releasing one or more free neutrons.

(44-2) *Induced fission* results when a nucleus absorbs a particle (usually a neutron) and then fissions.

(44-2) A *fissile nucleus* is a nucleus that can be induced to fission by absorbing a neutron of *any* energy. (Only three fissile nuclei are known: ^{233}U, ^{235}U, and ^{239}Pu.)

(44-2) *Uranium enrichment* is any process that increases the relative content of ^{235}U over its natural 0.72% concentration.

(44-2) In a *chain reaction,* the neutrons released in one fission reaction induce other fission reactions, each of which release more neutrons that induce still more fissions, and so on.

(44-2) The *critical mass* is the exact amount of fissile material needed to maintain a steady power output from a chain reaction. (A *subcritical mass* allows the number of reactions per second to decrease with time because neutrons escape from the system, and a *supercritical mass* allows an exponential growth in the reaction rate.)

(44-2) The *multiplication factor (k)* is the average number of neutrons from a fission event that cause other fissions events. ($k = 1$ maintains a constant rate of reactions. If $k < 1$ the rate diminishes, and if $k > 1$ the rate increases with time.)

(44-2) The *generation time* is the average time between successive generations in a fission chain reaction.

(44-3) A *moderator* is a material inserted into a reactor core whose purpose is to decrease the kinetic energy of the neutrons.

(44-3) A *control rod* is a neutron-absorbing material that is used to control the rate of a fission reactor by reducing the number of free neutrons in the core.

(44-3) Neutrons emitted at the moment of fission are known as *prompt neutrons.*

(44-3) Some of the fission fragments are unstable, emitting neutrons when they decay. These nuclei have half-lives that vary from a few tenths of a second to nearly a minute. The neutrons emitted during these subsequent decays are known as *delayed neutrons.*

(44-3) In a *boiling-water reactor,* the cooling water in the core is allowed to boil, producing the steam that passes through the turbines.

(44-3) In a *pressurized-water reactor,* the cooling water in the core is kept under pressure so that it does not boil. A heat exchanger then absorbs heat from this hot, high-pressure (radioactive) water and transfers it to fresh water in a secondary loop, which then boils and drives the turbines.

(44-3) A *breeder reactor* is designed to convert a significant amount of the ^{238}U in the reactor fuel into ^{239}Pu.

(44-4) The *proton-proton cycle* is a fusion process occurring in the core of the sun, the net effect of which is to convert four protons and two electrons into a single ^{4}He nucleus, plus 26.6 MeV of energy in various forms.

(44-4) The *critical ignition temperature* is the temperature at which fusion-generated power exceeds power loss by radiation.

(44-4) The Lawson criterion states that an energy-positive fusion process will occur if the product of particle density (n) and confinement time (τ) is greater than a specific value. ($n\tau > 10^{22}$ s/m^3 for D–D; $n\tau > 10^{20}$ s/m^3 for D–T.)

(44-4) *Inertial confinement* uses the inertia of the fuel pellets to contain them for the brief duration of the fusion process.

(44-4) *Magnetic confinement* employs magnetic fields to contain the fuel for the duration of the fusion reaction.

(44-4) A *tokamak* is a toroidal-shaped magnetic confinement vessel for fusion power generation.

SUMMARY OF EQUATIONS

1. Number of fission events:

$$N = \frac{k^{n+1} - 1}{k - 1} \qquad \text{(Text Eq. 44-2)}$$

Consider a fission chain reaction, beginning with one neutron. Each fission releases k neutrons *that cause additional fission reactions*. The total number of fission reactions that have occurred by the end of the nth generation is given by N.

2. Lawson criterion for fusion:

$$n\tau > 10^{22} \text{ s/m}^3 \quad \text{(D-D)}$$

$$n\tau > 10^{20} \text{ s/m}^3 \quad \text{(D-T)} \quad \text{(Text Eq. 44-5)}$$

For a fusion reaction to produce more energy than it requires for its initial heating, the Lawson criterion must be met. In these expressions, n is the particle density (in particles per m^3), and τ is the time (in seconds) during which the particle is confined. For deuterium-deuterium fusion, $n\tau$ must exceed 10^{22} s/m^3, but deuterium-tritium fusion becomes energy-positive when $n\tau$ exceeds 10^{20} s/m^3.

AVOIDING PITFALLS

1. **Beta decay:** When a nucleus decays by emitting a beta particle (which is really an electron, created in the decay $p \rightarrow n + \beta^- + \bar{\nu}_e$), the atomic number of the nucleus *increases* by 1: $Z_f = Z_i + 1$. The atomic mass, however, remains essentially unchanged.

2. **Absorption of neutrons:** The probability that a large nucleus will absorb a neutron is greater for *lower-energy* neutrons than for high-energy neutrons. (For this reason, fission chain reactions require some material to slow the fission neutrons down to "thermal speeds.")

3. **Control rods vs. moderators:** The purpose of the control rods in a reactor is to reduce the number of neutrons by absorption. An ideal moderator, in contrast, would absorb *no* neutrons: its purpose is to decrease the kinetic energy of the neutrons.

4. **Fission multiplication factor:** k is not simply the number of neutrons emitted during each fission, but it represents the (average) number of neutrons *that induce other subsequent reactions.* Thus, if a reaction produces 3 neutrons per fission, but 2 of these escape without causing any other fissions, the multiplication factor is $k = 1$.

5. **Number of fissions:** Be sure to distinguish between the number of fissions that occur during the nth generation alone (k^n), and the total number of fissions that have occurred during the first n generations [$N = (k^{n+1} - 1)/(k - 1)$].

6. **Power in a reactor:** The power (energy released per second) in a reactor is proportional to the number of decays occurring each second. Thus it is proportional to the number of decays occurring in each particular generation, so $P \propto k^n$.

7. **Conditions for fusion:** The condition for fusion *to occur* is simply that the temperature of the particles exceeds the critical ignition temperature, approximately 600 MK for D–D fusion, and 50 MK for D–T fusion. For fusion to be *energy positive* (*i.e.*, to release more energy than is needed to heat the plasma), the product of particle density and confinement time ($n\tau$) must exceed the Lawson criterion, about 10^{22} s/m^3 for D–D fusion, or 10^{20} s/m^3 for D–T fusion.

 Connections to *ActivPhysics*

Fission and fusion are both consequences of the principles of nuclear physics. In Activity 19.2 *Nuclear Binding Energy*, the light nuclei are built sequentially as different combinations of protons and neutrons are tested for stability. It may be helpful to review this activity before completing Activity 19.3 *Fusion*. All of the different elementary reactions of Eqs. 44-3 and 44-4 may be simulated in the activity, where the amounts of energy released by each fusion reaction are predicted and checked.

CHAPTER 45   FROM QUARKS TO THE COSMOS

This final chapter deals with the most recent developments in two of the most fundamental questions addressed by physics: "What are the fundamental constituents of matter?" and "Why does the universe appear as it does today?"

As we developed the ability to accelerate sub-atomic particles to higher and higher energies, we discovered hundreds of "elementary particles" whose existence was not even suspected just 50 years ago. By observing the creation and decay of these particles, we have been led to several new conservation laws that supplement the classical laws for conservation of momentum, energy, angular momentum, and electric charge. Each conservation law states that a certain property of the system (e.g., charge, parity, strangeness, etc.) remains unchanged by a particular (electromagnetic, strong, or weak) interaction.

We can separate all known particles into two general classes—the constituent particles of matter, and the particles they exchange during an interaction. The force carriers ("exchange particles") are known as gauge bosons because of their integral spin. The electromagnetic force occurs through an exchange of photons, the weak nuclear force with W^+, W^-, and Z^0 bosons, and the strong nuclear force with various "gluons."

The particles that make up matter can be subdivided into two major groups, according to whether or not they interact through the strong nuclear force:

1. The leptons consist of those particles that do not feel the strong nuclear force. (They do, however, experience gravitational, electromagnetic, and weak nuclear forces.) Six leptons (plus their antiparticles) exist: the electron (e^-) and its neutrino (v_e), the muon (μ^-) and its neutrino (v_μ), and the tau particle (τ^-) and its neutrino (v_τ).

2. The hadrons consist of those particles that interact through all forces, including the strong nuclear force. Each hadron is itself a composite system of three quarks (a "baryon") or a quark-antiquark pair (a "meson"). Six quarks (plus their antiparticles) exist: the up (u) quark, the down (d) quark, the strange (s) quark, the charm (c) quark, the top (t) quark, and the bottom (b) quark. The u, c, and t quarks carry a charge of $+\frac{2}{3}e$, and the d, s, and b quarks carry a charge of $-\frac{1}{3}e$. It seems that quarks cannot exist as free particles but always exist as a bound system of three quarks or a quark-antiquark pair. In addition, each quark comes in three "colors" (red, blue, and green), and each antiquark comes in three "anticolors" (antired, antiblue, and antigreen).

Quantum electrodynamics, developed in the 1940s, was our first complete understanding of the quantum nature of any of the fundamental forces. In the 1970s the weak nuclear force and electromagnetic forces were shown to be different manifestations of the same fundamental ("electroweak") interaction. The present form of this theory, known as the "standard model," includes the quarks, leptons, and gauge bosons described above. Recent grand unified theories (GUTs) have attempted to unite the strong and electroweak forces. Several variations have been proposed, and most predict the existence of magnetic monopoles and the (very slow) decay of free protons. One class of theories suggest that elementary particles may consist of tiny one-dimensional "superstrings" existing within a 10-dimensional space. The ultimate goal is a "theory of everything" that will unite gravity with the strong and electroweak interactions. So far, this remains an unachieved dream.

Finally, a great deal of progress has been made in the past few decades in answering questions about the early history of the universe. Two landmark discoveries (Hubble's discovery of the expansion of the universe, and Penzias and Wilson's detection of the 3 K microwave radiation) have shaped our present understanding of the early structure and behavior of the universe. The expansion of the universe, first observed by Edwin Hubble, suggests that the entire universe consisted of a single point about 15–20 billion years ago. High-energy photons that date back to within 1 million years of the big bang have since been drastically redshifted by the expansion of the universe, and appear today as the microwave background radiation discovered by Penzias and Wilson.

DEFINITIONS

You should know the definition of each of these terms. (The number in parentheses is the text chapter and section in which the term is introduced.)

(45-1) A virtual photon is a photon emitted by one particle and absorbed by another particle, unseen by the outside world (except through the force it exerts on the two interacting particles).

(45-1) Quantum electrodynamics was the first successful description of a fundamental interaction (electrodynamics) in terms of an exchange of intermediate bosons (photons).

(45-2) A fermion is any particle whose spin quantum number is a half-integral number (quarks and leptons are all spin-$\frac{1}{2}$ fermions). Fermions obey the Pauli exclusion principle, and bosons do not.

(45-2) A *boson* is any particle whose spin quantum number is an integer. (Photons, W^+, W^-, Z^0, and the gluons are all spin-1 bosons, and the graviton is predicted to be a spin-2 boson.)

(45-2) A *lepton* is a fundamental particle that interacts only through gravitational and electroweak forces. (That is, leptons do *not* feel the strong nuclear force.) Six leptons (plus their antiparticles) are known: the electron and its neutrino, the muon and its neutrino, and the tau and its neutrino.

(45-2) A *baryon* is a particle composed of three quarks. Baryons interact through all three (strong, electroweak, and gravitational) forces.

(45-2) A *meson* is a particle composed of a quark-antiquark pair. Like baryons, mesons interact through all three forces.

(45-2) A *hadron* is any particle made of quarks and/or antiquarks, so hadrons interact through all three forces. (Baryons and mesons together comprise the hadron class.)

(45-2) A *gauge boson* is any integer-spin particle that is exchanged between two interacting particles. Examples include photons, W, Z^0, gluons, and gravitons.

(45-2) The *parity* of a function is defined in terms of the effect on the function of replacing x with $-x$, y with $-y$, and z with $-z$. If the function is unchanged by this inversion, the function has *even parity*. If the inversion simply multiplies the function by (-1), the function has *odd parity*.

(45-2) *Charge conjugation* is the mathematical operation of changing the sign of each electric charge in a reaction.

(45-2) *Time reversal* is the mathematical operation of replacing *every* occurrence of t in a process with $-t$.

(45-3) A *quark* is a fundamental particle, carrying a charge of $+\frac{2}{3}e$ or $-\frac{1}{3}e$. Quarks come in six "flavors" (u, d, s, c, t, and b) and three "colors" (red, blue, and green.) Antiquarks ($\bar{u}, \bar{d}, \bar{s}, \bar{c}, \bar{t}, \bar{b}$) also exist and carry the opposite charge as the corresponding quarks.

(45-3) *Quantum chromodynamics* is the theory that explains the strong nuclear force in terms of exchanges of colored gluons between quarks.

(45-3) A *gluon* is a zero-rest-mass boson that is exchanged between quarks when they interact through the strong nuclear force. Eight gluons are predicted, each of which carries color charge.

(45-3) The *standard model* is a quantum field theory of the strong and electroweak interactions that describes matter in terms of quarks and leptons. The standard model successfully combines the electromagnetic and weak nuclear forces into a single (electroweak) interaction, but the strong and gravitational forces are treated as distinct phenomena.

(45-4) A *grand unified theory* describes the strong and electroweak forces in terms of one single interaction (only gravity is left out). A number of GUTs have been developed, and most predict a finite lifetime for a free proton, the existence of magnetic monopoles, and a nonzero neutrino rest mass. To date, only the neutrino's rest mass has been confirmed.

(45-4) One of the current GUTs portrays elementary particles as tiny one-dimensional *superstrings* that exist within a 10-dimensional space.

(45-4) At very high energies, it is believed that all the fundamental forces have the same behavior, a mathematically symmetric system. As the energy is reduced, the different interactions begin behaving differently, and the *symmetry* (among the interactions) is *broken*.

(45-5) *Hubble's law* states that the velocity of recession of a distant galaxy (or, presumably, any other distant object) is directly proportional to its distance from the point of observation.

(45-5) About 10^5 years after the big bang, atoms began forming. Since that time, the vast majority of photons no longer interact with matter. These leftover photons, now greatly redshifted by the expansion of the universe, today comprise the *cosmic background radiation*, whose spectrum matches that of a blackbody at a temperature near 3 K.

(45-5) To explain the homogeneity of the background radiation, Alan Guth and others have suggested that the universe underwent a sudden *inflation* that began 10^{-35} s after the big bang and lasted for the next 10^{-32} s. During this inflation, the volume of the universe increased by an extra factor of 10^{100}.

(45-5) The *critical density* of the universe is the density that would just barely bring the present expansion to a halt after an infinite time. If the universe's density is above ρ_c, the expansion will halt after a finite time, and the universe will begin to contract toward a "big crunch." If the universe's density is below ρ_c, the expansion will continue without end.

SUMMARY OF EQUATIONS

1. Hubble's law:

$$v = H_0 d \qquad \text{(Text Eq. 45-1)}$$

Edwin Hubble discovered that the speed with which a distant object is receding from any given point of observation (for example, the Earth) is directly proportional to the distance of the object from the point of observation. The exact value of Hubble's constant H_0 is hotly debated, with values quoted between 15 and 30 (km/s)/Mly.

2. Electromagnetic Doppler shift:

   a. *Nonrelativistic (u << c) form:*

   $$\frac{\Delta\lambda}{\lambda_0} = \frac{u}{c} \qquad \text{(Text Eq. 17-11)}$$

   In this expression, λ_0 represents the wavelength emitted by a source that is at rest with respect to the observer, and $\Delta\lambda$ is the *change* in wavelength due to the relative motion of the source and observer. If they are receding from each other (positive u), $\Delta\lambda > 0$, and a redshift is observed; if they are approaching each other (negative u), $\Delta\lambda < 0$, and a blueshift is observed.

   b. *Exact (relativistic) form:*

   $$\lambda = \lambda_0 \sqrt{\frac{1 + u/c}{1 - u/c}}$$

   As before, λ_0 is the wavelength observed when the relative velocity of source and observer is zero. λ represents the wavelength observed when their relative velocity is u. Recession (positive u) produces a redshift, and approaching (negative u) produces a blueshift. When $u << c$, this expression reduces to Eq. 17-11.

3. Critical density for the universe:

   $$\rho_c = \frac{3H_0^3}{8\pi G}$$

   This expression, from Example 45-4 in the text, gives an estimate for the critical density of the universe. If the average (mass) density is less than ρ_c, the curvature of the universe is negative and the expansion of the universe will continue forever. However, if the density is greater than ρ_c, the curvature is positive and the universe will eventually stop expanding and begin to contract back toward a "big crunch."

4. Blackbody radiation:

   (I am repeating two important results from Chapter 39 because of their relevance to the cosmic background radiation.)

   a. *Stefan-Boltzmann radiation law*

   $$P = \sigma A T^4 \qquad \text{(Text Eq. 39-1)}$$

   The total power radiated by a blackbody with surface area A is directly proportional to the fourth power of its kelvin temperature. The Stefan-Boltzmann constant has the SI value $\sigma = 5.67 \times 10^{-8}$ W/m²K⁴.

   b. *Wien's displacement law*

   $$\lambda_{max} T = 2.90 \times 10^{-3} \text{ m·K} \quad \text{(Text Eq. 39-2)}$$

   The wavelength of the most intense radiation from a blackbody is inversely proportional to the kelvin temperature of the object.

AVOIDING PITFALLS

1. **Rest lifetimes:** When the lifetime of a particle is given, it will almost always be τ_0, the "proper" or "rest lifetime." This is the lifetime of the particle as measured in a frame of reference in which the particle is at rest. If, in a different frame, the particle is moving with a speed v, its lifetime will be lengthened by a factor of $\gamma = (1 - v^2/c^2)^{-1/2}$. Note: If the particle's kinetic energy is given, rather than its speed, it is a simple matter to calculate γ from $K = (\gamma - 1)E_0$.

2. **Members of the Standard Model:** The large number of unfamiliar names and properties of all these particles makes it rather difficult to make sense of all this, so the chart shown in Figure 45.1 may help you sort out the relationships among the various "fundamental particles," as described by the Standard Model.

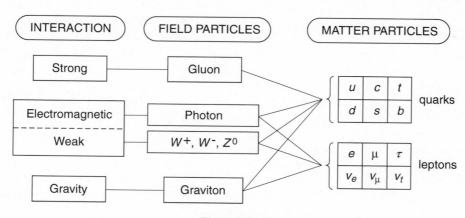

Figure 45.1

Organization of the Standard Model. Note that the field particles are all spin-zero "gauge bosons," and the matter particles are spin-1/2 "fermions." Also note that gravity and the weak force interact with *all* matter particles, the electromagnetic force acts on all charged particles, but the strong force does not affect the leptons.

The left column shows the three fundamental interactions (strong, electroweak, and gravitational), and the center column lists the gauge boson exchanged during each interaction. The constituent particles of matter can be grouped into two corresponding families: quarks and leptons. The connecting lines indicate that quarks (and all particles made up of quarks and/or antiquarks) can interact through all three forces, whereas leptons do not interact through the strong force.

3. **Conservation laws:** There are also a number of unfamiliar conservation laws that govern the reactions and decays of these particles. Some of these conservation laws are not always obeyed, but only during certain kinds of interactions. I am listing a few of these conservation laws below, along with the circumstances under which the law is known to hold.

Conserved Quantity	When Conserved
Mass-energy	Always*
Momentum	Always*
Electric charge	Always
Baryon number	Always
Lepton number	Always**
Strangeness	$\Delta S = 0$ in strong and electromagnetic interactions, and in weak interactions *not* involving s quarks; $\Delta S = \pm 1$ in weak interactions involving s quarks.

   * Temporary violations of these conservation laws can occur during intervals allowed by the uncertainty principle ($\Delta E \cdot \Delta t \geq \hbar$).

 ** There are actually three distinct lepton numbers (one that counts members of the electron family, one for members of the muon family, and one for members of the t family), each separately conserved.

4. **Big bang:** A common misconception of the big bang is that it was like a giant explosion, spewing atoms, quasars, planets, and galaxies out into empty, but already existing, space. A more accurate description is that *space itself* exploded, carrying matter and radiation with it.

5. **Hubble's law:** It's intuitive to think that Hubble's law relates an object's speed to its distance from "the center of the universe." However, *all* space is expanding, and we cannot point to a single spot and say, "That's where the big bang happened," because the big bang really happened *everywhere* in the universe!

   Hubble's law states that the distance between *any* two objects in the universe is directly proportional to their relative velocity of recession, and makes no reference to the distance from the "center of the universe."

 Connections to *ActivPhysics*

Table 45-1 on page 1230 lists the properties of 22 particle/antiparticle pairs. This table will be quite useful when completing Activity 19.5 *Particle Physics*. The purpose of the activity is to use the conservation laws to predict the pairs of particles that could result from an elementary particle reaction, similar to Example 45-1. The advantage of this activity is that almost any pair of particles may be chosen for the collision, which provides excellent practice for understanding the rules of particle interactions and may be very helpful in completing Exercises 7–9 and 11.

PART II

Guide to *ActivPhysics*

Christopher Wozny

UNIT 11 ELECTRICITY

Unit 11 is the first of four units that explore the topic of electromagnetism. Electricity is a force found in nature caused by the property known as *charge*. Since electricity is just another type of force, all of the theories and methods of kinematics, dynamics, and statics apply equally well to electric forces as to any other force. These activities explore the unique characteristics of the electric forces produced by stationary charges, which are called electrostatics. Some of the basic concepts of electricity are assumed, such as the existence of only two types of charges labeled positive and negative, and that opposite charges attract each other whereas like charges repel each other. However, a number of new and important concepts are introduced in this unit, including the electric field and electric potential.

An electric field is constructed by measuring the electric force acting on a "test charge" at every point in space. Since the magnitude of the test charge is constant and charge is a scalar quantity, its effect can be eliminated by dividing the magnitude of the electric force by the magnitude of the test charge. The resulting vector field labels every point in space with a magnitude and a direction. The field is not a force, but force can easily be found by placing a charge of *any* magnitude in the field. In this respect, the concept of a field is more general than the concept of a force, since a force acts at one particular location between two particular objects but a field is defined for overall space and exists independent of the interacting charge.

A second new concept introduced in this unit is electric potential. Since electric force is a function of position only, then there must also be an electrical potential energy. The potential, or voltage, is defined in a manner similar to the field by determining the potential energy of a test charge at some point in space and dividing it by the magnitude of the test charge. Electric field and electric potential are just two of a number of new useful mathematical methods for describing nature encountered in the twin fields of electricity and magnetism.

GAME PLAN

There are thirteen activities in this unit, but only six different simulations. The *Electric Force* simulation, found in the first five activities, 11.1–11.5, shows electric force vectors for two or three point charges interacting in space. In Activity 11.1 *Electric Force: Coulomb's Law*, the simulation is used to deduce Coulomb's law; in Activity 11.2 *Electric Force: Superposition Principle*, it is used to show how electric force vectors add, with sample calculations presented in Activity 11.3 *Electric Force:*

Superposition (Quantitative); and in Activities 11.4 *Electric Field: A Point Charge* and 11.5 *Electric Field: Due to a Dipole* the simulation is used to show the conceptual link between electric force and electric field. The sequence and content of these five activities develop the topics of electrostatics in the same manner as any standard textbook.

The second simulation of the unit displays electric field lines or equipotential lines for one or two point charges. This simulation is employed in Activities 11.4–11.6, 11.11, and 11.12. The first three activities—11.4 *Electric Field: A Point Charge*, 11.5 *Electric Field: Due to a Dipole*, and 11.6 *Electric Field: Problems*—explore the properties and construction of an electric field, and Activities 11.11 *Electric Potential: Qualitative Introduction* and 11.12 *Electric Potential, Field, and Force* do the same for the electric potential.

The field for a different configuration of charges, the *Parallel Plate Field* simulation, is also included in Activities 11.4 and 11.9–11.13. Two parallel plates with uniform but opposite charge distributions will result in an almost uniform electric field between the plates.

All of the introductory investigations cited so far explore fundamental electrostatic principles, and the application activities in this set are not that difficult. The last two activities and their accompanying simulations, 11.7 *Electric Flux* and 11.8 *Gauss's Law*, explore topics that are not always covered in an introductory course, so the decision to complete them will depend on the course and the instructor. However, both activities will be useful if Maxwell's equations are covered in the course.

THE DETAILS

11.1 Electric Force: Coulomb's Law

Coulomb's force law for two charges is deduced by observing the resulting magnitudes and directions of the force acting between two charges with variable magnitudes and positions.

Layout Introductory activity; one simulation showing the force vector acting on two particles with adjustable charge magnitudes and position (the *Electric Force* simulation).

Pointers This activity deduces Coulomb's law from observations of the direction and magnitude of electric force resulting from different combinations of two charges located in different positions. Another approach to this activity is to begin with the form of Coulomb's law and use the simulation to verify the form of the equation. In either case, the main points made in the text bar are worth noting and remembering.

11.2 Electric Force: Superposition Principle

Pair-wise interactive forces and the net force acting on each charged particle are displayed for a system of three charges, each with an adjustable magnitude and position.

Layout Introductory activity; one simulation, the *Electric Force* simulation of Activity 11.1 but with the addition of a third charge.

Pointers This activity investigates the net force acting in a space containing more than two charges. The short answer is that the force vectors acting on a charge add as vectors, but if the short answer in physics was able to explain things clearly, then everyone would take physics and the full course would only be one term long. It is worthwhile to complete all the questions in this activity to make sure you truly understand the superposition principle.

11.3 Electric Force: Superposition (Quantitative)

Calculations are made of the net force or charge magnitude for four different word problems.

Layout Application activity; one simulation, the *Electric Force* simulation of Activity 11.2.

Pointers The word problems created for this activity are not that different from the type found in a standard textbook; however, as in previous *ActivPhysics* units, the word problems presented here include a step-by-step guide to reach the final answer, which can be quite helpful for students with no experience with this topic.

11.4 Electric Field: A Point Charge

The concept of an electric field is developed by examining the force acting on "test charges" of different magnitudes near a single, fixed point charge. Once the concept of an electric field is explained, maps of electric fields for a point charge and two oppositely charged parallel lines of charge are displayed and explored by varying the magnitude and sign of the charge.

Layout Introductory activity; three simulations. Sim 1 is the *Electric Force* simulation of Activity 11.2; Sim 2 shows the electric field for either one or two point charges (the *Point Charge Field* simulation); and Sim 3 shows the electric field for two parallel lines of charge (the *Parallel Plate Field* simulation).

Pointers Of all the activities of this unit, this is probably the most important one. The three standard configurations of one and two point charges and uniformly charged parallel plates will be referred to frequently in a physics course, so understanding the behavior of the electric field for these configurations is very important.

11.5 Electric Field: Due to a Dipole

The electric field caused by two point charges is first constructed using the test charge method and then explored using the same approach as Activity 11.4.

Layout Introductory activity; four simulations. Sim 1 (= Sim 3) is the *Electric Force* simulation of Activity 11.2; Sim 2 (= Sim 4) is the *Point Charge Field* simulation of Activity 11.4.

Pointers The electric dipole has applications in condensed matter physics (liquids and solids), chemistry, and materials science. The focus in this investigation is to see how the fields of two point charges are able to combine into a logical result that matches our observations and experience.

11.6 Electric Field: Problems

Electric field lines are sketched for five different combinations of two point charges with different signs and magnitudes.

Layout Application activity; one simulation, the *Point Charge Field* simulation of Activity 11.4.

Pointers This activity will test if you truly understand the basic properties of the electric field. If you discover that you can't correctly sketch these fields, or if you don't understand the mistakes you may have made, then it is important to review the previous exercises or get extra help.

11.7 Electric Flux

The concept of electric flux and the relationship between flux and charge is explored by calculating flux through an adjustable surface surrounding one or two charges with variable signs and magnitudes. Three equivalent methods for determining flux are presented. The second half of the activity focuses on the integral method, in preparation for the next activity, 11.8 *Gauss's Law*.

Layout Introductory activity; two simulations, the first showing different configurations of point charges and the calculation of flux through an adjustable surface, the second showing the flux through either a charged solid sphere or a charged spherical shell.

Pointers Flux is not always covered in an introductory course but students with a strong interest in mathematical physics will enjoy this activity. This activity and the next one are quite useful if Maxwell's equations will be discussed in the course (which is usually a standard topic in a calculus-based course).

11.8 Gauss's Law

Gauss's law, which states that the integral of the flux over a closed surface is proportional to the magnitude of the charge enclosed by the surface, is used to determine the electric field at different locations in or near a charged, solid sphere or a charged spherical shell.

Layout Application activity; one simulation representing a three-dimensional charged sphere, including its field lines.

Pointers Gauss's law is one of Maxwell's four equations governing the behavior of electricity and magnetism; it is a necessary consequence of the inverse square nature of Coulomb's law. Gauss's law demonstrates one of the motivating factors that causes some individuals to become physicists: a logical consistency in the universe that some scientists call "elegance" and others refer to as "beauty."

11.9 Motion of a Charge in an Electric Field: Introduction

The position, velocity, and acceleration of a charged particle moving through a uniform electric field are explored for different signs and magnitudes on the point charge and for different field strengths and directions.

Layout Introductory activity; one simulation depicting the motion of a point charge through a uniform electric field produced by two oppositely charged plates (a variation of the *Parallel Plate Field* simulation).

Pointers After developing the theory of electric force and electric fields in the previous eight activities, we must remember that the ultimate purpose for doing so was to connect back to the behavior or charges in nature, and one fundamental concern in all of physics is how objects move. This simulation investigates the motion of charges that result from their electric properties.

11.10 Motion of a Charge in an Electric Field: Problems

Position, range, or time of flight are calculated for five particular combinations of a charged particle moving through a uniform electric field.

Layout Application activity; one simulation, the *Parallel Plate Field* simulation of Activity 11.9.

Pointers This activity presents simple application problems for a charged particle moving through a uniform electric field. The analogy to projectile motion (Unit 3 of *ActivPhysics*) is intentional. This investigation should remind you that electricity is still just another example of a force, and that all

the laws and principles of motion developed in mechanics still apply.

11.11 Electric Potential: Qualitative Introduction

The electric potential is constructed for one and two point charges, and for two parallel plates of opposite and uniform charge distribution. The rules and principles governing the behavior of the electric potential are developed by exploring the behavior of test charges in the electric potential.

Layout Introductory activity; two simulations. Sim l is the *Point Charge Field* simulation, and Sim 2 is the *Parallel Plate Field* simulation, both first encountered in Activity 11.4.

Pointers The electric field simulations always had the option of including the electric potential, so you may have observed them for these simulations, whether accidentally or intentionally. This activity and the next will demonstrate the construction and properties of the electric potential, in a similar fashion to the way Activities 11.4–11.6 explained the nature of the electric field. The unit of electric potential is voltage, and since batteries are rated by their voltage, it should be clear that it is important to understand the meaning of an electric potential. This activity should help you do that.

11.12 Electric Potential, Field, and Force

The interrelationships between and among electric potential, electric field, and electric force are explained using the examples of one and two point charges and uniformly charged parallel plates.

Layout Introductory activity; two simulations. Sim l is the *Parallel Plate Field* simulation, and Sim 2 is the *Point Charge Field* simulation, both first encountered in Activity 11.4.

Pointers This activity continues the discussion of the previous one. The conclusions drawn in this activity are just as important to understand and remember as the conclusions of Activity 11.4, concerning the properties of the electric field.

11.13 Electric Potential Energy and Potential

The motion of a charge in a uniform electric field is examined using conservation of energy instead of examining net forces.

Layout Introductory activity; one simulation, the *Parallel Plate Field* simulation of Activity 11.9.

Pointers Electric force, electric field, electric potential, and electric potential energy are all interrelated. In mechanics, we used calculus to show that conservation of energy is a consequence of Newton's laws of motion. The same type of mathematical relationship applies to the vector electric field and the scalar electric potential. Activity 11.4 showed the connection between electric force and electric field, so logically the same type of connection should exist between electric potential energy and the electric potential. In other words, if the electric field is electric force divided by charge, then the electric potential is electric potential energy divided by charge; and if the "real" force can be reconstructed by multiplying the field by the charge of the particle, then the "real" energy of a charged particle in a field can be calculated by multiplying the charge of the particle by the potential at that location.

Excess charges on a negatively or positively charged object will naturally repel each other due to the properties of electric forces. However, the same charges will be naturally attracted to opposite charges residing on another object. If two charged objects are allowed to make contact and if both of them are electrically conducting (meaning that charges are able to move freely), then charge will migrate from one object to the other, causing a conversion of stored electrical potential energy into other forms of energy. The released energy can be harnessed if the flow of charge is controlled by connecting the two objects with a conducting wire. For example, a toaster converts electrical energy into heat and a bulb converts electrical energy into light.

Instead of calculating changes in electrical energy directly, scientists usually measure the voltage (or potential) between two terminals. The rate at which charge flows between two terminals is the current. If current flows in one direction only, from a positive to a negative terminal, the result is a *direct current* or DC circuit. As charges flow through real materials, they lose energy due to collisions, which also prevent an instantaneous movement of charge and an infinite current. This property of a material is its resistance, and the relationship between voltage, current, and resistance is given by Ohm's law. This unit of *ActivPhysics* explores changes in voltage across resistors and capacitors and current flow in DC circuits.

GAME PLAN

A circuit diagram is a symbolic picture showing how electronic circuit elements are connected. All of the simulations in these activities include circuit diagrams. One important advantage of *Activ-Physics* is that you can construct your own circuit diagrams with the simulation tool; therefore, it may be possible to create many of the circuits presented in word problems in your particular textbook.

The basic circuit element is a wire, which does nothing but connect together other electronic elements. Almost all DC circuits require a power source (a single *cell*, or a series of cells, which is a *battery*). When a power source is added to an *ActivPhysics* circuit, its voltage may be set to a value ranging from −10 to +10 volts. A switch is another circuit element that can be added to a diagram to open and close a current loop while the simulation is running.

If the two terminals of a power source are connected to each other by a wire, the power source will "short out," because a power source must act on something. In Unit 12, three circuit elements that a power source can act on are a resistor, a capacitor, and a lightbulb. An active circuit element such as one of these either stores or dissipates voltage. A lightbulb is actually just a resistor, but the relative amount of voltage expended by different bulbs (resistors) in the circuit can be observed from their relative brightness, which in turn may represent either the relative currents flowing through the bulbs or the relative voltage loss of each bulb. The internal resistance of a lightbulb is fixed, but when a resistor element is added to a circuit, its resistance can be set to a value between 1 and 10 ohms.

A capacitor doesn't dissipate voltage, it stores voltage.

These three primary circuit elements—power source, capacitor, and resistor (or lightbulb)—can be used to construct an amazing variety of different circuits, because any two elements can be connected either *in series* or *in parallel*. When constructing a circuit, a scientist is generally concerned with two questions: What is the voltage expended or stored by each element in the circuit (the voltage drop), and what is the current flowing through each element in the circuit? All eight of the activities in this unit will explore different combinations of circuit elements in series and in parallel.

The place to start is with Activity 12.1 *DC Series Circuits: Qualitative*, which explains how to use the circuit simulation tools to create circuits, and the meaning and function of the different elements. I then recommend completing the short Activity 12.4 *Using Ammeters and Voltmeters*, which demonstrates how to correctly place ammeters (in series) and voltmeters (in parallel) in order to measure current and voltage drop, respectively. The rest of the activities may then be completed sequentially, since they build the general rules for resistors in DC circuits in the same traditional order as any textbook: series circuits, parallel circuits, combined circuits, and then Kirchhoff's laws, which are a set of principles governing the behavior of any DC circuit that are quite useful for very complicated circuits. The last three activities deal with the behavior of capacitors in DC circuits.

One final comment concerning this unit: Most textbooks and many instructors emphasize the use of DC circuit rules to calculate current flow and voltage drop. However, many of these circuit activities ask only whether a lightbulb will light when the circuit loop is closed, or how its brightness will compare to other bulbs in the circuit, or if the brightness of a bulb will change when the configuration of a circuit changes. These types of questions reflect the basic philosophy of *ActivPhysics* that understanding physics is more than just being able to calculate numerical answers from equations for word problems. Our assumption is that if students understand the basic concepts of physics, then the numerical problem solving will be easier for them—and they will be more likely to remember the physics principles after the course is completed.

THE DETAILS

12.1   DC Series Circuits: Qualitative

The first part of the activity shows how to construct working circuits using the circuit tool; the second part uses a simple circuit to test Ohm's law. In the third part of the activity, the rules of voltage drop and current flow in a series resistance circuit are developed and tested by observing the behavior of circuits containing either bulbs or resistors.

Layout   Introductory activity; four simulations. Sim 1 shows the circuit tool bar and an empty circuit board; Sims 2–4 are different circuit diagrams constructed with the circuit tool.

Pointers   This activity introduces the construction of circuits using the circuit tool. A simple circuit consisting of a power source, lightbulb, and an ammeter can easily demonstrate Ohm's law, $V = IR$, since the resistance of the lightbulb is a constant 1 ohm.

This investigation also shows the rules governing current and voltage for a bulb: how total current flow relates to flow through an individual bulb, and how total voltage relates to voltage drop through an individual bulb. The only measurement that is always unchanging for a bulb in a circuit is its resistance. In every DC circuit, particular relationships between current and voltage for its elements will depend on the configuration of the circuit.

Another important conclusion to be drawn from this activity is that the brightness of a lightbulb depends on both its current and the voltage. Later activities will ask for predictions of relative brightness of bulbs in a circuit, so it is important to consider both relationships between bulb currents and voltages before reaching a definite conclusion. In fact, the product of current and voltage is power, which is the time rate of change of energy. Therefore, the principle of energy conservation may also be used to make predictions about relative brightness.

12.2   DC Parallel Circuits

The rules governing voltage drop and current flow for a parallel resistance circuit are developed for circuits containing lightbulbs of equal resistance and tested by observation of the brightness of bulbs in more complicated circuit configurations.

Layout   Introductory activity; six simulations, each showing a different configuration of power source and lightbulbs, with some including ammeters.

Pointers   The relationships between voltages and currents for bulbs (or resistors) in parallel are different from those for bulbs and resistors in series. The equations for calculating the equivalent resistance of a circuit are also different. It may be useful to create a table listing those relationships and refer back to it when completing the rest of these activities or textbook word problems.

12.3   DC Circuit Puzzles

Voltage and current are predicted and measured for eight different circuit diagrams consisting of power sources and lightbulbs in different configurations.

Layout   Application activity; eight simulations, each showing a different configuration of power source and lightbulbs, with some including ammeters or voltmeters to measure current or voltage drop.

Pointers   As with many of the *ActivPhysics* application activities, this one tests whether you truly understand the relationships between voltage and current for series and parallel resistor circuits. Don't expect to get all of the circuit problems right, but do plan on learning from your errors. Having a table of relationships like the one suggested in the previous activity's *Pointers* should be helpful.

12.4   Using Ammeters and Voltmeters

The correct methods for inserting an ammeter in a circuit to measure current or a voltmeter across a circuit element to measure voltage are demonstrated and explained based on the principles of how they function.

Layout   Introductory activity; four simulations. Sim 1 and Sim 3 show the correct way to insert an ammeter and a voltmeter in a circuit; Sim 2 and Sim 4 show the incorrect way to insert an ammeter and a voltmeter in a circuit.

Pointers   This is a very short activity with a simple and direct conclusion. The rules for connecting ammeters and voltmeters are usually one of the first priorities of an electronics laboratory investigation, since burning out ammeters can get very expensive. Even so, don't miss the information in the text bar explaining *why* ammeters are put in series in a circuit and voltmeters are in parallel with the circuit element, since this represents a practical application of the rules of DC circuits developed thus far.

12.5 Using Kirchhoff's Laws

Kirchhoff's laws concerning current flow at a junction and voltage drop in a loop, which were deduced by observation in previous activities, are used to calculate voltage drop and current flow through each circuit element in six different circuits.

Layout Introductory activity; six simulations, each showing a different circuit configuration.

Pointers One method of determining voltage and current for every element in a circuit is by equivalent resistance; however not all circuits can be solved that way. Kirchhoff's laws are a more general solution that will never fail if the equations generated by them are solved correctly. Almost all graphing calculators include the ability to solve a matrix of equations. If you don't know how to program a calculator to do that, then it would be advantageous to learn to save yourself hours of algebraic manipulation.

12.6 Capacitance

The rules governing the behavior of a capacitor in a DC circuit are deduced by observing current flow over time and the voltage stored on capacitors in four different circuits with different configurations of lightbulbs and capacitors in series and in parallel.

Layout Introductory activity; four simulations, each showing a different configuration of power source, lightbulbs, and capacitors.

Pointers Resistors dissipate energy as current flows through them. Capacitors store electrical energy, so they typically begin with zero potential difference, which increases as the capacitor is charged. The positive and negative sides of the capacitor must be opposite those of the power source that is charging it, so that as the voltage on a capacitor increases, the current through it decreases. It is also true that a capacitor can't have a potential difference larger than the power source used to charge it. These principles will be helpful in completing this activity.

12.7 Series and Parallel Capacitors

The rules governing the amount of voltage stored on different capacitors connected in series or in parallel are developed by observation of different circuits.

Layout Introductory activity; five simulations, showing different configurations of power sources, lightbulbs, and capacitors.

Pointers Capacitors have a property known as capacitance, which in the SI system is measured in farads. Capacitance measures the ratio of total charge stored and voltage. Just as different resistance affects the voltage drop and current flow when resistors are connected in series or in parallel, the same is true of stored voltage for capacitors of different capacitance. In this activity, all capacitors have the same capacitance, so the values of the stored voltages tend to be the same in either a series branch or a parallel branch, but that is not the case generally.

12.8 Circuit Time Constants

The current flowing through a circuit consisting of only a charged capacitor and a resistor (an RC circuit with no power source) decreases exponentially over time, and the effects of capacitance and resistance on the time constant of the circuit are visualized.

Layout Introductory activity; one simulation showing a diagram of an RC circuit with variable resistance, capacitance, and total initial charge, and also a graph of the current in the circuit as a function of time.

Pointers The current through a capacitor as it is being charged must decrease over time since its stored voltage will oppose and therefore cancel the electromotive force of the power source that is causing current to flow in the first place. An analogy to this situation could be water flowing into a pond: as the pond fills up, the current from the stream feeding the pond decreases. This activity examines the discharging of a capacitor instead of its charging, but the mathematical relationship for current as a function of time will be the same in both cases.

UNIT 13 MAGNETISM

Magnetic force bears a number of similarities to electric force, but electricity and magnetism cannot be the same phenomenon because a stationary charge does not interact with a stationary magnet. However, in 1820 Hans Christian Oersted discovered quite by accident that *moving* charges do interact with a magnetic compass needle. Two long, straight current-carrying wires also interact with each other magnetically, either attracting or repelling each other based on the directions of the current flow. These types of observations ultimately led to the conclusion that magnetism is caused by moving charges, and therefore electricity and magnetism are intimately linked.

It is advantageous to describe both electricity and magnetism in terms of their fields instead of forces, but the magnetic field doesn't behave in quite the same way as the electric field. For example, the magnetic field vector acts at a right angle to the magnetic force vector instead of in the same direction, as with electricity. The cause of magnetism, current, is a vector and not a scalar, like charge; and current, magnetic field, and magnetic force are related to each other mathematically by a cross product. (Torque was also defined in terms of a cross product; see Unit 7.) In fact, a charge moving through a magnetic field will not accelerate in the direction of motion but is more likely to follow a "corkscrew" path as it travels through the field (see Activity 13.4).

Magnetic fields can be difficult to comprehend because their interactions are always three-dimensional; however, there is one extremely important practical consequence of magnetism. Oersted discovered that a moving charge interacts magnetically with a stationary magnet, but it is equally true that a moving magnet interacts *electrically* with a stationary charge, creating (or inducing) a voltage in a conducting material. It is this principle of electromagnetic induction that is the basis of generators, motors, and almost all of our modern technological culture.

GAME PLAN

The activities of this unit build very nicely on one another, so I recommend completing all of the activities sequentially. Magnetism is one topic where a conceptual understanding, especially of the three-dimensional nature of magnetic effects, can be much more important than numerical problem solving. In fact, the calculations found in word problems on magnetism tend to be very simple algebraically, but you must understand what is happening in the magnetic field in order to set up

and solve them correctly, which is why having a firm grasp of the interrelationships between and among the force, the field, and the velocity of a moving charge is so important.

The first three activities, 13.1 *Magnetic Field of a Wire*, 13.2 *Magnetic Field of a Loop*, and 13.3 *Magnetic Field of a Solenoid*, show the construction of magnetic fields for different current-carrying wire configurations. These investigations shouldn't take long and will help you understand the general relationships between and among current strength, the form of the field lines, and the direction of the magnetic field vector. A test of that understanding can be found in the next three activities, 13.4 *Magnetic Force on a Particle*, 13.5 *Magnetic Force on a Wire*, and 13.6 *Magnetic Torque on a Loop*. These investigations demonstrate the three-dimensional nature of magnetism and the importance of understanding the cross-product relationship between magnetic field and magnetic force.

The next two activities, 13.7 *Mass Spectrometer* and 13.8 *Velocity Selector*, are practical applications of magnetic fields, and both of these devices are often found in the laboratory. The last two activities, 13.9 *Electromagnetic Induction* and 13.10 *Motional EMF*, demonstrate the connection between electricity and magnetism, which is pivotal in the theory of electromagnetism (Maxwell's equations) and the description of light as an electromagnetic wave. Unit 14 shows how electromagnetic induction can be used to create an electric circuit element, the inductor.

THE DETAILS

13.1   Magnetic Field of a Wire

Magnetic field lines are drawn for a single current-carrying wire.

Layout Introductory activity; one simulation, showing magnetic field lines for a current-carrying wire, where current magnitude and direction are adjustable parameters in the simulation.

Pointers The electric field lines for a point charge radiate outward from a positive charge or inward to a negative charge. For an instantaneous vector current, modeled by a long, straight wire carrying a constant current, the field lines circulate around the wire in either a clockwise or a counter-clockwise direction. This is one fundamental difference between electric and magnetic fields; however, other aspects, such as the effect of increasing or decreasing the magnitude of the field-creating source, are quite similar.

The addition of the magnetic field vector at any point in space in the simulation helps make the meaning and behavior of the magnetic field more understandable. The simulation also includes the option of showing how iron filings would behave in a real experiment instead of plotting magnetic field lines. This option, which is also included in the next activity, may be useful since field lines cannot be seen directly but the orientation of the filings confirms their existence and the behavior of field lines shown in the simulation.

13.2   Magnetic Field of a Loop

Magnetic field lines are drawn for a current-carrying loop of wire.

Layout Introductory activity; one simulation, showing magnetic field lines for a current-carrying circular loop of wire, where current magnitude and direction are adjustable parameters in the simulation.

Pointers If field lines loop around a straight current-carrying wire, then what is their structure for a current-carrying loop? This activity is a necessary and logical step to the next activity, the magnetic field of a solenoid. Solenoids in magnetism serve a similar function as charged parallel plates in electrostatics (Unit 11). The *Pointers* for the next activity will discuss the magnetic properties of a solenoid further.

13.3   Magnetic Field of a Solenoid

Magnetic field lines are drawn for a solenoid, which is often constructed by coiling a current-carrying wire.

Layout Introductory activity; one simulation, showing magnetic field lines for a current-carrying solenoid. The magnitude and direction of the current in the solenoid are adjustable parameters in the simulation.

Pointers The magnetic field inside a solenoid tends to be constant and uniform, just like the electric field between two uniformly and oppositely charged plates. In the electric field of parallel plates, the field lines run perpendicular between the two plates; in the solenoid, the field lines run parallel to the length of the solenoid's cylindrical tube. In the simulation, the X's represent current entering the planar "cut" through the solenoid perpendicular to the plane; whereas the dots represent current exiting the plane perpendicular to it. This is a standard notation in magnetism, and the X's and dots can represent any vector quantity, such as the magnetic field vector B in the next set of activities.

13.4   Magnetic Force on a Particle

Two views of a charged particle moving through a uniform magnetic field are simulated: one view is a full, three-dimensional picture; the other view looks down the axis of the magnetic field vector.

Layout Introductory activity; one simulation, showing two views of the three-dimensional trajectory of a charged particle in a uniform magnetic field. The magnetic field strength, and the x- and z-components of the particle's velocity are adjustable parameters in the simulation.

Pointers Magnetic fields, like electric fields, are ultimately linked to forces that can act on objects that possess magnetic properties. However, the electric force acts in the direction of the electric field, whereas the magnetic force acts perpendicular to the magnetic field and the magnitude of the magnetic force is also proportional to the component of the velocity vector that is perpendicular to both the force and the field. Therefore, the z-component of the velocity vector has no effect on the magnetic force because it is parallel to the magnetic field. The y-component has been set to zero in the simulation only to simplify the picture, so that the component of the velocity vector perpendicular to the magnetic field is just the magnitude of the x-component of the velocity. This simplification makes the relationship between the component's speed and the magnetic force easier to observe, and causes the orientation of the circular path to remain constant as parameters are changed.

13.5   Magnetic Force on a Wire

Magnetic field lines for two current-carrying wires are drawn and the magnetic force vectors of each wire resulting from the interaction of their fields are shown. The relationship between current magnitude and distance is deduced by varying the magnitude and direction of the two currents and the separation distance of the two wires.

Layout Introductory activity; one simulation, showing the field lines, magnetic field vector, and magnetic force vectors for two current-carrying wires.

Pointers Compare this simulation to the *Electric Force* simulation of Activity 11.1. The similarities between Coulomb's law and the behavior of these two wires is striking; however, because current is a vector and not a scalar, like charge, the calculation of magnetic forces based on small current elements (current per unit length) becomes very complicated very quickly. That is one reason why the study of magnetism focuses almost exclusively on the behavior of magnetic fields instead of referring back to a fundamental magnetic force law.

13.6 Magnetic Torque on a Loop

The magnetic force acting on a current-carrying loop is observed, which causes it to twist if the magnetic dipole is not aligned with the magnetic field vector.

Layout Introductory activity; one simulation, showing the magnitudes and directions of current and magnetic force for a current-carrying loop in different orientations in a magnetic field. The magnetic field strength and orientation of the loop in the field are adjustable.

Pointers The previous two activities investigated magnetic force on particles and wires; this activity is another application of magnetic force following the same basic principles. The idea of magnetic field lines passing through an area will result in a definition of magnetic flux (see also Activity 11.7 *Electric Flux*). The magnetic torque acting on a current-carrying loop is the basis of the electric motor.

13.7 Mass Spectrometer

Pairs of charged isotopes with a common speed enter a uniform magnetic field and experience different degrees of deflection. The known velocity, magnetic field strength, and radii of curvature for a pair of unknown isotopes are used to determine their chemical identity.

Layout Application activity; one simulation showing the paths of pairs of isotopes traveling through a uniform magnetic field. The isotope pair, their initial speed, and the magnetic field strength are all adjustable parameters in this simulation.

Pointers The mass spectrometer is an application of a charged particle moving through a constant magnetic field (Activity 13.4). The magnetic force is a centripetal force, and the principles of mechanics show that centripetal force is proportional to the mass and the square of the speed, and inversely proportional to the radius of curvature. However, the magnetic force is also proportional the charge and the perpendicular velocity component of the particle. So if two particles with the same charge and speed but different masses enter the same uniform magnetic field, they will follow circular paths of different radii. Therefore, the ratio of their radii will be proportional to the ratio of their masses, and the relative amounts of different charged particles in a sample (for example, atomic isotopes) can be determined. That is the theory and operation of the mass spectrometer.

13.8 Velocity Selector

The magnetic and electric field strengths and the speed of a particle of known charge are set so that the particle travels in a straight-line path through the fields.

Layout Application activity; one simulation, showing the motion of a charged particle traveling through a space that contains uniform magnetic and electric fields. The type of particle, its speed, and the field strengths are all adjustable parameters in this simulation.

Pointers Activity 11.9 *Motion of a Charge in an Electric Field: Introduction* showed that a charged particle moving through a uniform electric field will follow a curved path due to the electric force. If a uniform magnetic field is also present in that space perpendicular to both the electric field and the direction of the moving particle, it is possible for the particle to experience a magnetic force in a direction opposite to that of the electric force. If the two forces are perfectly balanced, then the particle will continue to travel through the fields in a straight line and experience no deflection at all.

However, the magnetic force is a function not only of field strength and charge (like the electric force) but also of the speed of the particle. Therefore, if the particle moves too slowly, it will still be deflected in the direction of the electric force; if it moves too quickly, it will be deflected in the opposite direction by the magnetic force. That is the principle behind the velocity selector.

13.9 Electromagnetic Induction

An oscillating current is produced in a rotating loop of wire located in a uniform magnetic field.

Layout Introductory activity; one simulation, showing a rotating wire loop in a uniform magnetic field and also showing plots of the magnetic flux and induced voltage as a function of time. The magnetic field strength and frequency of rotation are adjustable parameters in the simulation.

Pointers Electrons located in a metal wire loop in the simulation are moving through space because the loop is rotating. When the velocity vector is perpendicular to the magnetic field vector, a magnetic force pushes the electrons in the direction of the wire and current flows. The metal wire will have a resistance, so Ohm's law implies that a voltage has been induced in the wire due to its motion through the magnetic field. The motion depicted in the simulation is the basis of electrical power generation and alternating current.

Experimental observations show that electromagnetic induction does not occur for uniform motion through a uniform field; in fact, it is a variation in magnetic flux that induces a voltage in the wire. The definition of magnetic flux is analogous to the definition of electric flux (Activity 11.7): it is the product of the field strength, an enclosed area, and the orientation angle between the field and area. In this simulation, it is the orientation angle that is varying over time.

13.10 Motional EMF

A moving conducting bar laying on a U-shaped conducting rod in a uniform magnetic field develops a voltage due to changing magnetic flux.

Layout Introductory activity; one simulation, showing the change in flux and induced voltage for a conducting bar moving through a uniform magnetic field. The velocity, length, and resistance of the bar and the strength of the magnetic field are all adjustable parameters in this simulation.

Pointers An electromotive force will be induced if the magnetic flux varies over time. The flux is defined as the magnetic field strength multiplied by the area enclosed by a loop and also multiplied by the angle between the magnetic field vector and a vector normal to the plane of the area. In the previous activity, an induced current was produced by varying the orientation angle; in this activity, the area contained by the loop shrinks, which changes the magnetic flux. Of course, the third possibility (not simulated in this unit of *ActivPhysics*) would be to vary the strength of the magnetic field.

UNIT 14   AC CIRCUITS

In Activity 13.9 *Electromagnetic Induction*, a uniform magnetic field induced a voltage in a rotating rectangular metal loop, causing current to flow in accordance with Ohm's law. Because a particular side of the rectangle first moved in the direction of and then against the direction of the magnetic field, the induced voltage was first positive and then negative, producing an alternating current (AC). The pattern of the oscillating induced voltage over time was a cosine function with a specific amplitude, frequency, and phase angle.

A resistor in an AC circuit functions in the same way as a resistor in a DC circuit, and current flowing from the power source through a single resistor in an AC circuit oscillates as a cosine function with the same frequency and phase angle as the applied voltage. A capacitor, which only served to stop current flow in a DC circuit (see Activities 12.6 *Capacitance* and 12.7 *Series and Parallel Capacitors*), becomes a useful device in AC circuits because the voltage stored on it is continually changing due to the constantly varying applied voltage. A third useful device in AC circuits is the inductor, which produces a changing magnetic field in response to the changing current, creating an induced voltage in the circuit that is always opposite to the voltage produced by the AC power source. Inductors, like capacitors, have a very limited use in a DC circuit because current flow becomes effectively constant soon after the circuit is closed, and inductance only occurs if the current varies.

The voltage stored on a capacitor and the electromotive force (emf) produced by an inductor in a simple AC circuit will also behave as cosine functions over time with the same frequency as the AC power source but with a different phase angle. Because capacitors and inductors in AC circuits "resist" current flow by producing an opposing voltage, these electronic devices have a property called "reactance" which has the same units as resistance. Like resistance, reactance also follows Ohm's law; but unlike resistance, reactance is also a function of the applied AC frequency. Resistance and reactance may be combined in a simple series AC circuit using a vector method to calculate the overall "impedance" of the circuit. The behavior of resistors, capacitors, and inductors in AC circuits is the subject of this unit of *ActivPhysics*.

GAME PLAN

The first activity of the unit explores the properties of inductors in a DC circuit. Without any resistance, current flow would be instantaneous, so Activity

14.1 *The RL Circuit* examines a DC circuit consisting of a power source, a resistor, and an inductor in series. The behavior of an inductor in a DC circuit has a number of similarities to that of a capacitor in a DC circuit, so it may be worthwhile to first review Activity 12.8 *Circuit Time Constants*, which simulates an RC circuit consisting of a resistor and a capacitor, and where the resistor in the circuit serves the same function as in the LC circuit.

Activity 14.2 *The RLC Oscillator* replaces the DC voltage source of the previous activity with a charged capacitor. A DC power source has definite positive and negative terminals, but a capacitor does not, so the result is oscillating voltage and current. An LC (or RLC) circuit has a natural frequency that is a function of the inductance and capacitance of the circuit's elements. The simulation opens with the resistance set to zero, and the effect of the resistor is later demonstrated by assigning it a nonzero value. In the third activity, 14.3 *The Driven Oscillator*, an AC power source with a variable frequency is added to the RLC circuit. It is at this point that the relative phase of the voltage cosine functions through the inductor, capacitor, and resistor (which is the phase of the AC power source) becomes important, and the vector addition of these voltages creates a resonance in a driven RLC circuit, which is thoroughly investigated in the activity.

The amount of time spent on AC circuits in an introductory physics course will vary greatly, depending on the interest of the instructor and time constraints. All three of these activities (and Activity 12.8) will make the function of inductors, capacitors, and resistors in an AC circuit, and their phase-dependent interrelationships, easier to understand. The level of difficulty of these three activities is not that great, so just the everyday reality of alternating current in our technologies may be a sufficient motivation to at least skim these activities.

THE DETAILS

14.1   The RL Circuit

The behavior of an inductor in a DC circuit is investigated when it is combined in series with a single resistor.

Layout Introductory activity; one simulation, showing a diagram of the RL circuit and also a plot of the current in the circuit as a function of time.

Pointers The RC circuit of Activity 12.8 displayed a

voltage that decreased exponentially over time as the capacitor discharged to zero volts, and a plot of current versus time will have the same functional form as the voltage due to Ohm's law. The LC circuit simulation plots the current in the circuit over time, which increases from zero to a maximum value (determined by the resistance in the circuit), but it also follows an exponential function. It is worth the effort to consider the causes of the behavior of each circuit and the basic characteristics of each electronic device before exploring the next activity.

14.2   The RLC Oscillator

The charge on a capacitor and the current through an RLC circuit are plotted as a function of time for a charged capacitor connected in series to a resistor and an inductor.

Layout   Introductory activity; one simulation, showing a diagram of the RLC circuit and also a plot of the current in the circuit and the charge stored on the capacitor as a function of time.

Pointers   The current in an LC circuit oscillates over time. Furthermore, the cosine function of the current through the loop is 90 degrees out of phase with respect to the stored voltage on the capacitor. The text bar points out that it is possible to draw an analogy to a mechanical oscillator, such as a mass on a spring. The reasons for this behavior must be traced back to the fundamental principles governing the behavior of each device, and under-

standing the LC and RLC circuit is crucial for understanding the behavior of the RLC in a circuit with an external AC power source, as discussed in the next activity.

14.3   The Driven Oscillator

A capacitor, inductor, and resistor are connected in series with a variable-frequency AC power source, and a plot of current as a function of driving frequency is displayed.

Layout   Introductory activity; one simulation showing a diagram of the RLC circuit with a variable AC power source, a plot of the current in the circuit as a function of driving frequency, and a voltage phasor diagram. The resistance, capacitance, inductance, and driving frequency are all adjustable. Varying the first three changes the shape of the current vs. the frequency curve; varying the driving frequency affects the phasor diagram.

Pointers   After learning that AC circuits involve an oscillating power source, and after discovering that the LC displays an oscillating voltage and current, you may be surprised to discover that there are no oscillations in this simulation. The key to understanding this activity is to realize that voltage on an inductor and capacitor either lead or follow the phase of the driving frequency, and that the reactance, and therefore voltage drop, across the capacitor and inductor are both a function of the driving frequency.

UNIT 15 GEOMETRIC OPTICS

Optics is the study of the behavior of light. There are four fundamental properties of light that receive most of the attention in an introduction to optics, and two of these properties, reflection and refraction, are explored in this unit on geometric optics. Both of these properties are best understood by defining the *light ray* as a straight-line path of light as it travels from its source through empty space or through a transparent medium. Reflection occurs when a light ray bounces off a nontransmitting and nonabsorbing material; refraction occurs when a light ray passes from one transmitting medium into another. The law of reflection and the law of refraction express the relationships between the incident (or incoming) angle of the light ray and the reflected or refracted angle of the light ray, where the angles are defined with respect to the flat interface where the light ray changes direction.

The laws of reflection and refraction are simple relationships that become quite useful when the reflecting or refracting surfaces are curved, such as spherical mirrors and thin lenses. Light rays guided by curved mirrors or lenses produce a *real* image at a location where light rays meet, or a *virtual* image where they appear to originate. The image may be magnified and appear larger or smaller than the object that produced the original light rays, and in some cases the image is inverted.

Any curved mirror or lens will have a focal point located somewhere along the axis of the mirror or lens. The focal point is the position where all incident light rays parallel to the axis meet after reflection or refraction, and the distance from the mirror surface or the center of the lens to the focal point is the focal length. Knowledge of the focal length and the location of the object can be used to locate the image either geometrically or algebraically using an equation that relates image distance, object distance, and focal length.

GAME PLAN

The principles of geometric optics are easy to comprehend, and the algebraic equations are relatively simple. Furthermore, because optics by its very nature is a visual topic, this unit of *ActivPhysics* can be very enjoyable.

Like Unit 11 on electricity, only a few simulations do most of the work in this unit. The first three activities, 15.1 *Reflection and Refraction*, 15.2 *Total Internal Reflection*, and 15.3 *Refraction Applications*, employ the same simulation to illustrate the basic principles of reflection and refraction. The next five activities show the application of the

law of reflection to mirrors, and the remaining seven activities explore the properties of lenses, which produce images based on the law of refraction.

Activity 15.4 *Plane Mirrors* illustrates the concept of image formation as the location where reflected or refracted light rays meet, or appear to meet. Activities 15.5 *Spherical Mirrors: Ray Diagrams*, 15.6 *Spherical Mirror: Mirror Equation*, 15.7 *Spherical Mirror: Linear Magnification*, and 15.8 *Spherical Mirror: Problems* all employ a single simulation that is able to represent mirrors of different curvatures, either curving inward toward the object (concave, or converging mirrors) or curving outward away from the object (convex, or diverging mirrors). The simulation allows the object to be placed at different points along the axis of the mirror and uses two light rays to locate the image. These four activities thoroughly cover all possible arrangements of object and image for all possible types of spherical mirrors.

Activities 15.9 *Thin-Lens Ray Diagrams*, 15.10 *Converging Lens Problems*, and 15.11 *Diverging Lens Problems* follow the same course for lenses as the spherical mirror activities. In this case, a single simulation allows the lens to possess different curvatures. The last four activities illustrate important applications of lenses, including microscopes, telescopes, and eyeglasses. Activity 15.12 *Two-Lens Optical Systems* illustrates an important principle of multiple-lens systems: that the image formed by one lens can become the object of a second lens. One practical application of two-lens systems is explored in Activity 15.13 *The Telescope and Angular Magnification*. Activity 15.14 *The Eye* shows how the eye is able to focus light on the retina, and Activity 15.15 *Eyeglasses* demonstrates how corrective lenses solve the problem when it can't.

THE DETAILS

15.1 Reflection and Refraction

The reflection and refraction of light are simulated for an incident light ray striking a semicircular transparent medium, and the laws of reflection and refraction are verified from the observed behavior of the reflected and refracted light rays.

Layout One simulation, showing both the reflection and refraction of an incident light ray striking at the center of the flat side of a semicircular transparent medium. The angle of the incident light ray and the indices of refraction of both mediums are adjustable parameters in the simulation.

Pointers This simulation reproduces a common figure found in most textbooks, with the added advantage of allowing you to adjust the important variables in the reflection and refraction equations.

15.2 Total Internal Reflection

The behavior of a light ray passing from a medium with a larger index of refraction to a medium with a lower index of refraction results in the phenomenon of total internal reflection and the definition of the critical angle.

Layout Introductory activity; one simulation, the *Reflection and Refraction* simulation of Activity 15.1.

Pointers The discussion of the text bar follows the same format as most textbooks when presenting the concept of total internal reflection, which is a logical necessity based on the form of the equation for refraction. The shape of the medium is semicircular so that an incident light ray from the curved side will always be perpendicular to the surface of the block, resulting in no angular deflection at the surface due to refraction.

15.3 Refraction Applications

The law of refraction is used to calculate either the angle or the index of refraction for four different word problems, and the solutions are verified by the simulation.

Layout Application activity; one simulation, the *Reflection and Refraction* simulation of Activity 15.1.

Pointers The four word problems in this activity are similar in scope and difficulty level to most textbook problems on this topic, and some of them may be exactly the same as assigned problems. That means that this simulation can be employed to verify the solutions of certain textbook problems, just as it is used to verify the answers to these word problems.

15.4 Plane Mirrors

A set of light rays originating from a point source and reflected off a plane mirror illustrate the principles of image location and magnification for a plane mirror.

Layout Introductory activity; one simulation, showing the reflection of four light rays originating from the point of an arrow representing an object and the physical location of the arrow's image. The *x*- and *y*-positions of the object are adjustable parameters in the simulation.

Pointers It is important to understand that *all* reflected light rays originating from a single point meet (or in this case, appear to meet) at a single point, which is the location of the image. In the rest of these activities, only two light rays will be drawn, which are chosen based on the knowledge of how they must reflect or refract. Other rays could be drawn, but their correct paths are not as easy to determine.

15.5 Spherical Mirrors: Ray Diagrams

Ray diagrams are drawn for light rays from an object that are reflected off a spherical mirror, showing the location and magnification of its image.

Layout Introductory activity; one simulation showing an object and its image formed by a spherical mirror. The position of the object on the mirror's axis and the curvature of the mirror are adjustable parameters in the simulation.

Pointers This first activity investigating spherical mirrors encourages you to explore the simulation without being concerned about the particular results. It also defines the focal point and focal length and explains why the path of an incident light ray traveling parallel to the axis must be reflected through the focal point. A third ray with a known path that is not included here is an incident ray that first passes through the focal point, which must be reflected parallel to the axis. Examining the ray diagram should convince you that this third ray, too, would pass through the same image point. These concepts will be important for the next two activities, where two equations are able to specify numerically the exact location and height of the image.

15.6 Spherical Mirror: Mirror Equation

The mirror equation is introduced; it establishes the relationships between and among object distance, image distance, and focal length. Calculations using the mirror equation are verified using the *Spherical Mirror* simulation.

Layout Introductory activity; one simulation, the *Spherical Mirror* simulation of Activity 15.5.

Pointers The six combinations of object distance, image distance, and focal length should thoroughly test your understanding of the mirror equation. Positive focal lengths correspond to convex mirrors, and negative focal lengths correspond to concave mirrors.

15.7 Spherical Mirror: Linear Magnification

An equation for the magnification of an image, which is the ratio of image height to object height, is deduced from the behavior of an image formed by a spherical mirror.

Layout Introductory activity; one simulation, the *Spherical Mirror* simulation of Activity 15.5.

Pointers Image and object height are related to image and object distance, which in turn are related to each other by the mirror equation. The positive or negative sign of the magnification identifies whether the image is inverted or not.

15.8 Spherical Mirror: Problems

Five word problems involving spherical mirrors are posed, and the *Spherical Mirror* simulation is used to verify their solutions.

Layout Application activity; one simulation, the *Spherical Mirror* simulation of Activity 15.5.

Pointers The word problems in this activity are similar in scope and difficulty level to most textbook problems on this topic, and some of them may be exactly the same as assigned problems. That means that this simulation can be employed to verify the solutions of certain textbook problems, just as it is used to verify the answers to these word problems.

15.9 Thin-Lens Ray Diagrams

Ray diagrams are constructed for light rays refracted through both converging and diverging thin lenses.

Layout Introductory activity; one simulation, showing an object and its image formed by a thin lens. The position of the object on the mirror's axis and the curvature of the mirror are adjustable parameters in the simulation.

Pointers The ray diagrams for a thin lens are very similar to the ray diagrams of a spherical mirror, except that light rays pass through the lens and out the other side of the lens. Note that light rays passing through the center of the lens on the axis experience no net refraction. The similarities between this activity and Activity 15.5 are intentional, since the behavior of light rays with respect to the focal point and the equations governing the position and magnification of the image are exactly the same as those for spherical mirrors.

15.10 Converging Lens Problems

The lens equation and magnification equation are used to calculate image distances or heights for converging lenses with positive focal lengths.

Layout Application activity; one simulation, the *Thin-Lens* simulation of Activity 15.9.

Pointers After the calculation of image position and image height for six different object locations, three different word problems are posed. The format of this activity is just a condensed version of Activities 15.6–15.8 on spherical mirrors.

15.11 Diverging Lens Problems

The lens equation and magnification equation are used to calculate image distances or heights for diverging lenses with negative focal lengths.

Layout Application activity; one simulation, the *Thin-Lens* simulation of Activity 15.9.

Pointers Image position and image height are calculated for six different object locations and one word problem. The format of this activity is just like that of the previous activity.

15.12 Two-Lens Optical Systems

Ray diagrams for a two-lens system show the location and magnification of an image.

Layout Application activity; one simulation, showing the full ray diagram for a two-lens system. Both focal lengths and lens locations are adjustable parameters in the simulation.

Pointers The lens equations for image magnification and position still apply in a two-lens system, but the key principle is that the image of one lens becomes the object of the other lens. In a two-lens system, the final image is focused at a point closer to the lens than for a single lens, and the magnification of the final image is a function of both focal lengths.

15.13 The Telescope and Angular Magnification

The properties of a telescope are demonstrated using a two-lens simulation.

Layout Application activity; one simulation showing the ray diagram for a two-lens system with the object an infinite distance from the first lens. Both focal lengths and the angle of incidence are adjustable parameters in the simulation.

Pointers In a telescope, the two lenses are adjusted so that the focal points of the two lenses coincide. The most important property of a telescope when viewing distant stars is not that it makes them bigger, since they will still appear to be point objects, but that it will make them brighter. This fact can be seen in the simulation, since the parallel light rays of the image are in a more condensed region of space compared to the object light rays.

15.14 The Eye

The physiology of the eye is simulated, and the principle of accommodation is explained.

Layout Application activity; one simulation, showing the focusing ability of the eye.

Pointers An object is in focus when its image is located on the retina. The eye accomplishes this task by changing the thickness of the lens, and therefore its focal length, which is accommodation. Eyeglasses are needed when the eye can't accommodate to the degree needed to keep an object in focus.

15.15 Eyeglasses

The function of eyeglasses is demonstrated when the eye can no longer accommodate an image. Both nearsightedness and farsightedness are investigated.

Layout Application activity; one simulation, showing the effect of glasses on the focusing ability of the eye. This simulation is the same as that of Activity 15.14.

Pointers An object is in focus when its image is located on the retina. The eye accomplishes this task by changing the thickness of the lens, and therefore its focal length, which is accommodation. Eyeglasses are needed when the eye can't accommodate to the degree needed to keep an object in focus. These two activities should appeal to anyone interested in how the eye and eyeglasses function.

The properties of reflection and refraction are called geometric optics because the paths of light rays can be understood without any knowledge of the wave nature of light. However, interference, diffraction, and polarization are properties of light that are a direct consequence of its wave nature, and these topics are investigated in this unit on *Physical Optics*.

Light waves interact with each other according to the superposition principle, which states that the combined wave form of two waves passing through a medium is just the sum of their amplitudes at any given point. If two waves with the same wavelength and amplitude meet each other "in phase" then the result is a single wave with the same wavelength as the original pair but twice the amplitude of either wave. If the two waves meet "out of phase" then their amplitudes cancel and the result is zero wave amplitude. (See Activity 10.7 *Beats and Beat Frequency*.)

Two light waves with a common wavelength (or monochromatic light) and amplitude may be produced by sending one monochromatic light wave through two slits. The light waves emerging from the slits propagate as a circular wave front like ripples traveling across the surface of a pond after a stone is dropped into it, and the interference of light can be seen by setting up a screen some distance in front of the two-slit source. The two light waves will travel different distances at different locations on the screen, so at some positions they meet at the screen in-phase and at other positions they meet out of phase. The resulting interference pattern is a series of light and dark bands.

Diffraction is a property that allows wave fronts to bend around barriers. The theory of diffraction assumes that a wave front can be thought of as a superposition of propagating circular "wavelets." As wavelets pass through a single narrow slit, they interfere with each other and also produce a pattern of light and dark bands. The diffraction pattern can be sharpened by using a grating, which is just a series of equally spaced narrow slits.

GAME PLAN

The first three activities in this unit investigate the superposition of monochromatic light waves originating from two sources. Activity 16.1 *Two-Source Interference: Introduction* deduces the bright line interference equation from the superposition principle and geometry; Activity 16.2 *Two-Source Interference: Qualitative Questions* adjusts the variables of the equation to observe the effects on the interference pattern; and Activity 16.3 *Two-*

Source Interference: Problems creates a set of word problems with numerical answers based on the interference equation. All three activities employ the same simulation; the advantage of these activities, as so often is the case with *ActivPhysics*, is that the meaning of the different terms in an equation and their effects on the physical result are visualized and can therefore be more clearly understood.

The next two activities, Activity 16.4 *The Grating: Introduction and Qualitative Questions* and Activity 16.5 *The Grating: Problems*, examine the behavior of an optical grating, which produces multiple sources of interfering light. The equation and principles behind the interference pattern for the grating are exactly the same as for the two-source case, but the bright lines are much sharper. Therefore, it isn't necessary to complete these two activities if the physics of a grating is not one of the course objectives. However, the subject of Activity 16.6 *Single-Slit Diffraction* will certainly be a key concept of physical optics in any course, and this activity may therefore be as helpful to you as the first three activities.

The next two activities, 16.7 *Circular-Hole Diffraction* and 16.8 *Resolving Power*, present their subject matter effectively, but those topics are not often emphasized in a general physics course. The last activity, 16.9 *Polarization*, is a very different topic compared to the previous ones, but the simulation is an excellent one if polarization problems have been assigned from the text and if real polarizing filters are not available.

THE DETAILS

16.1 Two-Source Interference: Introduction

Two sources of monochromatic light separated by a certain distance produce an interference pattern on a distant screen. This activity investigates the causes of that pattern.

Layout Introductory activity; one simulation, showing two sources of light, their circular wave crests, and the interference pattern produced by the sources on a screen. Wavelength and source separation distance are both adjustable parameters in the simulation.

Pointers The equation for two-source interference developed in this activity is a result of both the superposition principle and geometry. It is important to remember that the equation $D \sin \theta = m \lambda$ is the exact solution, and the equation $\Delta y = m \lambda D / d$ is an approximation that applies only for small angles and large distances from the two sources. It should also be clear that if the maxima are located at the mth positions for in-phase superposition, then *exactly* halfway between those points minima should occur at values of $m + 1/2$ in the interference equation where out-of-phase superposition predominates.

16.2 Two-Source Interference: Qualitative Questions

The effects of wavelength and separation distance are investigated for two-source interference.

Layout Application activity; one simulation, the *Two-Source Interference* simulation of Activity 16.1.

Pointers One of the best aspects of this simulation is that it enables us to see the effects of changing the variables of the investigation on the interference pattern. Notice that the bright bands appear where two circular crests would strike the screen. Try to explain how (and why) the crest-on-crest location changes with each parameter. (The way the color of the wave crests in the simulation changes with wavelength is neat, too.)

16.3 Two-Source Interference: Problems

The equation for constructive interference is used to calculate wavelength, angle, or separation distance for six different word problems, and the solutions are verified by adjusting the parameters of the simulation.

Layout Application activity; one simulation, the *Two-Source Interference* simulation of Activity 16.1.

Pointers The word problems in this activity are similar in scope and difficulty level to most textbook problems on this topic, and some of them may be exactly the same as assigned problems. That means that this simulation can be employed to verify the solutions of certain textbook problems, just as it is used to verify the solutions to these word problems.

16.4 The Grating: Introduction and Qualitative Questions

Monochromatic light passing through a multislit grating produces an interference pattern on a distant screen. This activity investigates the causes of that pattern.

Layout Introductory activity; one simulation, showing the interference pattern of a multislit grating. The wavelength of light and slit width are adjustable parameters in the simulation.

Pointers The physical principles that produce the interference pattern of a grating are almost exactly the same as those that produce the two-source interference pattern. Two interesting things about

the grating and this particular simulation: (1) the interference pattern is much sharper because the wave front from one slit is more likely to be exactly canceled by a wave front from some other slit *except* at the correct constructive interference location; and (2) the simulation also plots a curve showing the relative intensity of light as a function of vertical position on the screen. This intensity distribution is the result of diffraction. Note that the width of the intensity plot is a function of wavelength but not slit width.

16.5 The Grating: Problems

The equation for constructive interference from a grating is used to calculate wavelength, angle, or separation distance for six word problems, and the solutions are verified by adjusting the parameters of the simulation.

Layout Application activity; one simulation, the grating interference simulation of Activity 16.4.

Pointers The word problems in this activity are similar in scope and difficulty level to most textbook problems on this topic, and some of them may be exactly the same as assigned problems. That means that this simulation can be employed to verify the solutions of certain textbook problems, just as it is used to verify the solutions to these word problems.

16.6 Single-Slit Diffraction

Monochromatic light passing through a single narrow slit produces an interference pattern on a distant screen. This activity investigates the causes of that pattern.

Layout Introductory activity; one simulation, showing a source of light and the interference pattern produced by it on a distant screen. Wavelength and slit width are both adjustable parameters in the simulation.

Pointers The form of the equation for diffraction is quite similar to that of two-source interference, but with some notable differences. First, the separation distance between two sources is replaced by the slit width; and second, the locations of constructive interference are a function of $(m + 1/2)$, whereas the locations of destructive interference are associated with an integer m. The one exception is $m = 0$, which is always a point of constructive interference.

16.7 Circular-Hole Diffraction

Monochromatic light passing through a pointlike hole produces an interference pattern on a distant screen. This activity investigates the causes of that pattern.

Layout Introductory activity; one simulation

showing the two-dimensional interference pattern on a distant screen produced by monochromatic light passing through a single pointlike hole. The wavelength of light and the diameter of the aperture are both adjustable parameters in the simulation.

Pointers One of the advantages of this activity is that the results can be easily reproduced with just a darkened room, a flashlight or laser, a piece of paper, and a pin. It also demonstrates the tangible reality of interference.

16.8 Resolving Power

The ability to identify the distinctness of two point sources of light is investigated.

Layout Introductory activity; one simulation showing the pattern of monochromatic light produced on a screen from two point sources with a small apparent separation distance.

Pointers This activity clearly shows how resolving power is related to the principle of diffraction. It is also important to note that resolving power depends on the distance of separation of the two light sources, the aperture width, and also the wavelength being resolved. In this respect, the investigation incorporates many principles and concepts of physical optics.

16.9 Polarization

The intensity of light passing through two polarizing filters set at different angles is observed.

Layout Introductory activity; one simulation showing the intensity of light on a screen after the light passes through two polarizing filters. Both polarizing angles are adjustable parameters in the simulation.

Pointers Polarization is a property of transverse waves only, so light must be a transverse and not a longitudinal wave. The equation for light intensity as a function of relative angle is included in the simulation and is easily verified by running it. The calculations for eleven different sets of data in the activity will test your understanding of the polarization equation.

Classical physics is a set of laws and theories governing the observed behavior of matter on a human scale. Modern physics emerged as scientists began to invent apparatus and techniques for probing beyond the limits of our sensory experiences into the extremes of the universe: the very large and small, the very hot and cold, and the very fast. This is the first of four units surveying modern physics, and it begins with two topics that revolutionized physics around the turn of this century: special relativity and quantum theory.

Both of these subjects had their origins in fundamental inconsistencies between the behavior of light and its description as an electromagnetic wave. If all known waves are disturbances propagated through a medium, then there should be a medium for a light wave. Since light can travel through a vacuum, its medium can't be any particular form of matter, so a nonmaterial *ether* was postulated. Michelson and Morley performed a series of experiments from 1881 through 1887 designed to detect the presence of the ether, but none was ever found. Einstein proposed in his special theory of relativity that the ether wasn't detected because it didn't exist. Instead, he postulated that the speed of light in a vacuum was the same in all reference frames and was not determined by the properties of a medium. But by doing so he had to sacrifice the immutable nature of mass, length, and time. None of these properties of the universe are absolutes in relativity; instead, their measured values depend on the speed at which an object is moving with respect to an observer.

Another problem in classical physics was the discrepancy between the predicted distribution of radiated light frequencies and the experimentally obtained results for a particular type of glowing object known as a "blackbody." The solution to this problem was proposed by Planck in 1900. He was able to obtain the correct distribution of blackbody radiation by assuming that light can only be emitted or absorbed in discrete amounts, or quanta, even though no part of electromagnetic theory suggested that such a condition should exist. Planck proposed that the energy of a light wave is not a function of its amplitude but instead is proportional to its frequency.

Once again it was Einstein who took Planck's theory to its logical conclusion. Hertz discovered in 1887 that certain materials are able to release electrons after absorbing light by a process known as the photoelectric effect. Einstein was able to explain the photoelectric effect by assuming that light could only be absorbed and released in discrete packets of localized energy which he called "photons." This implied that a light wave also behaves like a particle, even though the properties of particles and waves are often contradictory. Einstein's explanation of the photoelectric effect was specifically cited in his award of the 1921 Nobel Prize in physics.

GAME PLAN

Unlike most other units of *ActivPhysics*, where the activities are designed to illustrate basic concepts or present applications of physics principles, six of the seven activities in this unit investigate important experiments in the development of modern physics. The theories of modern physics were often proposed to explain experimental observations, so the *Pointers* for these activities generally focus on the implications of the experiments and their relation to our modern understanding of how the universe behaves.

I recommend reading the section of the text dealing with each of these experiments first, completing the activity, and then rereading the text. If these experiments or their underlying concepts are discussed in class, then it would be useful to complete each activity after the lecture in order to clarify these ideas in your mind. Each activity is a "stand alone" investigation, so it isn't necessary to do all of them or to complete them in any particular order, except that Activity 17.2 definitely builds on Activity 17.1.

Activities 17.1 *Relativity of Time* and 17.2 *Relativity of Length* reproduce Einstein's "thought experiments" that introduced the world to the principles and predictions of special relativity. These two investigations serve to animate standard textbook figures and illustrations in a way that makes the scientific arguments more plausible.

Activities 17.3 *Photoelectric Effect* and 17.4 *Compton Scattering* reproduce results of two experiments that confirmed that light waves have particlelike properties. Both of these activities do a very good job of showing the logical but erroneous predictions of the wave model and how a particle model could correctly explain the data. Activity 17.5 *Electron Interference* takes the opposite view, showing how particles must necessarily have wave-like properties. This property of nature is called "wave–particle duality."

Activity 17.6 *The Uncertainty Principle* uses experimental data to demonstrate a law of nature with important implications on the subatomic scale. The uncertainty principle is one of the foundational concepts of quantum theory, although it is rarely invoked without reference to some other problematic issue in quantum mechanics. The last activity, 17.7 *Wave Packets*, introduces a reasonable mathematical model that not only shows the plausibility of wave-particle duality but also explains the necessity of the uncertainty principle.

THE DETAILS

17.1 Relativity of Time

The paths of a light pulse in two different frames of reference are compared, and when combined with the condition that the speed of light must be the same in all frames of reference, the result is the Lorentz γ factor and the prediction of time dilation.

Layout Introductory activity; three matched simulations. Sim 1 recreates Einstein's light-clock "thought experiment"; Sim 2 adds clocks timing the event from the stationary observer's perspective; and Sim 3 adds clocks timing the event from the moving observer's perspective. Sim 2 and Sim 3 are not shown in the text bar as icons.

Pointers This activity presents the classic argument for relativistic time first proposed by Einstein and repeated in any general physics textbook. Completing this activity and the next one will require concentration, so make sure you understand each step of the argument before moving on to the next step. Time dilation may seem impossible or illogical at first since we never personally experience it, but the reality of time dilation has been conclusively demonstrated in particle accelerators.

17.2 Relativity of Length

A comparison of the paths of a light pulse in two different frames of reference, along with the condition that the speed of light is constant in all frames of reference, results in the prediction of length contraction for an object moving relativistically.

Layout Introductory activity; three matched simulations. Sim 1 shows Einstein's light clock oriented in the direction of the relative velocity; Sim 2 adds clocks timing the event from the stationary observer's perspective; and Sim 3 adds clocks timing the event from the moving observer's perspective. Sim 2 and Sim 3 are not shown in the text bar as icons.

Pointers This activity follows the same line of argument as the previous one, so make sure you understand that investigation before tackling this one. In Activity 17.1, the light pulse moved perpendicular to the direction of relative motion; in this activity, the light pulse moves in the direction of relative motion. Because the speed of light *must* be constant in all reference frames no matter what the direction of travel, and because time dilation and the γ factor derived in the previous activity must apply, it is not possible to measure the same length in all reference frames. In fact, Fitzgerald proposed a length contraction (including the correct γ factor!) to explain the null result of the Michelson-Morley experiment *before* the development of special relativity and the prediction of time dilation.

17.3 Photoelectric Effect

The experimental observations of the photoelectric effect showing the consequences of adjusting light intensity and light frequency on the number of electrons ejected from a metal surface are re-created as a simulation.

Layout Exploratory activity; one simulation recreating the photoelectric effect experiment.

Pointers It is important to remember that the photoelectric effect is not just an academic exercise but the actual behavior of certain materials found in nature. In fact, it is the photoelectric effect that causes sliding doors to open and close automatically. Therefore, the photoelectric effect presents undeniable evidence for the existence of photons—and that is the reason why it is important to understand this key experiment in the development of quantum theory.

17.4 Compton Scattering

The angle and frequency of light recoiling after a collision with a subatomic particle are recorded by a detector. The data is used to demonstrate the existence of photons, which carry both energy and momentum.

Layout Exploratory activity; one simulation, showing the relative intensity of photon wavelengths before and after a Compton scattering event as a function of detector location.

Pointers The significance of this activity is that Compton scattering presents further evidence for the existence of photons. The speed and direction of the electron after an interaction with light correlate with the direction and frequency of light after the interaction, assuming that Planck's law correctly predicts the energy of light from its recorded frequency. The data shows that both energy and momentum are conserved. Since momentum has always been associated with massive particles, it is logical to conclude that light, in the form of a photon, can also have the characteristics of a particle with mass. This investigation will help clarify the details of the photon-particle scattering experiment.

17.5   Electron Interference

The wave properties of the electron are demonstrated by recreating the Davisson-Germer electron diffraction experiment, and thus confirming the de Broglie relation for electrons.

Layout   Exploratory activity; one simulation showing the relative intensity of electrons at different locations after having passed through a regular crystal. The speed of electrons and the interatomic spacing are both adjustable parameters in the simulation.

Pointers   If the concept of diffraction is unclear to you, it may be worthwhile to review some of the activities in Unit 16. In particular, compare this simulation to the grating simulation of Activities 16.4 and 16.5. Diffraction angle is related to both the wavelength of the incoming wave and the spacing of the slits. The wavelength of the electron is determined from its speed and mass, using the de Broglie relation. Once both the wavelength of the electron is known and also the most likely locations where electrons strike the screen, the slit spacing (which is the separation distance between atoms in the crystal) can be calculated. The activity concludes with a number of real calculations of the scattering locations of electrons.

The experimental observation that electrons scatter off a regular crystal in a "banded" pattern that is a function of their velocity cannot be explained by any classical theory. The conclusion that the pattern is the result of diffraction, and that an electron has an associated wavelength that is a function of its momentum, is one of the rare cases in the sciences where a theory has suggested a key experiment, instead of an experiment resulting in a fundamentally new theory.

17.6   Uncertainty Principle

The intensity pattern of electrons on a distant screen after having passed through one or two slits is used to demonstrate the uncertainty principle, which postulates that the position and momentum of a particle cannot be simultaneously specified with unlimited accuracy.

Layout   Introductory activity; one simulation, showing the intensity pattern of electrons hitting a distant screen after having passed through one or two slits. The speed of the electrons and slit width are adjustable parameters in the simulation.

Pointers   Compare this simulation to the two-source simulation of Activity 16.1 and the single-slit diffraction simulation of Activity 16.6. Uncertainty is represented by a range or a "width" in measured values: $\Delta x = x^{max} - x^{min}$ and $\Delta p = p^{max} - p^{min}$. The uncertainty principle states that these quantities are inversely related: a small width in Δx requires a larger width in Δp and vice versa, and the product of the two uncertainties must be greater than Planck's constant. The activity shows how real data confirms the uncertainty principle. This law of nature is also one of the foundational principles leading to the probability interpretation of quantum mechanics.

17.7   Wave Packets

Wave-particle duality and the uncertainty principle are unified by creating a wave packet from the superposition of many periodic waves of similar wavelength.

Layout   Introductory activity; one simulation, showing a wave packet constructed from the superposition of waves about a central wavelength λ and with a spread in wavelength of $[+/- 1/2\ \lambda]$.

Pointers   Since particles and waves have very different and often contradictory properties, how is it possible for light or an electron to have characteristics of both? And *why* is it impossible to know the position and momentum of a particle to any desired accuracy simultaneously? The wave packet model constructed in this activity provides a plausible explanation to both of these questions. A wave packet is constructed from periodic waves, but it is localized in space (it has a width) like a particle. Wave packets also travel through space, like particles, with a "group velocity" that is a function of the wavelengths used to construct it. Therefore, a wave packet has both "particlelike" and "wavelike" properties.

Activity 10.7 *Beats and Beat Frequency* may provide a useful review for this topic, but imagine a larger collection of superposing waves with a similar wavelength than just the two shown in the simulation. Mathematically, the result of a spread of wavelengths is just a single beat envelope, the wave packet, instead of a chain of wave packets as that simulation shows.

Wave packets can also be used to justify the uncertainty principle. (Since momentum is a function of wavelength, a single periodic wave has a completely specified momentum, but the wave extends infinitely in both directions, so the position of a particle represented by the wave is completely uncertain.) The only way to construct a wave packet at one completely specified point is to use *all* possible wavelengths, so the momentum of the pointlike wave packet is completely uncertain.

UNIT 18 ATOMIC PHYSICS

The fundamental principle of quantum theory is that energy on the atomic and subatomic scales comes in discrete amounts, or quanta. The application of quantum theory to the behavior of electrons in atoms is the subject of this unit of *ActivPhysics*.

The first successful quantum model of the atom was proposed by Niels Bohr for the single-electron hydrogen atom. Bohr proposed that electrons travel in orbits and follow all the laws of classical physics except that the angular momentum of the electron is quantized. The discrete amounts of allowed angular momentum were multiples of $h/2\pi$ where h is Planck's constant. The implications of quantized angular momentum led to quantized speeds and energies for the electron as it orbited the nucleus at well-defined radii.

The test of Bohr's theory was the prediction of the frequencies of light that an atom could absorb or emit, which is the experimental field of spectroscopy. Bohr claimed that the frequencies of light absorbed or emitted by an atom corresponded to the differences between electron orbital energies. His model worked quite well for the hydrogen atom only, but his success spurred other scientists to continue to develop quantum theory. One important theory that grew out of Bohr's work was Heisenberg's uncertainty principle; another was de Broglie's relation. Both of these ideas helped lay the foundation of quantum mechanics.

GAME PLAN

This unit of *ActivPhysics* consists of four models describing the behavior of electrons in atoms. The value of these activities is that they serve to illustrate and clarify some of the early concepts of quantum theory, even though Bohr's model was superseded by a more general theory of quantum mechanics (explored in Unit 20 of *ActivPhysics*).

Activity 18.1 *The Bohr Model* visualizes all of the key features of his theory for the hydrogen atom. The simulation is an animated version of a standard textbook figure. Activity 18.2 *Spectroscopy* uses the technology of computer simulations to demonstrate how Bohr's theory of spectroscopy could be used to reconstruct spectra. This procedure is actually used by spectroscopists to deduce the potential energy surfaces of atoms, molecules, and crystals. Activity 18.3 *Standing Electron Waves* presents a semiclassical model to show that Bohr's assumption that angular momentum is quantized is at least plausible. This basic idea will be extended and generalized in Unit 20 of *ActivPhysics*. Activity 18.4 *The Laser* simulates a well known consequence of quantum atomic the-

ory and should be of interest to anyone curious about the operation of a laser.

THE DETAILS

18.1 The Bohr Model

The Bohr model of hydrogen and the spectral lines absorbed or emitted by the electrons obeying the predictions of the model are visualized.

Layout Exploratory activity; one simulation, showing electrons revolving around the hydrogen nucleus in the orbits calculated by Bohr at the speeds and with the energies predicted by his model, and also showing the spectrum resulting from transitions between quantum states.

Pointers The simulation animates the motion of electrons in Bohr's model and visualizes the transition of electrons between orbits. This should help clarify the written description of the model found in most textbooks and clarify the figures that typically accompany that explanation. One advantage of this simulation is that a particular spectral line clearly corresponds to a particular orbital transition.

18.2 Spectroscopy

The energy levels of a model atom are adjusted until the complete spectrum of the atom is correctly reproduced.

Layout Application activity; one simulation showing the wavelengths of light resulting from adjustable energy levels for an ideal Bohr-like atom.

Pointers One of the differences between classical physics and modern physics is that it is very difficult to create simple experiments in the laboratory with readily available equipment to test quantum principles. Unfortunately, it is usually through real-life application that we ultimately understand physical concepts and their implications. Therefore, although this is a somewhat contrived exercise, it should be very helpful for understanding the relationship between electron energy levels and the resulting spectrum. It may also help convince you that discrete energy levels for electrons in atoms really do exist, since all atomic spectra are discrete spectra, like those simulated in this and the previous activity. In fact, it is this very process of spectral matching that scientists used to determine the correct spacing of electron quantum states in atoms, molecules, and solids.

18.3 Standing Electron Waves

The electron wavelength postulated by de Broglie is simulated by a wave following a circular path representing the orbit of the electron.

Layout Introductory activity; one simulation, showing the circular wave pattern of an orbiting electron that results from an adjustable rotational energy.

Pointers This activity visualizes a circular standing wave. As in other activities, this simulation serves to animate a standard figure found in most textbooks and help clarify the written explanation of this quantum condition. It also demonstrates that only circular standing wave patterns are stable for the electron in Bohr's theory, and that the condition of quantized angular momentum results from this fact.

18.4 The Laser

The principles of the laser are illustrated by simulating the transition of electrons between quantum states under the conditions of stimulated emission.

Layout Introductory activity; one simulation, showing photons of a particular wavelength either absorbed or emitted under different conditions.

Pointers The prediction of the laser was one of the hallmarks of quantum theory. Although lasers have become an important component of our technological society (a laser is used to read the *ActivPhysics* CD), the principle of "light amplification by the stimulated emission of radiation" is not generally well understood. Completing this activity should allow you to explain the different steps of the laser process, the meaning of each word in the acronym, and also the concept of "coherence."

UNIT 19 NUCLEAR PHYSICS

Scientific laws and theories are always the product of experimental observation; but as scientists probe deeper into the heart of matter obtaining experimental data and interpreting it becomes much more difficult. This is especially true in the case of nuclear physics, where the volume occupied by the nucleus is extremely small and the forces holding the nucleus together are extremely strong compared to any other physical system studied so far.

Data concerning nuclear processes can be obtained in one of two ways: either the nucleus undergoes a natural change that is detected by some appropriate device, or the nucleus is probed artificially by some means and the results of the induced change are collected and analyzed. Radioactive decay is a natural process but the number of naturally radioactive nuclei is relatively few. For that reason, the data obtained from natural radioactivity does not provide enough information to produce a complete theory of the structure and physics of the nucleus.

However, it is possible to probe the nucleus by bombarding it with high-energy particles and interpreting the resulting scatter pattern. If the energy of the probing particle is larger than the forces holding the nucleus together, then the nucleus may fragment into smaller pieces, which then can be studied further. In other circumstances, two colliding particles are transformed into other particles. The current generation of particle accelerators is able to create energies large enough to probe not only nuclei but the protons and neutrons as well, reaching into the most basic structure of matter. Therefore, it isn't surprising that this field of physics at the limits of our scientific understanding is often called "high energy" or "elementary particle" physics.

GAME PLAN

Like the other three units of *ActivPhysics* exploring topics in modern physics, the activities of this unit help clarify certain key ideas of nuclear physics instead of presenting a complete and unified theory of protons and neutrons in atomic nuclei. Activity 19.1 *Particle Scattering* shows how statistical data from scattering experiments may be used to calculate separation distances or particle diameters. (See also Activity 7.17 *Scattering*.) Activity 19.2 *Nuclear Binding Energy* demonstrates how the theory of nuclear binding arose from a large body of data collected for as many known isotopes as possible. Activities 19.3 *Fusion* and 19.4 *Radioactivity* are

a matched set in that the first investigation builds larger, stable nuclei from smaller ones whereas the second splits large, unstable nuclei into smaller ones. These two activities, along with Activity 19.2, show that stability results from a balance of forces and cannot be predicted from one principle alone. Activity 19.5 *Particle Physics*, like Activity 19.3 *Fusion*, gives you the opportunity to experiment with subatomic particles following known principles but in ways that are virtually impossible to recreate in any laboratory.

THE DETAILS

19.1 Particle Scattering

The statistical results of a large number of particles scattered off a material composed of equally spaced particles of a set diameter is used to calculate the most likely radius of the particles.

Layout Introductory activity; one simulation recording the total number of particles impacting a material with an unknown internal structure and the number of them scattered and transmitted.

Pointers This activity is similar in spirit to Activity 17.17 *Scattering*. In both cases, the parameters of an object that cannot be observed directly are inferred from scatter patterns. The methods modeled by these activities are actually used by scientists to discover the properties of materials: in fact, Rutherford used the exact same method as Activity 17.17 to calculate the radius of the gold atom's nucleus, and to demonstrate that the atom is mostly empty space.

19.2 Nuclear Binding Energy

Trends in nuclear binding energy are observed by checking for stability of some simple nuclei and calculating the binding energy per nucleon for the stable ones.

Layout Introductory activity; one simulation, which constructs simple nuclei from protons and neutrons and checks their stability.

Pointers This activity uses known data and simple arithmetic to calculate the binding energies of certain small nuclei and predict the amount of energy absorbed or released in some simple nuclear reactions. The principle of stability then results from simple energy considerations.

19.3 Fusion

The relationship between collision speed and fusion, and the amount of energy released as a result of the fusion of different combinations of light nuclei, are explored in this activity.

Layout Introductory activity; one simulation, showing the head-on collision of different nuclei at different speeds and the amount of energy released when fusion occurs.

Pointers In the previous activity, the binding energies of small nuclei were predicted, along with the energy released by some nuclear reactions. This activity continues that investigation by simulating nuclear reactions such as those that might occur in the sun. The focus of this activity is calculating Q-values, just as the focus of the previous one was calculating nuclear binding energies. The fundamental conclusion of this activity is that it isn't enough to have a stable process; the external conditions of the reaction (the speeds of the particles) must be correct as well.

19.4 Radioactivity

Four different nuclei are allowed to decay over different time scales. The half-life of the radioactive decay is calculated from a plot of remaining nuclei as a function of time, and the decay mechanism is determined from the identity of the transformed nucleus.

Layout Exploratory activity; one simulation, which represents radioactive nuclei as collections of circles that change color as an individual nucleus decays and also plots the number of remaining nuclei as a function of time. The particular nuclear isotope and the time scale are adjustable parameters in the simulation.

Pointers Radioactive particles decay exponentially, and the exponential nature of this decay is effectively simulated by this activity. If you are unclear at all about half-life or decay constants, this will be an extremely helpful activity to complete.

19.5 Particle Physics

The identity of one of two particles resulting from the collision of a pair of elementary particles is determined from the application of conservation principles.

Layout Introductory activity; one simulation showing the collision of different combinations of elementary particles and the identity of one of two particles produced by the reaction.

Pointers In order to complete this activity, it will be necessary to have a table of elementary particles available that includes the charge, lepton number, and baryon number of each. This particular simulation will be helpful for understanding the meaning of these conserved quantities.

UNIT 20 QUANTUM MECHANICS

Sir Isaac Newton proposed a theory of mechanics in order to explain how and why objects moved. The laws of motion that Newton formulated survived in their original form for almost 300 years. However, in the end they proved inadequate to accurately explain the extremes of nature: the very fast and the very small. Quantum mechanics has superseded Newtonian mechanics as the best explanation of the behavior of matter on the atomic and subatomic scales. The perspective and methods of quantum mechanics are quite different from those of classical dynamics, where the goal is to know the position and momentum of a particle at any point in time. According to the Heisenberg uncertainty principle, that goal is literally impossible at the atomic level.

The motion of a particle in the classical framework is the result of forces acting on it and its initial conditions. In quantum mechanics, the dynamics of subatomic particles is defined by the *wave function*. The wave function for a given set of dynamical conditions is a solution of the Schrödinger equation, which at one level seems to be a restatement of conservation of energy: that the sum of the kinetic and potential energies is constant. In practice, the theory and the mathematics of the Schrödinger equation aren't quite that simple. The wave function doesn't correspond to any one measurable property of a particle, such as position or momentum. Instead, all measurable properties of the particle—including position, momentum, and energy—can be derived mathematically by "operating" on the wave function. According to the Born interpretation of quantum mechanics, the wave function and the results of operations performed on a particle correspond to statistical probabilities. Therefore, it isn't possible to know exactly where a particle is and how it is moving, but one can predict where the particle *might* be located if one was to look for it or what its most likely momentum *might* be if such a measurement were to be made.

GAME PLAN

No one will ever claim that quantum mechanics is easy to understand or that the mathematical equations that describe the quantum world are easy to solve. The four activities of this unit have been constructed to teach some of the most important conclusions and concepts of quantum mechanics through particular ideal examples. One of the emphases of this unit is to compare and contrast the expectations of classical mechanics with quantum reality. My recommendation is to complete these four activities sequentially. This unit can be completed without reference to a textbook discussion of quantum mechanics, and it may be better to deliberately separate these activities from any other presentation of the material in order to see two perspectives on a very difficult and abstract subject.

Activity 20.1 *Potential Energy Diagrams* begins by presenting the classical interpretation of particle dynamics from the energy perspective. The importance of probability in quantum mechanics is suggested by the Strobe function, which shows the instantaneous location of the particle at certain times. It may be useful to write down and refer to the main conclusions of the activity, especially those concerning turning points and where the particle is most likely to be found, since the next three activities will show how quantum mechanics predicts very different conclusions about these issues compared to the classical model.

Activity 20.2 *Particle in a Box* is the simplest possible dynamical model, a discussion of which can be found in any general physics textbook. There are two advantages of this investigation over the textbook description of the particle in a box: First, the adjustable parameters in the simulation demonstrate the effects of different parameters on the quantum results, and thus help illustrate the meaning of the equations that describe this system. Second, the activity stresses the link between quantum and classical dynamics by including questions concerning the behavior of the particle under different conditions. The natural and logically consistent transformation from the description of a system using quantum mechanics to the correct classical description of the same system on the macroscopic scale using Newtonian mechanics is known as the correspondence principle.

Activity 20.3 *Potential Wells* moves from the infinite potential at the walls of a particle in the box to finite values. One of the most important learning objectives for this activity is to understand how only certain particle energies result in stable wave functions. The last activity, 20.4 *Potential Barriers*, serves to illustrate one of the most famous predictions of quantum mechanics, the process known as tunneling. In quantum theory, it is possible for a particle to traverse a barrier even if the total energy of the particle is less than the potential energy of the barrier.

THE DETAILS

20.1 Potential Energy Diagrams

A point particle with a set total energy moves classically in a region of space defined by a potential function.

Layout Introductory activity; one simulation, tracking the classical motion of a point particle in either a multilevel square potential well or in a harmonic potential well.

Pointers Before one can understand the implications of quantum mechanics, it is important to recognize the expectations of the classical model. The questions in this activity ask you to consider two major predictions of the classical model: first, where in space a classical particle will *not* be found if its total energy is less than the energy of a potential in certain parts of that space; and second, where the particle will spend most of its time in the allowed regions of space. Remember these classical conclusions as you explore the next three activities, because quantum mechanics will provide very different answers to these questions.

20.2 Particle in a Box

The allowed energies for a particle in a box are predicted based on the assumption that only standing wave patterns are acceptable solutions for the wave function defining the dynamical particle.

Layout Exploratory activity; one simulation, showing the standing wave function or its square for a particle with an adjustable energy in a one-dimensional box with an adjustable length.

Pointers The activity asks you to predict the relationship between allowed energies, the mass of the particle, and the length of the box based on the definition of kinetic energy and the de Broglie relation. Note in particular the locations in the box where the particle is most likely to be found, and compare them to the classical result of the previous activity. Also notice that there are places within the box in the quantum model where the particle will *never* be found.

This activity should help you understand why only certain discrete energy levels are allowed for this system, as well as functional relationships among those levels. The questions concerning the limits of very large mass and very large "n" should help you see how quantum mechanics transforms into the classical result (including the locations where the particle is most likely to be found) following the correspondence principle.

20.3 Potential Wells

The allowed energies for a particle in a box with finite walls and the behavior of its wave function are simulated under different physical parameters.

Layout Introductory activity; one simulation, showing the first three stable wave functions for a particle in a box with finite walls. The length of the box, the barrier height, and the mass of the particle are adjustable parameters in the simulation.

Pointers The only difference between the particle in a box of the previous activity and the square well of this one is that the potential isn't infinite at the walls. Note that the wave function no longer ends abruptly at the walls but "spills over" into the walls. The distance it penetrates is a function both of the potential height and the energy of the particle, and the importance of this result is examined in greater detail in the next activity.

20.4 Potential Barriers

The phenomenon of tunneling is illustrated when a particle with finite energy encounters a potential barrier of greater energy but finite width.

Layout Introductory activity; one simulation, showing the wave function traveling through three regions of space: (1) the region on the left side of the simulation represents the origin of the wave function and has a relative potential energy of zero; (2) the region in the center of the simulation represents a rectangular barrier of finite and adjustable height and width; and (3) the third region on the right side of the simulation represents the region of space the wave is traveling toward, also with a zero relative potential energy. The wave function energy, barrier height, and barrier width are all adjustable parameters in the simulation.

Pointers It is always important to remember that the behavior of waves and particles simulated in these activities is based on real data collected from real experiments. The universe can appear to be a mysterious place, and sometimes its behavior seems irrational. Even so, the quantum tunneling phenomenon illustrated by this simulation actually does occur; it is the principle behind a number of important experimental devices, including the scanning tunneling electron microscope.

PART III

ActivPhysics2 Workbook

Alan Van Heuvelen
Paul D'Alessandris

11. ELECTRICITY

12. dc CIRCUITS

13. MAGNETISM

14. ac CIRCUITS

About the Authors

Alan Van Heuvelen, of The Ohio State University, is a respected physics professor, author, and pioneer of active learning methods. His Active Learning Problem Sheets (the ALPS Kits) encourage student participation and learning in large and small classes and while working alone and in small groups. Now these same interactive techniques are easily extended and better visualized with the ActivPhysics simulations and activities.

Paul D'Alessandris has been teaching physics and engineering science at Monroe Community College since 1990. During this time his focus has been on developing curriculum that both incorporates the results of physics education research and effectively deals with a diversity of student abilities. Professor D'Alessandris has received several National Science Foundation grants in support of his work.

11

ELECTRICITY

Questions 1–2 Compare the force magnitudes. Draw arrows representing the force that each charge exerts on the other for the two situations shown. Make the arrows the correct relative lengths.

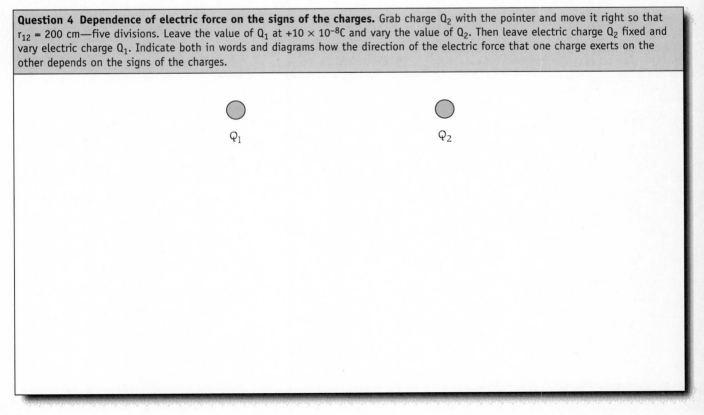

$$Q_1 = 10 \times 10^{-8} \text{ C} \qquad Q_2 = 5.0 \times 10^{-8} \text{ C}$$

$$Q_1 = 10 \times 10^{-8} \text{ C} \qquad Q_2 = -2.0 \times 10^{-8} \text{ C}$$

Question 3 Test your predictions by adjusting the magnitudes of the charges on the simulation. Then write a general rule that compares the relative magnitude of the force that charge Q_1 exerts on charge Q_2 to the magnitude of the force that Q_2 exerts on Q_1.

Question 4 Dependence of electric force on the signs of the charges. Grab charge Q_2 with the pointer and move it right so that $r_{12} = 200$ cm—five divisions. Leave the value of Q_1 at $+10 \times 10^{-8}$C and vary the value of Q_2. Then leave electric charge Q_2 fixed and vary electric charge Q_1. Indicate both in words and diagrams how the direction of the electric force that one charge exerts on the other depends on the signs of the charges.

Q_1 $\qquad\qquad\qquad$ Q_2

Question 5 Dependence of electric force on charge separation. Set the values of both Q_1 and Q_2 equal to $+10 \times 10^{-8}$ C. Construct a table that indicates the distance r separating the charges and the magnitude of the electrical force that one exerts on the other. Start with a separation r = 40 cm (0.40 m or one division on the screen) and record the force that one charge exerts on the other. Then try a separation of 80 cm and record the force. Before trying 120 cm, see if you can predict the force. Then try it. Predict the magnitude of the force for separations 160 cm and 200 cm. Finally, devise a rule that indicates how the magnitude of the force that one electric charge exerts on another depends on the distance between the two charges. When finished, compare your thinking to that of the Advisor.

Question 6 Force law between two point charges. Set the values of both Q_1 and Q_2 equal to zero and their separation equal to 100 cm (1.0 m or 2.5 divisions on the screen). Now, increase the value of each charge to the maximum possible and record the magnitude of the electric force that one exerts on the other. Then, leave the separation fixed and try different charge combinations and note the magnitude of the force for each charge combination. Finally, devise a rule that indicates how the magnitude of the force that one electric charge exerts on another depends on the values of the two charges. When finished, compare your thinking to that of the Advisor.

Question 7 Ratio calculation. Change the separation of Q_1 and Q_2 to $r_{12} = 200$ cm and their charges to $Q_1 = +8.0 \times 10^{-8}$ C and $Q_2 = -4.0 \times 10^{-8}$ C. Note the electric force that one exerts on the other. Predict the magnitude of the force if you decrease the separation to 100 cm and change the charges so that $Q_2 = +2.0 \times 10^{-8}$ C and $Q_2 = -8.0 \times 10^{-8}$ C. After your prediction, grab Q_2 and change its separation from Q_2 to 100 cm and adjust the charge-value sliders to the new values in order to check your work.

$+$

Q_1

$-$

Q_2

Question 8 In-your-head ratio calculation. Place charges 1 and 2 in a horizontal line separated by 100 cm. Set $Q_1 = +2.0 \times 10^{-8}$ C and $Q_2 = +3.0 \times 10^{-8}$ C. Note the magnitude of the electric force that one exerts on the other. Suppose that you increase the separation of the charges to 200 cm. Decide two pairs of values for the charges so that they exert the same sign and magnitude force on each other as before their separation was increased.

Q_1

Q_2

Question 1 Force diagrams. Construct a separate force diagram for each charged ball shown and indicate with an arrow the direction of the net force. Include only the electric forces. The objects are equally spaced.

(−) $Q_1 = -2q$ (+) $Q_2 = +q$ (−) $Q_3 = -q$

(−) $Q_1 = -2q$

(+) $Q_2 = +q$

(−) $Q_3 = -q$

Question 2 Force diagrams. Construct a separate force diagram for each charged ball shown and indicate with an arrow the direction of the net force. Include only the electric forces. The objects are equally spaced.

(+) $Q_1 = +2q$ (+) $Q_2 = +q$ (−) $Q_3 = -q$

(+) $Q_1 = +2q$

(+) $Q_2 = +q$

(−) $Q_3 = -q$

Question 3 With the charges still separated by 200 cm, determine one set of values for the charges so that the net force on $Q_1 = +10 \times 10^{-8}$ C is zero. When finished, adjust the charges in the simulation to check your prediction.

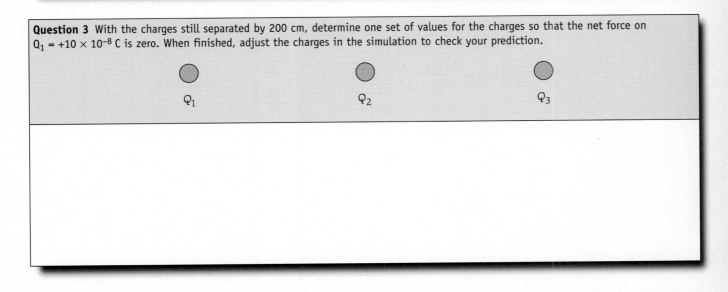

Q_1 Q_2 Q_3

Question 4 Construct a force diagram for each charged ball and estimate the direction of the net electric force on each ball. **Note:** $Q_1 = +2q$, $Q_2 = +2q$, and $Q_3 = -q$. The charges are at the corners of a square 200 cm on each side.

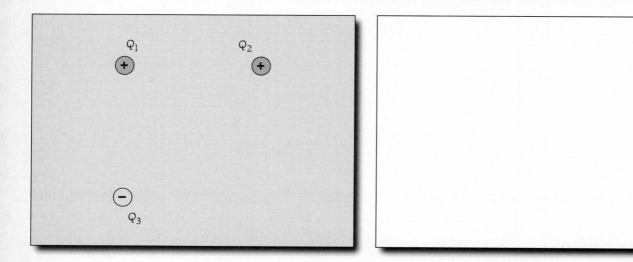

Question 5 Heart dipole. (a) Construct a force diagram for charge Q_3 and determine the direction of the net electric force exerted on Q_3 by the electric dipole if Q_3 has a positive charge and (b) if it has a negative charge. Can you understand how the dipole electric charges on the heart, caused by contracting heart muscles, push oppositely charged ions in the body tissue in opposite directions—like a little battery?

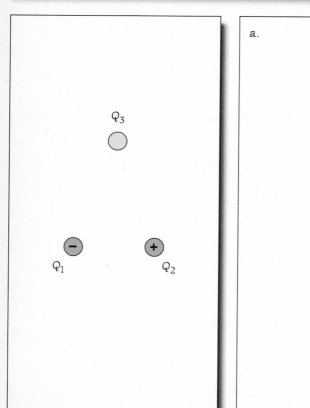

a.

$Q_3 > 0$

b.

$Q_3 < 0$

©1999 Addison Wesley Longman, Alan Van Heuvelen and Paul D'Alessandris

Question 1 Construct a force diagram for each charged ball shown and determine the net electric force on each ball. The balls are separated by 2.00 m.

$Q_1 = -10.0 \times 10^{-8}$ C

$Q_2 = +5.0 \times 10^{-8}$ C

$Q_3 = -5.0 \times 10^{-8}$ C

Question 2 Construct a force diagram for each charged ball shown and determine the net electric force on each ball. The balls are separated by 2.00 m.

$Q_1 = +10.0 \times 10^{-8}$ C

$Q_2 = +5.0 \times 10^{-8}$ C

$Q_3 = -5.0 \times 10^{-8}$ C

Question 3 Construct a force diagram for each charged ball and determine the net electric force on each ball. **Note:** $Q_1 = +10.0 \times 10^{-8}$ C, $Q_2 = +10.0 \times 10^{-8}$ C, and $Q_3 = -5.0 \times 10^{-8}$ C. The charges are at the corners of a square 1.00 m on each side.

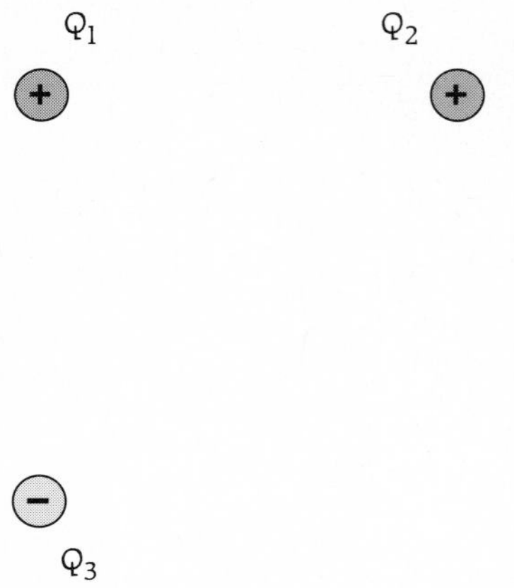

Q_1 (+) Q_2 (+)

(−)
Q_3

Question 4 Determine the net electric force exerted by the "heart" dipole charge on $Q_3 = +3.0 \times 10^{-8}$ C and on $Q_3 = -3.0 \times 10^{-8}$ C. The dipole charges $Q_1 = +10.0 \times 10^{-8}$ C and $Q_2 = -10.0 \times 10^{-8}$ C. The dipole charges are separated by 1.60 m and are 1.44 m from Q_3.

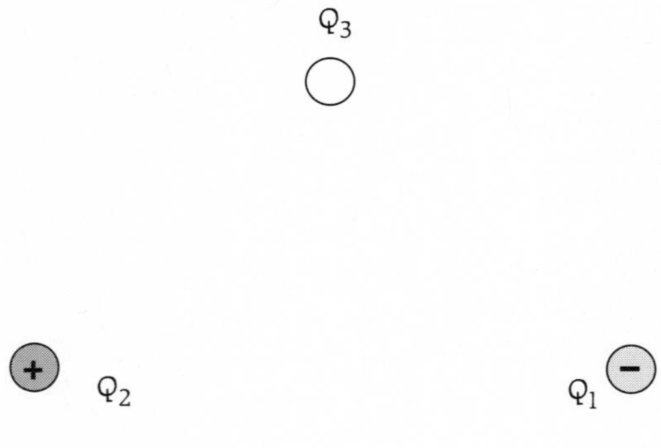

Q_3
○

(+) Q_2 Q_1 (−)

Question 1 Electric field. A positive charge $Q_1 = +10.0 \times 10^{-8}$ C is the source of an electric field. Use a positive test charge $Q_2 = +4.0 \times 10^{-8}$ C to explore the electric field at the positions of the four dots shown in the figure. Summarize your observations in words.

Question 2 Electric field. Determine the direction and calculate the magnitude of the electric field produced by Q_1 at the position 1.0 m to the right of Q_1. On a separate paper, find **E** at the other three positions. Each division on the paper is 0.40 m.

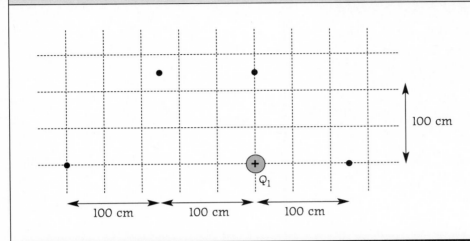

Question 3 Representing the electric field. The lines in the figures below represent the electric field produced by a +2-µC positive charge (left sketch) and a −5-µC charge (right sketch). Develop rules for the way the electric field is represented in these diagrams.

Consider in particular:
• the direction of the lines
• the places where lines start and end relative to the sign of the source charges
• the separation of the lines in a particular region relative to the strength of the field
• the number of lines starting or ending on a charge relative to the magnitude and sign of the charge

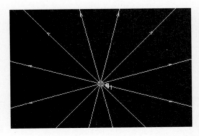 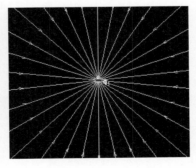

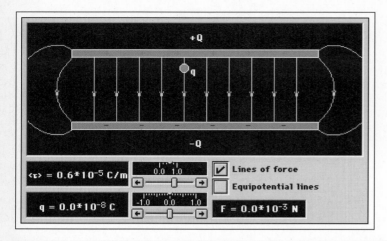

Question 4 The charge q can be placed at different positions between the plates, a region where the field is said to be uniform. Why is the field between the plates called uniform?

Question 5 Is the magnitude of the force exerted by the field on q greater, the same, or less if the charge is moved down near the lower negatively charged plate? Explain.

Question 6 Place the positive charge q in the middle between the plates. What happens to the force on q if you change its sign? Explain. After your prediction, change the sign and magnitude of q and move it to different positions. Note in particular the force on the charge when in the central region where the field is "uniform" compared to the force on the charge in the side fringe regions where the field is not uniform.

Question 1 In light pencil, indicate the direction and relative magnitude of the force that each dipole charge exerts on a positive test charge placed at the six positions indicated by the black dots. Graphically, add the forces to estimate the direction and magnitude of the dipole electric field at each position. When finished, move test charge Q_3 in the simulation to see the forces exerted on it. Also, compare your predicted field direction to the field direction shown in Question 2 below.

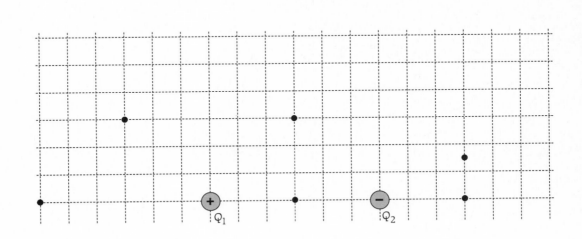

Question 2 The field produced by an electric dipole is shown below. The magnitude of each charge is 3.0 μC and the charged particles are separated by 2.0 m. Indicate (yes or no) if the field line pattern is consistent with the following rules for such representations.

- The electric field direction at a point is in the direction of the field line at that point. _____
- Lines start at positive charges and end at negative charges. _____
- The electric field in a particular region varies continuously and, between lines, points in about the same direction as neighboring lines. _____
- The distance between adjacent field lines at a particular point is proportional to the magnitude of the electric field at that point. _____
- The number of lines leaving or entering a charged particle is proportional to the particle's charge. _____

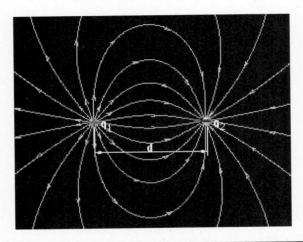

Question 3 Calculate the magnitude and direction of the electric field at the position shown in the diagram.

Your calculation should involve

- a force diagram
- the addition of the force components exerted on a pretend positive test charge +q placed at that point
- the calculation of the net force and the electric field (**E** = **F**/q) at that point

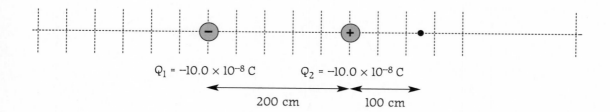

$Q_1 = -10.0 \times 10^{-8}$ C $Q_2 = -10.0 \times 10^{-8}$ C

200 cm   100 cm

Question 4 Calculate the magnitude and direction of the electric field at the position shown in the diagram.

Your calculation should involve

- a force diagram
- the addition of the force components exerted on a pretend positive test charge +q placed at that point
- the calculation of the net force and the electric field (**E** - **F**/q) at that point

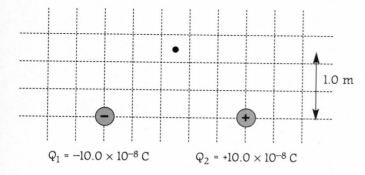

1.0 m

$Q_1 = -10.0 \times 10^{-8}$ C $Q_2 = +10.0 \times 10^{-8}$ C

Question 1 Plotting the electric field. Draw the electric field lines that represent the electric field caused by two equal positive charges.

Question 2 Plotting the electric field. Draw the electric field lines that represent the electric field caused by the two unequal positive charges. The left ball has twice the positive charge as the right ball.

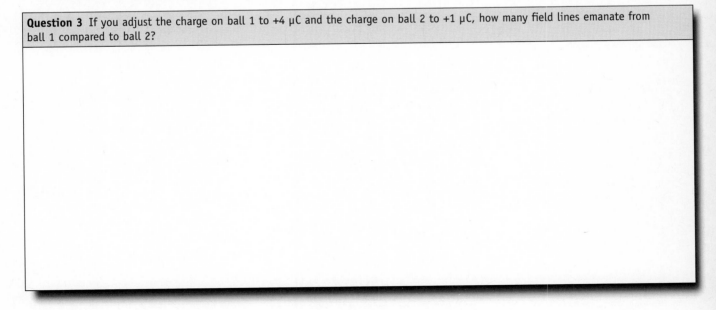

Question 3 If you adjust the charge on ball 1 to +4 μC and the charge on ball 2 to +1 μC, how many field lines emanate from ball 1 compared to ball 2?

Question 4 Where on the x-axis is the electric field zero? The charges are separated by 2.0 m.

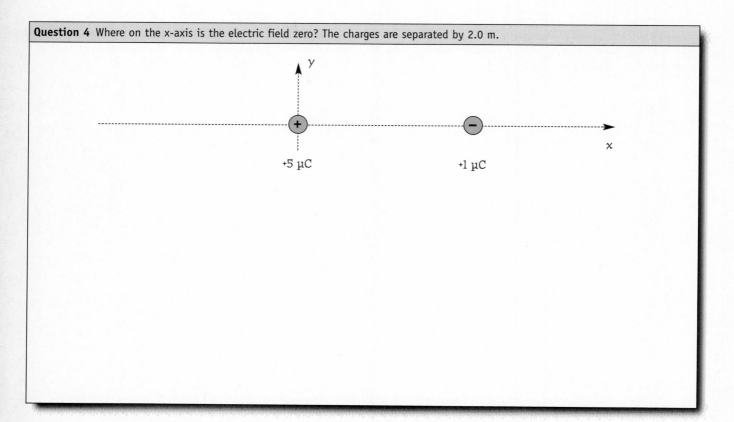

Question 5 Determine the value of Q_2 so that the electric field at the origin is zero. The left charge is 1.50 m from the origin and Q_2 is 1.00 m from the origin.

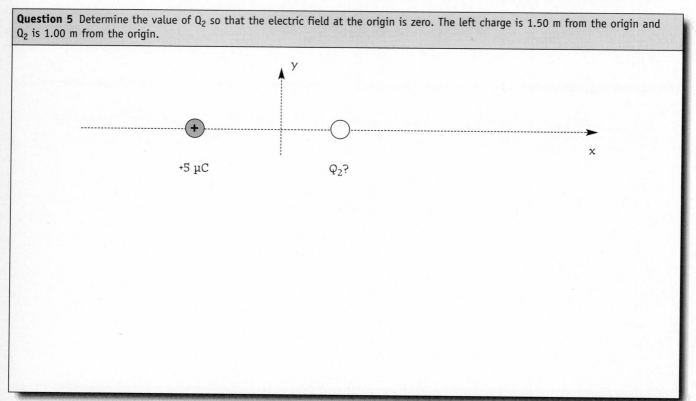

Question 1 Flux into or out of an oval. Design your own experiments to see how electric charge affects the flux into or out of the oval.

In your experiments, you can
- change the shape of the oval
- move the center of the oval so that it surrounds the charge or does not surround the charge
- change the magnitude and sign of the electric charge

When finished, develop in words a qualitative rule to determine the electric flux flowing into or out of the oval. Give examples to support your rule.

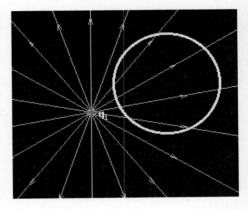

Question 2 Electric flux with two charges. In the simulation, click the "two charges" configuration. You can now adjust the sign, magnitude, and separation of two electric charges. Repeat the experiments done in Question 1. Does your rule apply for this two charge system?

You can
- change the shape of the ring
- change the position of the center of the ring (move it all over)
- change the magnitudes and signs of the electric charges

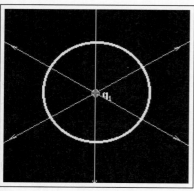

Question 3 First way to determine electric flux. The meter indicates the electric flux ϕ into or out of the oval and the net electric charge q_1 inside the oval. What happens to the flux if you double or triple the positive electric charge inside the oval?

What happens to the flux if you double or triple the negative electric charge inside the oval?

Find an equation with a proportionally constant that relates the electric flux into or out of the oval and the electric charge inside the oval.

Question 4 Second way to determine electric flux. The green electric field lines in the simulation screen represent the electric field surrounding the source charges. Develop a rule for the electric flux passing out of or into the oval by counting the electric field lines passing out of or into the oval.

Question 5 Integrate to find the electric flux leaving a sphere that surrounds a +3.0-μC point charge: $\phi = \iint \mathbf{E} \cdot \mathbf{dA}$. We do this in steps.

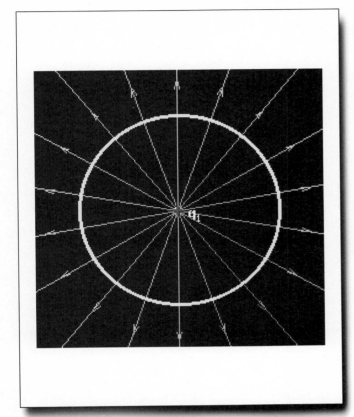

(b) For the situation shown in the figure on the left, explain why $\mathbf{E} \cdot \mathbf{dA} = E\,dA$ for every element on the surface.

(c) Why can you take E outside the integral—the last step below?

$$\text{flux} = \iint \mathbf{E} \cdot \mathbf{dA} = \iint E\,dA = \iint E\,dA$$

(a) What is the direction of **dA**, a small part of the sphere's surface area?

(d) Why can you now simply multiply the magnitude of the electric field at the surface times the total area of the sphere's surface—the last step below?

$$\text{flux} = \iint \mathbf{E} \cdot \mathbf{dA} = \iint E\,dA = \iint E\,dA = E(\text{Area}) = E\,(4\pi r^2)$$

Question 6 Determine the electric flux leaving or entering the oval shown using the charge inside the oval and the number of flux lines crossing the oval surface methods. The charge is +4 µC.

Question 7 Determine the electric flux leaving or entering the oval in the simulation using the charge inside the oval and the number of flux lines crossing the oval surface methods, $q_1 = +4$ µC and $q_2 = -2$ µC.

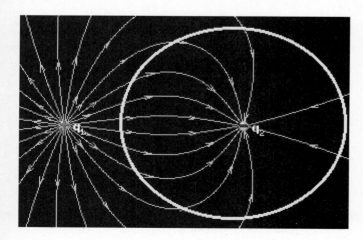

©1999 Addison Wesley Longman, Alan Van Heuvelen and Paul D'Alessandris

Question 8 Use the charge inside and integral methods to determine the electric flux leaving the 15-mm-radius sphere surrounding a $+10 \times 10^{-10}$ C charge. The electric field at the surface of the 15-mm-radius sphere is 40,000 N/C.

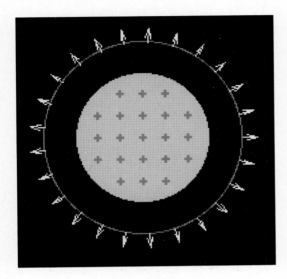

Question 9 Repeat the calculations in Question 8, only this time with the 15-mm-radius sphere surrounding a -10×10^{-10} C charge. The electric field at the surface of the 15-mm-radius sphere is 40,000 N/C and points into the spherical surface.

Question 1 Electric field outside a charged sphere. A 10-mm-radius solid sphere has $+10 \times 10^{-10}$ C of electric charge distributed uniformly throughout the sphere. Use Gauss's law to determine the electric field caused by this charge at a distance of 15 mm from the center of the sphere. $\iint \mathbf{E} \cdot \mathbf{dA} = 4\pi\, Q_{\text{inside}}$. We do this in steps.

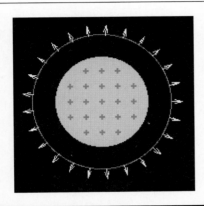

(a) First, determine an expression for the electric flux out of the Gaussian surface.

- What is the direction of **dA**, a small part of the Gaussian sphere's surface area?

- For the situation shown above, explain why **E • dA** = E dA for every element on the surface.

- Why can you take E outside the integral—the last step below?

  flux $= \iint \mathbf{E} \cdot \mathbf{dA} = \iint E\, dA = \iint E\, dA$

- Why can you now simply multiply the magnitude of the electric field at the surface times the total area of the sphere's surface— the last step below?

  flux $= \iint \mathbf{E} \cdot \mathbf{dA} = \iint E\, dA = \iint E\, dA = E(\text{Area}) = E(4\pi R^2)$

(b) Determine the charge inside the Gaussian surface Q_{inside}.

(c) Insert the electric flux and Q_{inside} into Gauss's law and find the electric field.

Question 2 Electric field outside a charged spherical shell. A 10-mm-radius spherical shell, like a basketball, has $+10 \times 10^{-10}$ C of electric charge distributed uniformly on its surface. Use Gauss's law to determine the electric field caused by this charge at a distance of 15 mm from the center of the sphere. $\iint \mathbf{E} \cdot \mathbf{dA} = 4\pi k \, Q_{inside}$

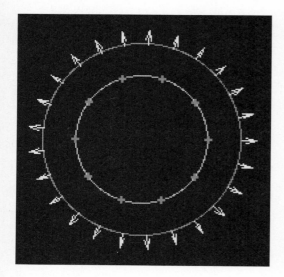

Question 3 Electric field inside the charged spherical shell. For the charged spherical shell in Question 2, use Gauss's law to predict the value of the electric field inside the shell. If you want, you can calculate the magnitude of the electric field at R = 5 mm from the center of the 10-mm-radius spherical shell. $\iint \mathbf{E} \cdot \mathbf{dA} = 4\pi k \, Q_{inside}$

Question 4 Electric field inside a charged solid sphere. Predict the value of the electric field 5.0 mm from the center of a 10-mm-radius solid sphere. The sphere is uniformly charged with $+10 \times 10^{-10}$ C of electric charge.

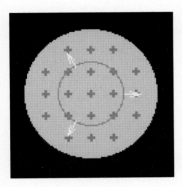

(a) First, determine the electric charge inside (Q_{inside}) a 5.0-mm-radius Gaussian surface. To do this, find the charge density in the bigger 10-mm-radius sphere, the volume of the 5-mm radius Gaussian sphere, and then the charge inside that Gaussian sphere.

(b) Then use Gauss's law to determine the electric field 5.0 mm from the center of the charged sphere. $\iint \mathbf{E} \cdot \mathbf{dA} = 4\pi k \, Q_{inside}$

Question 5 Electric field inside a charged solid sphere. Show that the electric field INSIDE the solid uniformly charged sphere varies as

$$E = \left(\frac{kQ}{R_{charged\ sphere}}\right)^2 \left(\frac{R}{R_{charged\ sphere}}\right)$$

where $R_{charged\ sphere}$ is the radius of the charged sphere (10 mm in the simulation), Q is the total charge on the sphere (adjustable with the Q slider), and R is the distance from the center of the sphere to the point where the electric field is being calculated.

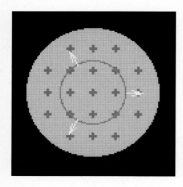

Question 1 Electron path. A negatively charged electron moves through a uniform electric field that points up. The electron enters the field moving in the horizontal direction; draw a line showing its subsequent motion after entering the field.

Question 2 x Velocity component. How does the x-component of velocity change as the electron moves through the vertical electric field?

Question 3 Electron path. Make the electron's x-component of initial velocity positive and its y-component of initial velocity zero.

- Construct a force diagram for the electron when passing through the electric field.
- Apply the y-component form of Newton's second law for the electron.
- Calculate the electron's acceleration in the y-direction.
- Run the simulation. Use the simulation y-component and time numbers to independently calculate the electron's acceleration in the y-direction. Compare these numbers to your previous Newton's second law prediction.

Question 4 Time of flight. Note the time interval needed for the electron to hit the lower plate.

If you reduce the initial x-component of velocity by one-half, is the time of flight: **(a)** less? **(b)** the same? **(c)** more? Explain.

Question 5 Effect of electric field on motion. If you reduce the electric field by half, what is the effect on

(a) the electron's acceleration in the x-direction?

(b) the electron's acceleration in the y-direction?

(c) the time of flight (the time to reach the bottom plate)?

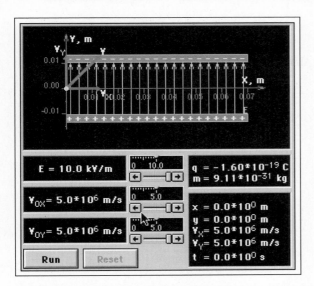

Question 1 Maximum y-position. Predict the maximum y-position of the electron. Does the initial horizontal velocity component affect the outcome?

Question 2 Time of flight. With the same settings as in Question 1, determine the time of flight for the electron (the time interval to reach the bottom plate).

Question 3 Maximum time of flight. Adjust the electric field and the initial y-velocity component so that the electron takes the longest time to return to y = 0.0 m. Note that its flight stops if it hits the upper plate at y = 0.010 m.

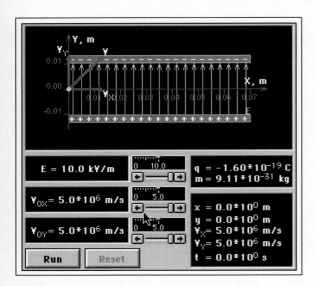

Question 4 Range. With E = +1.0 kV/m and v_{ox} = 5.0 x 10^6 m/s, predict the initial vertical velocity v_{oy} component that causes the electron on the first try to reach position x = 0.07 m and y = 0.00 m.

Question 5 Another problem. (a) Set the electric field to + 1.0 kV/m and the initial horizontal velocity component to +5.0 × 10^6 m/s. Determine the initial vertical velocity component so that the electron reaches x = 0.07 m and y = −0.01 m (on the first try). **(b)** If you double the value of the answer to (a), what value of the horizontal velocity component is needed to reach that same point? Do this work on a separate paper.

Question 6 A final problem. Set the electric field to + 10.0 kV/m and the horizontal and vertical velocity components to +5.0 × 10^6 m/s. Where will the electron hit the plate?

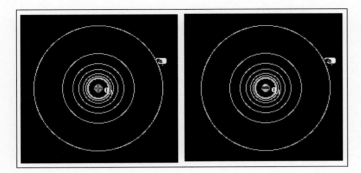

Summarize your observations for both Questions 1 and 2 in the space below.

Question 1 Electric potential due to positive charge. A +3.0-μC point charge produces the circular equipotential lines shown in the left figure above. The electric potential (sometimes called voltage) along each line is the same. The lines are analogous to constant elevation lines on a topological map.

- Move the pointer to one line and press down on the mouse to see the electric potential on that line. Continue moving along the line with the finger down and note the potential at other points on the line. What would an analogous hike in the mountains be like?

- Now, place the pointer near the positive charge and move away from it. What would an analogous hike in the mountains be like?

Question 2 Electric potential due to negative charge. Change the electric charge to −3.0 μC and repeat the two activities in Question 1 for a negative electric charge. In particular, how would you describe the quantity electric potential to another student? Indicate any analogies between charge and electric potential and large massive objects such as the earth and gravitational potential (gy).

Question 3 Electric potential due to an electric dipole. A +3.0-μC charge on the left and a −3.0-μC charge on the right produce the equipotential lines shown. The finger is on a +20-mV line.

- Move the pointer along several lines and note the potential at different positions along a line. What would an analogous hike in the mountains be like?

- Now, place the pointer near the positive charge and move it directly toward the negative charge. What would an analogous hike in the mountains be like?

- What is the potential half way between the charges?

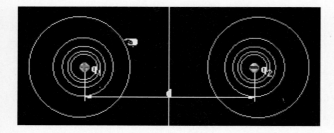

Question 4 Determining the electric potential. Suppose you knew the potential at every point in space that is caused by the positive charge if there alone and by the negative charge if there alone. How would you determine the potential when both charges are present? Note that the potential at the point where the finger tip is located in the sketch in Question 3 is +20 mV. If the positive charge was there alone, the potential would be +27 mV at that point. What do you think the potential would be at that point if the negative charge was there alone?

Question 5 Electric potential due to two positive charges. Suppose you have two +3.0 µC in a region, as shown. Choose several special points on the simulation window and measure the potential at those points with both charges present. Then reduce the right charge q_2 to zero and measure the potential at these points again. (**Warning:** The positions of the equipotential lines change, so they cannot be used to identify special points on the simulation window.) Now predict the potential at these points if the left q_1 charge is zero and the right charge q_2 is returned to +3 µC. Check your predictions by changing the charges and measuring the potential with the finger pointer.)

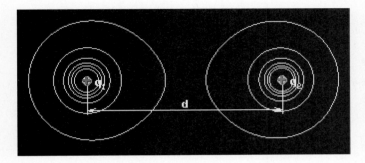

Question 6 Potential due to multiple charges. In the sketch below, you see equipotential lines caused by positive charges +Q distributed uniformly on the top metal plate and by negative charges –Q distributed uniformly on the lower metal plate. In the region between the plates, the equipotential lines are evenly spaced. The lines near the top positively charged plate are at higher potential than the lines near the bottom negatively charged plate. The line in the middle is at zero potential.

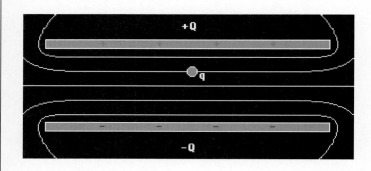

What is the direction of the force on a positively charged (q) ball when it is near the upper plate?

Is the force on that positively charged ball greater, the same, or less if it is closer to the lower plate (at lower potential)? Explain.

Does the magnitude of the electric force exerted on the charge q depend on the value of the potential or on some other property of the potential? Describe the property.

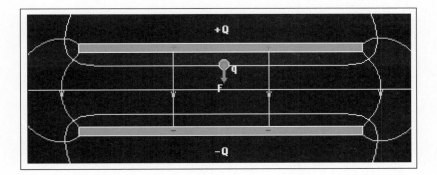

Question 1 Parallel plate electric field lines, equipotential lines, and electric force. The figure above shows a charge density of $+0.2 \times 10^{-8}$ C/m^2 distributed uniformly on the top plate and a charge of -0.2×10^{-8} C/m^2 distributed uniformly on the lower plate. The vertical electric field lines and horizontal equipotential field lines between the plates are also shown, as is the electric force exerted on a positive charge between the plates. On a separate paper, draw the **E** lines, the equipotential lines, and the force on the same charge if the magnitude of charge density is changed to 0.4×10^{-8} C/m^2 and then again to 0.6×10^{-8} C/m^2.

Question 2 Point charge electric field lines and equipotential lines. Are the representations of the electric field lines and the equipotential lines consistent with the following rules?

- Equipotential lines are perpendicular to electric field lines. _____

- The electric field at a position depends on how the potential is changing rather than on the value of the potential at a particular position. _____

- The electric field is greater in the regions where the equipotential lines are closer to each other. _____

- The electric field points "downhill," that is, from higher to lower electric potential. _____

Question 3 Electric force and relation between field and potential. Devise and describe some experiments to decide whether the simulation is consistent with the following relations: $F_y = qE_y$ and $E_y = -\Delta V/\Delta y$.

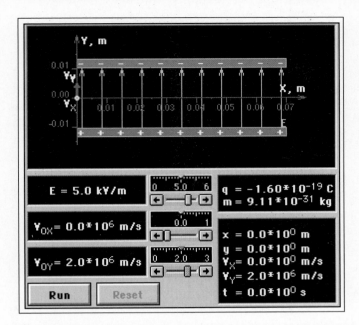

Question 1 Potential difference and electric field. Use the equation $E_y = -\Delta V/\Delta y$ to determine the potential difference between the lower plate and the upper plate.

Question 2 Changes in electric potential and electric potential energy. Suppose the electron moved from its present starting position between the plates to the top plate. Determine its change in electrical potential energy $U_q = qV$.

Question 3 An energy transformation problem. Our goal is to predict the initial vertical speed the electron needs so that it just reaches the top plate but does not hit it. Construct a qualitative energy bar chart for a process in which the electron starts with upward velocity and stops at the instant it reaches the top plate. Assume that the electrical potential energy is zero when the electron is at $y = 0.00$ m. The possible types of energy are kinetic (K), gravitational potential energy (U_g), elastic potential energy (U_s), and electrical potential energy (U_q).

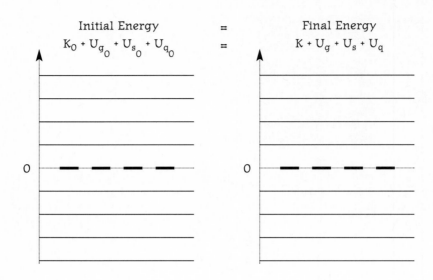

Speed to reach top plate. Use an energy approach and the energy bar chart to determine the initial y-component of velocity that is needed for the electron to just reach the top plate (its speed should be zero when $y = 0.010$ m). Use the conditions from Questions 1–3.

Question 4 Another problem. Start the electron moving upward at 5.0×10^6 m/s. Use an energy approach to determine the potential difference from its starting position to the top plate so that the electron stops at the top. Then determine the electric field that would produce this potential difference in a distance of 0.010 m.

Question 5 A final problem. Set the initial vertical velocity component to $+3.0 \times 10^6$ m/s and the initial horizontal velocity component to $+5.0 \times 10^6$ m/s. Use an energy approach to determine the electric field that will just deflect the electron when it reaches the top plate.

12

dc CIRCUITS

Hints for Using the Electric Circuit Construction Tools

◆ To add one of the elements to the circuit, click on it in the toolbox. Release the mouse and move the mouse between two dots in the circuit-building area. Then click and the element should appear between the dots.

◆ To remove an element, click on it.

The simulation has tools on the right side that can be used to construct an electric circuit. The tools, starting at the top, are

The Wire Tool makes a wire.

The Switch Tool produces an open switch. The switch can be closed and opened by clicking on it only while the simulation is running.

The Bulb Tool creates a 1.0-ohm resistance bulb.

The Capacitor Tool has two equally long parallel vertical lines and produces the capacitors used in Activities 12.6 and 12.7.

The Battery Tool is a source of potential difference. You can adjust the potential difference (often called voltage) across the battery terminals with a slider.

The Ammeter and Voltmeter Tools create meters that measure the current along a circuit and the potential difference (voltage) across a circuit element, respectively.

The Grounding Tool has an elbow and can set the electric potential in the circuit to zero at some point of your choice.

The Pointer Tool (an arrow) selects some element to adjust its value. The pointer can also indicate the voltage at different points in a circuit if the circuit is grounded with the Grounding Tool. Just click the pointer down at points in the circuit and the voltage is shown in the bottom-right panel of the simulation screen.

Question 1 First circuit. Consider the circuit as shown below. Adjust the battery voltage across the bulb to 10.0 V and observe the brightness of the bulb. How does the bulb brightness change as the voltage across the bulb is decreased?

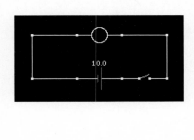

Question 2 Bulb resistance. Adjust the battery voltage and observe the brightness of the bulb and the electric current through the bulb. Complete the following table showing the voltage V across the bulb (for this circuit, the same as the voltage across the battery) and the electric current I passing through the bulb. Use this data to determine the electric resistance R in ohms of the bulb: $R = V/I$.

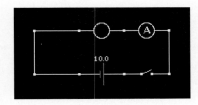

Voltage (V)	10	8	6	4	2	0
Current (A)						

Question 3 Two bulbs in series. Consider the circuit shown below. Which bulb will be brightest when the switch is closed? Add more bulbs in series, and compare the brightnesses of each bulb with others in the circuit. What do your observations tell you?

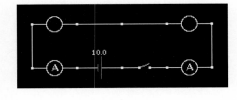

Question 4 Equivalent resistance for series resistors. With the circuit shown below, keep the potential difference across the battery at 10 V. In the table, record the current through the circuit as you replace wires with more 1.0-Ω bulbs in series. Based on your observations, state a rule for the equivalent resistance of a group of series resistive elements (like the bulbs).

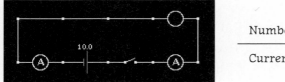

Number of bulbs	1	2	3	4
Current (A)				

The **equivalent resistance** of the bulbs is $R_{equivalent} = V / I$ where V is the potential difference across all of the resistive elements (the bulbs in this case) and I is the current through them. A single resistor with this equivalent resistance would have the same current passing through it if the same potential difference was placed across it.

Question 5 More series resistors. Use the idea for the equivalent resistance of series resistors to predict the current through the circuit shown below for different potential differences across the resistors. The resistors in this case have different resistances. You will have to adjust the resistances in the simulation.

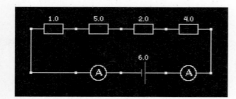

Voltage (V)	10	5	0
Current (A)			

Question 1 Parallel bulbs. With one switch closed, note the brightness of the bulb. How will the brightness of that bulb change if the switch for the second bulb is closed? Compare their brightnesses. How will the brightnesses of the two lower bulbs change if the switch for the third bulb is closed? How do the brightnesses of the three bulbs compare?

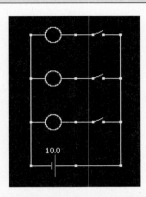

Question 2 Current through different branches.

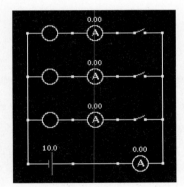

Predict the current through all ammeters when the switch for the lowest bulb is closed. After your prediction, close the switch to see how you did.

Predict the current through all the ammeters when the switches for the two lowest bulbs are closed. After your prediction, close the switches to see how you did.

Finally, predict the current through all the ammeters when the switches for all three bulbs are closed. After your prediction, close the switches to see how you did.

Question 3 Junction rule.

Turn on the switch for the lowest bulb. Look at the two middle junctions along the right side of the circuit (middle two dots on the right side of the circuit). How does the current flowing into each junction compare to the current flowing out of each junction?

Turn on the switches for the two lowest bulbs. How does the current flowing into each of the middle two junctions on the right side of the circuit compare to the current flowing out of each of these junctions?

Turn on the switches for all three bulbs. How does the current flowing into each of the middle two junctions on the right side of the circuit compare to the current flowing out of each of these junctions?

Question 3 Junction rule continued.

Write a general rule that seems to be consistent with your observations for the two junctions just analyzed.

Question 4 Equivalent resistance of parallel resistors. Complete the following table, which shows the current through the 5.0-V battery when placed in parallel across one or more 1.0-Ω bulbs. Use these numbers to write an equation for the equivalent resistance of the parallel resistors. In general equivalent resistance is defined as $R_{equivalent} = V / I$ where V is the voltage across the resistors and I is the total current flowing through them.

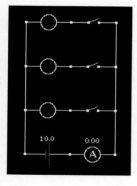

Bulbs in circuit	1	2	3
Voltage (V)	10	10	10
Current (A)			
$R_{equivalent}$ (Ω)			

Question 5 The battery—a constant current source or a constant voltage source? Based on your observations in this and the previous activity, would you say that the battery is a constant potential difference (constant voltage) source or a constant current source? Provide an example to support your choice.

Question 6 Using the equivalent resistance and junction rules. Apply the equivalent resistance rule you developed in Question 4 to predict the total current through the circuit shown below.

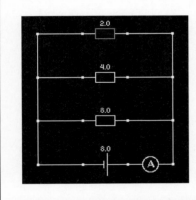

Question 7 Junction rule. Is the junction rule consistent with the current readings for the circuit shown here? Provide two examples.

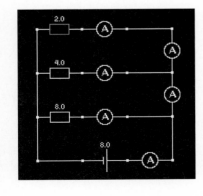

Puzzle 1 Rate the bulbs in this circuit according to brightness, listing the brightest bulb first. Indicate whether any bulbs are equally bright.

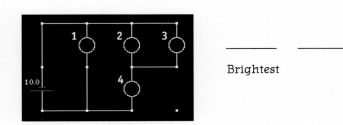

_____ _____ _____ _____

Brightest   Dimmest

Puzzle 2 Rate the bulbs in this circuit according to brightness, listing the brightest bulb first. Indicate whether any bulbs are equally bright.

_____ _____ _____ _____ _____

Brightest   Dimmest

Puzzle 3 Rate the ammeters in this circuit according to current flowing through them, the largest current ammeter first. The ammeters have zero resistance. Indicate whether any currents are equal. (**Hint.** It might be easier to visualize the circuit if you redraw it without the ammeters.)

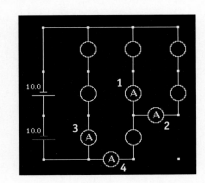

_____ _____ _____ _____

Largest   Smallest

Puzzle 4 When the switch is open, three bulbs shine with equal brightness. Indicate how the brightness of each bulb changes when the switch is closed. Justify your choices.

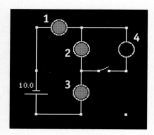

Bulb 1: _____ Becomes brighter
         _____ Remains same
         _____ Becomes dimmer

Bulb 2: _____ Becomes brighter
         _____ Remains same
         _____ Becomes dimmer

Bulb 3: _____ Becomes brighter
         _____ Remains same
         _____ Becomes dimmer

Puzzle 5 Indicate how the brightness of each bulb changes when the switch is closed. Justify your choices.

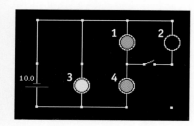

Bulb 1: _____ Becomes brighter
         _____ Remains same
         _____ Becomes dimmer
                   Explanation:

Bulb 2: _____ Becomes brighter
         _____ Remains same
         _____ Becomes dimmer
                   Explanation:

Bulb 3: _____ Becomes brighter
         _____ Remains same
         _____ Becomes dimmer
                   Explanation:

Bulb 4: _____ Becomes brighter
         _____ Remains same
         _____ Becomes dimmer
                   Explanation:

Puzzle 6 Three separate circuits each have one bulb. Rate the circuits according to the brightness of the bulb in the circuit, listing the brightest bulb circuit first. Indicate whether any bulbs are equally bright.

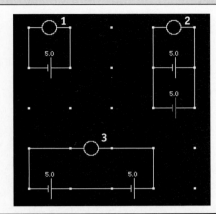

_____ _____ _____

Brightest   Dimmest

Puzzle 7 (a) Determine the current in each ammeter and the relative brightness of the four 1-Ω bulbs when the switch is open. Be sure to note that the left battery has a potential difference of −10 V.

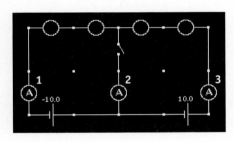

(b) Determine the current in each ammeter and the relative brightness of the four 2-Ω bulbs when the switch is closed. Note that the left battery has a potential difference of −10 V.

Puzzle 8 **(a)** Rate the relative brightnesses of the 1-Ω bulbs.

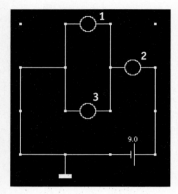

(b) Determine the voltage at each point in the circuit. The circuit is grounded (zero volts) on the left side of the battery.

Measuring Electric Current with an Ammeter

- ◆ An ammeter measures the flow of electric charge.

- ◆ To measure the current in a branch of a circuit, it must be inserted in series into the circuit branch so that all of the current passing through that branch must also pass through the ammeter.

- ◆ If inserted in the branch of a circuit through which we want to measure the electric current, the ammeter must not affect that current flow. Consequently, the ammeter has very low electric resistance (ideally, zero resistance).

- ◆ Both the correct and incorrect ways to insert the ammeter in the circuit are shown here. If used as shown on the right, a very large current will flow through the low resistance ammeter and possibly damage it (or blow its fuse).

Correct Ammeter

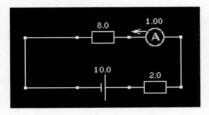

Incorrect Ammeter

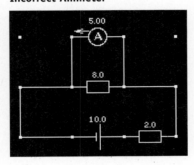

Measuring Potential Difference with a Voltmeter

- ◆ A voltmeter measures the potential difference between two points in an electric circuit.

- ◆ To measure the potential difference, the voltmeter terminals are touched to the two points. The voltmeter is in parallel with the circuit elements across which the potential difference is being measured.

- ◆ If placed in parallel across some part of the circuit, we do not want the voltmeter to provide an alternative path for the circuit's electric current. Consequently, the voltmeter should have somewhat higher electric resistance than the circuit elements across which the terminals are placed—ideally, the voltmeter has infinite resistance.

- ◆ Both the correct and incorrect ways to use a voltmeter to measure potential difference are shown here.

Correct Ammeter

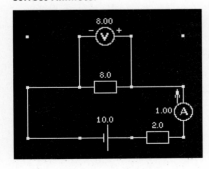

Incorrect Ammeter

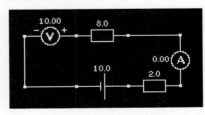

SUMMARY: Kirchhoff's Laws

Loop rule. The net change in electric potential (the voltage change) around any closed loop is zero. This is because the electric potential at *every* point in the circut can have only one value. A charged particle returns to the same electric potential if it returns to the same point in a circuit after a trip around a loop.

Junction rule. The electric current entering any point in a direct-current (dc) electric circuit equals the electric current leaving that point. If this were not true, electric charge would accumulate or dissipate at that point. This happens on capacitor plates but not at dc circuit junctions.

Question 1 The loop rule. (a) Use the loop rule to predict the electric current through the circuit shown below. **(b)** Then, determine the electric potential (voltage) at each point in the circuit..

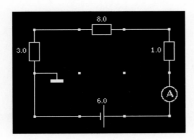

Question 2 **(a)** Apply the loop rule twice and the junction rule once to get three equations that can be used to determine the ammeter current readings for the circuit shown below. **(b)** Then, determine the electric potential at each point in the circuit.

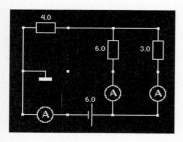

Question 3 **(a)** Apply the loop rule twice and the junction rule once. Be sure to note that the top battery produces −6.0 V (the left side is the positive terminal). **(b)** Use the three independent equations developed in part (a) to determine the current in each branch of the circuit.

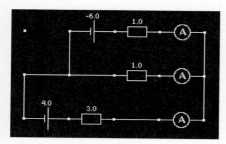

Question 4 The circulatory system. Here, we use a very simple electric circuit as an analog for the heart (the battery) and the vessels in the circulatory system (the resistors). The electron current is the "blood flow."

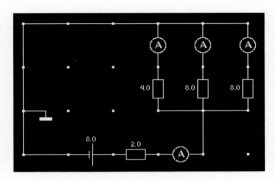

(a) Predict the equivalent resistance of this circuit. Then calculate the battery current and the current through each resistor. Also, determine the electric potential at every position in the circuit.

(b) Suppose the "person's" aorta (the large vessel that leaves the heart—it has a 2-Ω resistance in our simulation) becomes clogged, causing its resistance to blood flow to quadruple (to 8.0 Ω in the simulation). Now, determine the current flow (blood flow) in the other parts of the circuit.

Question 5 A circuit with three identical bulbs is shown below. Run the simulation with the switch open. Then answer the following questions before closing the switch.

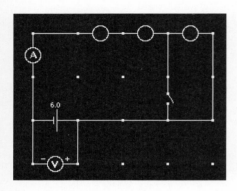

After you have answered the questions, run the simulation and turn the switch on and off to see how you did.

(a) What happens to the brightness of each bulb when the switch is closed?

(b) What happens to the current through the battery when the switch is closed?

(c) What happens to the potential difference across the battery?

(d) What happens to the total power use of the bulbs when the switch is closed?

Question 6 Blowing a fuse. The circuit shown here is analogous to a line in your home that is connected to a fuse that blows if the current exceeds 25.0 A.

As you prepare dinner, you have the following items connected across a 10-V potential difference:

10-Ω light

1-Ω burner

5-Ω mixer

1-Ω oven

5-Ω crock

4-Ω light

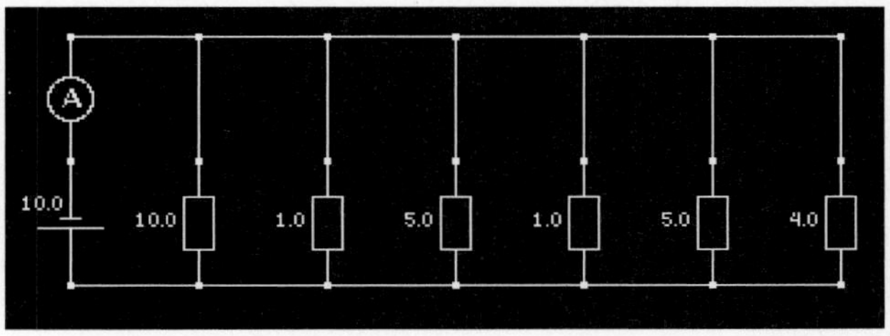

(a) Will you blow the fuse?

(b) If the current does exceed 25 A, remove one or more of the appliances so that the current is 25 A or less but as close to 25 A as possible. Which appliances will you remove?

Capacitance C A capacitor consists of two conducting surfaces separated by a nonconducting region. The capacitance C of the capacitor is a measure of its ability to store opposite electric charge (+q and −q) on the conducting surfaces when a potential difference V is placed across the surfaces. In particular, C = q/V.

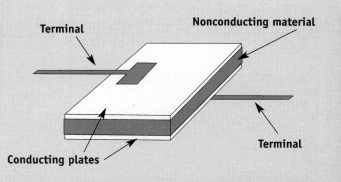

Question 1 Capacitor in an electric circuit. Predict how the brightness of each bulb, the current reading in each ammeter, and the voltage across the capacitor change with time as you run the simulation. Remember that the capacitor has two very large metal plates that do not touch. Thus there is a gap in the circuit—the space between the plates. After your predictions, run the simulation.

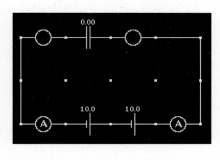

Question 2 Review questions.

(a) Does an open gap between the conducting plates of a capacitor mean that current cannot flow in other parts of the circuit or in that branch of the circuit?

(b) What happens on the capacitor plates when this current flows?

(c) Why does the current flow decrease over time in this particular situation (but not in general)?

Question 3 A capacitor in parallel with a bulb. With the switch open in the circuit below, note in the simulation the ammeter readings and bulb brightnesses for each bulb. If you were to close the switch, there would now be a capacitor in parallel with the bulb on the right (don't close the switch yet).

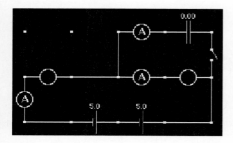

Immediately after closing the switch, would the brightness of the bulb on the right in parallel with the capacitor increse, decrease, or remain the same? Explain.

Immediately after closing the switch, would the brightness of the bulb on the left increase, decrease, or remain the same? Explain.

A long time after closing the switch, predict the relative brightnesses of the bulbs. Explain your reasoning.

After your preditions, close the switch and see what happens. You may have to open the switch, reset the simulation and try the experiment again while focusing on one bulb at a time.

Question 4 Bulb between two capacitors. This circuit has three bulbs and two capacitors all in series across a 30-V potential difference (three 10-V batteries in series). Predict what happens to each bulb immediately after the simulation begins to run. Justify your predictions.

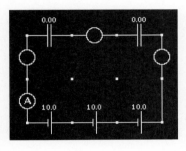

Predict what happens to each bulb 10 or 20 s after the simulation starts. Justify your predictions, then run the simulation to check your reasoning.

Question 5 Three bulbs and a capacitor. Predict the relative brightnesses of the three bulbs and the approximate voltage across the capacitor shown below immediately after the simulation starts to run. Justify your predictions.

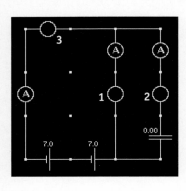

Repeat your predictions, only this time about 3 s after the simulation starts to run. Justify your predictions.

Repeat your predictions, only this time after the simulation has run 10 or 20 s. Justify your predictions.

Question 1 Series capacitors. Run the simulation and decide whether the group of three capacitors in series has more, the same, or less capacitance than the circuit with a single capacitor. All capacitors have the same capacitance, the bulbs the same resistance, and the ammeters zero resistance. Justify your conclusion.

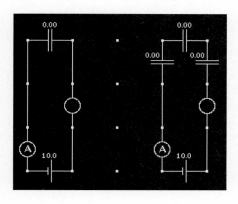

Question 2 Parallel capacitors. Run the simulation and decide whether the group of three capacitors in parallel has more, the same, or less capacitance than the circuit with a single capacitor. All capacitors have the same capacitance, the bulbs the same resistance, and the ammeters zero resistance. Justify your conclusion.

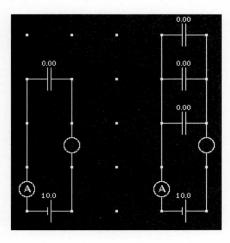

Question 3 Answer the following questions about the circuit shown below.

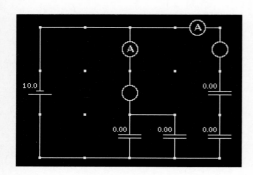

(a) Compare the relative brightness of the two bulbs shortly after the switch is closed. Explain your reasoning.

(b) Compare the relatve brightness of the two bulbs after the capacitors are completely charged. Explain why the brightnesses are as observed.

(c) Determine the potential difference across each capacitor after it becomes fully charged.

Question 4 Answer the following questions about the circuit shown below.

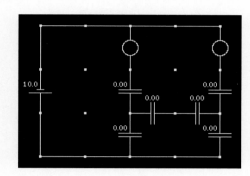

(a) Compare the relative brightness of the two bulbs shortly after the switch is closed.

(b) Compare the relative brightness of the two bulbs after the capacitors are completely charged.

(c) Determine the potential difference across each capacitor after it becomes fully charged.

Question 1 Discharging a capacitor. Set the initial charge on the capacitor to 4.0×10^{-4} C, the resistor resistance to 1.5 MΩ, and the capacitor's capacitance to 9.6 µF. Run the simulation and record the charge on the capacitor each 10 s starting at time zero. State in the form of a rule any systematic variation that you observe in the charge on the capacitor.

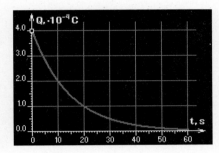

Question 2 Effect of R and C on half-life. With the resistor resistance at 1.5 MΩ and the capacitor's capacitance at 9.6 µF, the half-life for the discharge of the capacitor is 10 s.

(a) Increase the resistance to 3.0 MΩ. Find a value for the capacitance so that the half-life is again 10 s.

(b) Adjust the capacitance again to get a 10-s half-life only this time with the resistor resistance at 6.0 MΩ.

(c) Return the resistance to 3.0 MΩ and the capacitance to 4.8 µF. Increase the resistance and observe the graph. Does the half-life increase or decrease as the resistance increases? If you double the resistance, how does the half-life change?

(d) Return the resistance to 3.0 MΩ and the capacitance to 4.8 µF. Increase the capacitance and observe the graph. Does the half-life increase or decrease when the capacitance increases? If you double the capacitance, how does the half-life change?

(e) Now, write an equation that indicates how the half-life for capacitor discharge depends on the values of the resistance and the capacitance in the RC circuit.

(f) Does the half-life depend on the initial charge on the capacitor?

Question 3 Charge and current. Start with an initial charge of 4.0×10^{-4} C, a resistance of 3.0 MΩ, and a capacitance of 4.8 μF. The half-life is 10 s and the equation for the charge on the capacitor as a function of time is $Q = Q_0 e^{-0.693\, t\, /\, R\, C}$. Determine the current ($i = dQ/dt$) through the resistor as a function of time. Then, determine the value of the current at times 0, 10, 20, and 30 s. Run the simulation to check your work.

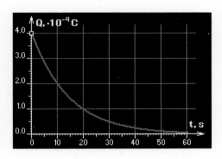

Question 4 Loop rule during discharge. Start with an initial charge of 4.0×10^{-4} C, a resistance of 3.0 MΩ, and a capacitance of 4.8 μF. In the space below, draw a series RC circuit. Assume that the capacitor is initially charged. Use the numbers on the simulation screen to see whether Kirchoff's loop rule applies to the discharge of this RC circuit at times 10, 20, and 30 s after the discharge starts.

MAGNETISM

Question 1 Direction of the magnetic field. What will the magnetic field look like when positive current flows through the wire? (Positive current is defined to flow out of the screen.) Sketch the field.

Question 2 Orientation of the magnetic field. What angle does the magnetic field make relative to the position vector connecting the wire to the point of interest? Answer below, and indicate this angle on your sketch in Question 1.

Question 3 Magnitude along a radial line. Does the magnitude of the field change along a line extending radially away from the wire? If so, describe the change.

Question 4 Magnitude along a field line. Does the magnitude of the field change along the circular field lines? If so, describe the change.

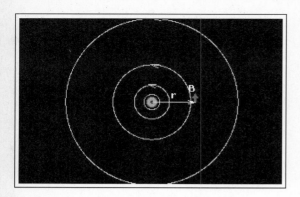

Question 5 Dependence on current. What happens to the magnitude and direction of the magnetic field, at the point in space you are examining, if the current is increased?

Question 6 Flipping the current. What happens to the magnitude and direction of the magnetic field, at the point in space you are examining, if the current is flipped from positive to negative?

Question 7 Iron fillings pattern.

Sketch the pattern formed by the iron filings for a negative current.

Sketch the pattern formed by the iron filings for a positive current.

Why does the pattern formed by the filings not depend on the direction of the current?

Could iron filings be used to determine the direction that current flows? Why or why not?

Question 8 Functional dependence on current. Select an arbitrary point in space. Vary the current through the wire and record the magnitude of the magnetic field at this point.

I ———|——— B

Sketch your data.

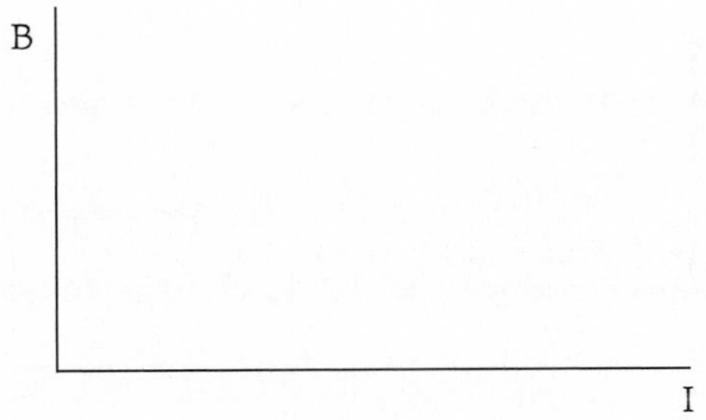

B

|_____ I

What is the functional dependence of magnetic field on current for a straight, current-carrying wire?

Question 9 Functional dependence on distance. Vary the distance between the point of interest and the wire, and record the magnitude of the magnetic field.

d ———|——— B

Sketch your data.

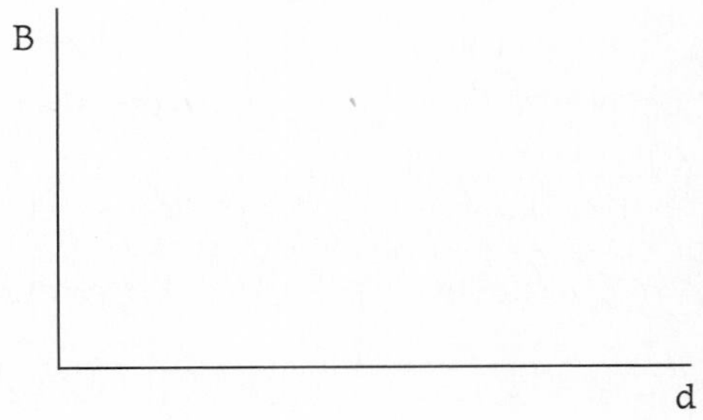

B

|_____ d

What is the functional dependence of magnetic field on distance from a straight, current-carrying wire?

Combine your results to express the dependence of magnetic field on both current and distance from the current-carrying wire.

Question 10 Biot–Savart law. What is the distance from a wire carrying +10 A beyond which the magnetic field is less than 15 μT?

Question 11 Biot–Savart puzzler. A 2-cm-long object is placed in the magnetic field of a 15-A wire. One end of the object is exposed to a 35-μT field. What range of magnetic fields may the other end of the object be exposed to?

At what distance is the magnetic field of a 15-A wire equal to 35 μT?

Given your previous answer, at what minimum and maximum distance can the other end of the object be located?

Given this range of positions, compute the range of magnetic fields to which this object may be exposed.

Question 1 Magnetic field lines. What will the magnetic field look like when positive current flows through the loop? (Positive current is defined to flow out of the screen at the top of the loop and into the screen at the bottom of the loop.) Sketch the field.

Question 3 Orientation of the magnetic field. What angle does the magnetic field make relative to the central axis?

Question 2 Direction of the magnetic field along the central axis. Why does the magnetic field point to the right along the central axis when positive current flows through the loop? Explain using the right-hand rule.

Question 4 Magnitude along the central axis. Does the magnitude of the field change along the central axis? If so, describe the change.

Where is the maximum field located?

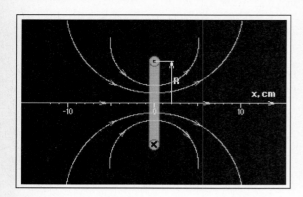

Question 5 Dependence on current. What happens to the magnitude and direction of the magnetic field, at the point in space you are examining, if the current is increased?

Question 6 Flipping the current. What happens to the magnitude and direction of the magnetic field, at the point in space you are examining, if the current is flipped?

Question 7 Iron filings pattern. What happens to the iron filings pattern if the current is flipped between positive and negative values?

Question 8 Functional dependence on current. Select an arbitrary point on the central axis. Vary the current through the loop and record the magnitude of the magnetic field at this point.

I ___ B

Sketch your data.

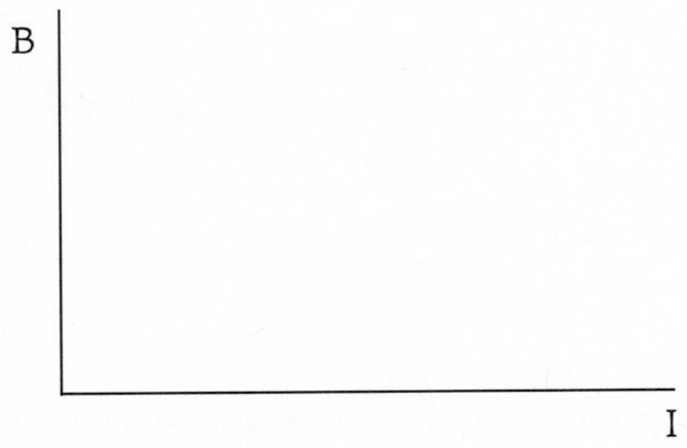

B
|
|
|_____ I

What is the functional dependence of the magnetic field along the central axis on current?

Question 9 Functional dependence on distance. Vary the distance between the point of interest and the center of the loop, along the central axis, and record the magnitude of the magnetic field.

d ___ B

Sketch your data.

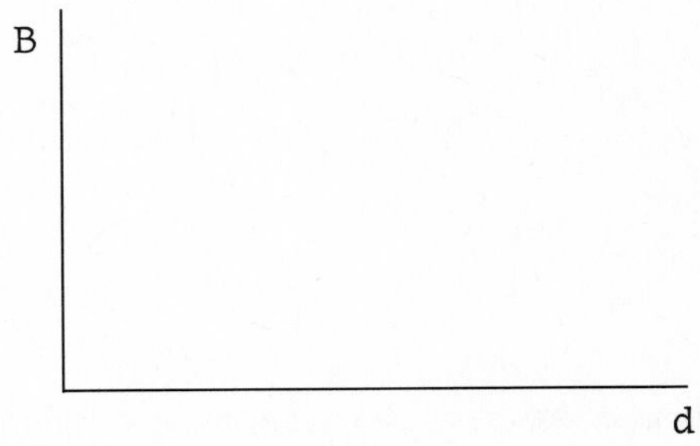

B
|
|
|_____ d

Does there appear to be a simple functional dependence of the magnetic field along the central axis on distance from the loop? If so, what is it?

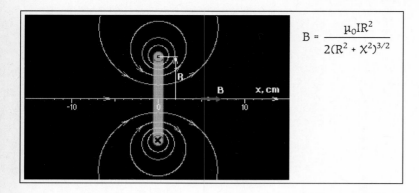

$$B = \frac{\mu_0 I R^2}{2(R^2 + X^2)^{3/2}}$$

Question 10 Finding the maximum field. What is the maximum field along the central axis of a loop carrying −5 A?

Question 11 Using the relationship. What is the distance along the central axis from a loop carrying 10 A beyond which the magnetic field is less that 100 μT?

Question 1 Magnetic field lines. What will the magnetic field look like when positive current flows through the solenoid? (Positive current is defined to flow out of the screen at the top of the loop and into the screen at the bottom of the loop.) Sketch the field.

⊙⊙⊙⊙⊙⊙⊙⊙⊙⊙⊙⊙⊙⊙⊙⊙⊙⊙

⊗⊗⊗⊗⊗⊗⊗⊗⊗⊗⊗⊗⊗⊗⊗⊗⊗⊗

Question 2 Direction of the magnetic field inside the solenoid. Why does the magnetic field point to the right inside the solenoid when positive current flows through the loop? Explain using the right-hand rule.

Question 3 Orientation of the magnetic field. What angle does the magnetic field make relative to the central axis?

Question 4 Magnitude along the central axis. Does the magnitude of the field change along the central axis?

If so, does it change as rapidly as the field of a single loop?

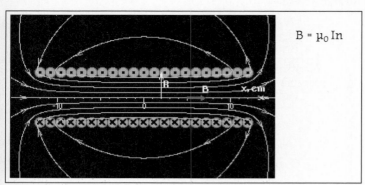

$$B = \mu_0 I n$$

Question 5 Uniformity. What is the magnetic field at the center of the solenoid?

Record the value of the magnetic field at various locations along the central axis.

d	B

Over what portion of the length of the solenoid is the field within 10% of the field at the center? Express this length as a percentage of the entire length of the solenoid.

Question 6 Testing the model. How many loops comprise the solenoid in the simulation?

How long is the solenoid?

What is n, the number of loops per unit length?

Does the theoretical value for the magnetic field of an infinitely long solenoid agree with the simulation?

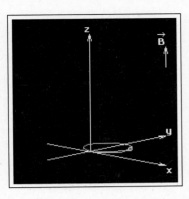

Question 1 Positive or negative? When the particle is initially launched in the +x-direction, what is the direction of the magnetic force on the particle?

Given the directions of the magnetic field, initial magnetic force, and initial velocity, use the right-hand rule to deduce the sign of the electric charge of the particle.

Question 2 Flipping the magnetic field. If the magnetic field is flipped, will the electron traverse its orbit *clockwise* or *counterclockwise*, when viewed from the +z-axis?

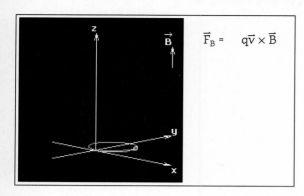

$$\vec{F}_B = q\vec{v} \times \vec{B}$$

Question 3 Increasing the magnetic field: Radius. What happens to the force on the electron if the magnetic field is increased?

Therefore, what will happen to the radius of the electron's path if the magnetic field is increased in magnitude?

Question 4 Increasing the magnetic field: Time. What happens to the electron's velocity if the magnetic field is increased?

From Question 3, what happened to the radius of the electron's path when the magnetic field was increased?

Therefore, what will happen to the time it takes for the electron to complete one orbit if the magnetic field is increased in magnitude?

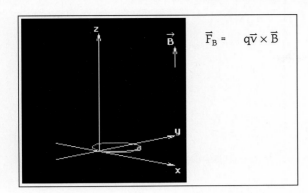

$$\vec{F}_B = q\vec{v} \times \vec{B}$$

Question 5 Increasing the velocity: Radius. What is the relationship between net force and velocity for an object undergoing circular motion?

What happens to the magnetic force on the electron if its velocity is doubled?

Given the changes to both the net force and velocity in the circular motion relationship, what happens to the radius of the electron's path if the initial x-velocity is doubled?

Question 6 Increasing the velocity: Time. From Question 5, what happened to the radius of the electron's path when the velocity was doubled?

Given the change in orbit radius and the change in electron velocity, what will happen to the time it takes for the electron to complete one orbit if the initial x-velocity is doubled?

$$\vec{F}_B = \quad q\vec{v} \times \vec{B} \qquad\qquad F_{radial} = m\frac{v^2}{r}$$

For Questions 7–9, the initial x-velocity is 4.0×10^7 m/s and the applied magnetic field is 1.0 mT.

Question 7 Varying the field and the velocity I. What happens to the radius and period of the orbit if the x-velocity of the particle is doubled and the magnetic field is doubled?

Explain the change in radius.	Explain the change in period.

Question 8 Varying the field and the velocity II. What happens to the radius and period of the orbit if the x-velocity of the particle is halved and the magnetic field is doubled?

Explain the change in radius.	Explain the change in period.

Question 9 Varying the field and the velocity III. What happens to the radius and period of the orbit if the x-velocity of the particle is doubled and the magnetic field is halved?

Explain the change in radius.	Explain the change in period.

Question 10 z-Velocity. Does the path of the particle change if it is given an additional velocity component in the z-direction?

Sketch your prediction for the electron's path.

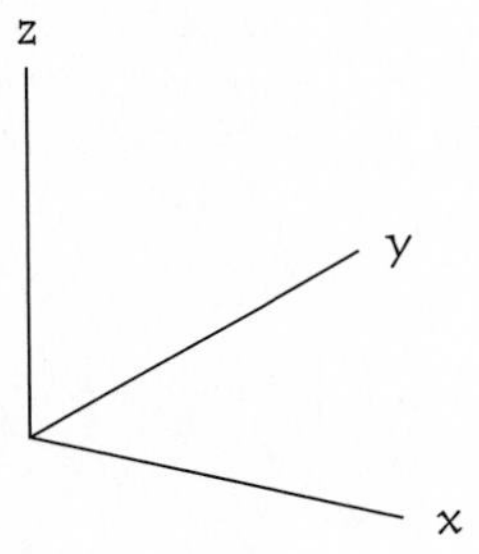

Prediction

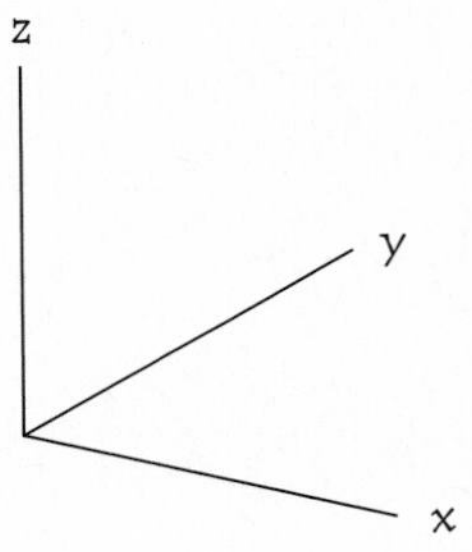

Actual

Question 11 Exclusively z-velocity. Predict the resulting motion when the particle is launched along the z-axis.

Question 1 Field produced by wire 1. If a positive (directed out of the screen) current flows through the left wire, is the direction of the magnetic field produced at the location of the right wire *up, down, left,* or *right?* Sketch the field due to wire 1.

⊙
1   ⊙
         2

Question 3 Field produced by wire 2. Since a positive (directed out of the screen) current flows through the right wire, is the direction of the magnetic field produced at the location of the left wire *up, down, left,* or *right?* Sketch the field due to wire 2.

⊙
1   ⊙
         2

Question 2 Force on wire 2. If a positive current flows through the right wire, does the magnetic field produced by the left wire exert a force directed *up, down, left,* or *right* on the right wire? Sketch the force on wire 2.

⊙
1   ⊙
         2

Question 4. Force on wire 1. Since a positive current flows through the left wire, does the magnetic field produced by the right wire exert a force directed *up, down, left,* or *right* on the left wire? Sketch the force on wire 1.

⊙
1   ⊙
         2

13.5 Magnetic Force on a Wire continued

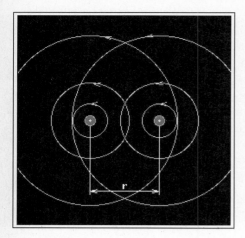

Question 5 Separation dependence.
What happens to the magnitude of the magnetic field at the location of each wire when the wires are brought closer together?

What happens to the magnitudes of the magnetic forces acting on the wires when the wires are brought closer together?

Question 6 Reversing current.
What happens to the directions of the magnetic forces acting on the wires when the current through wire 1 is reversed?

Does it matter whether current 1 or current 2 is reversed?

Question 7 Unequal forces. Is it possible, by varying the currents and/ or the separation, for the forces of interaction between the two parallel wires to be unequal?

If so, what combination of currents and/or separations accomplishes this task?

Question 8 Remembering mechanics. What law of mechanics is illustrated by the preceding question?

$$\vec{F}_B = I\vec{L} \times \vec{B}$$

$$B = \frac{\mu_0 I}{2\pi r}$$

Question 9 Calculating the field. What is the magnetic field at the location of each wire in a pair of wires, one carrying 2.0 A and the other −1.2 A, 0.5 m apart?

Magnetic field at 2.0-A wire, due to −1.2-A wire:	Magnetic field at −1.2-A wire, due to 2.0-A wire:

Question 10 Calculating the force per unit length. What is the force per unit length acting on each wire in a pair of wires, one carrying 2.0 A and the other −1.2 A, 0.5 m apart?

What is the force per unit length acting on the 2.0-A wire, due to the −1.2-A wire?	What is the force per unit length acting on the −1.2-A wire, due to the 2.0-A wire?

Question 11 Varying the current. What happens to the force between the wires if both the currents are halved?

What happens to the magnetic fields produced?	What happens to the force between the wires?

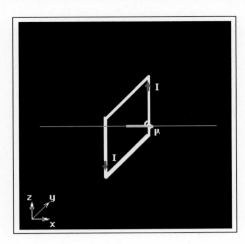

Question 1 Magnetic force on the top of the loop. What is the direction of the current flowing through the wire comprising the top of the loop?

If a magnetic field is applied in the positive x-direction, what is the direction of the magnetic force on the wire comprising the top of the loop?

Question 2 Reversing the field. If the direction of the magnetic field is reversed, what happens to the direction of the magnetic force on each of the four sides of the loop?

13.6 Magnetic Torque on a Loop continued

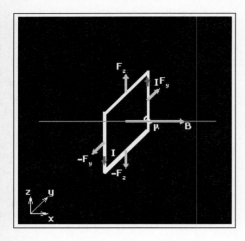

Question 3 Net force on the loop. What is the net force acting on the loop?

Question 4 Rotating the loop: Forces. What happens to the magnitude and direction of the magnetic forces acting on the four wire segments if the loop is rotated to a small positive angle?

Top wire:

Bottom wire:

Left wire:

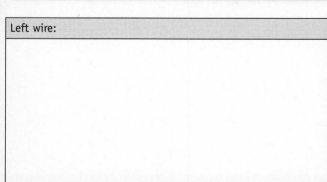

Right wire:

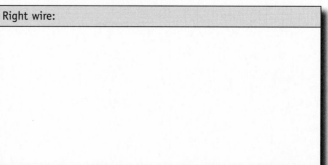

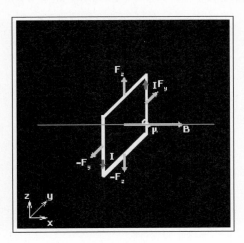

Question 5 Rotating the loop: 90°.

What is the direction of current flow through the top wire when the loop is rotated to +90°?	What happens to the magnitude of the force on the top wire when the loop is rotated to +90°?

Question 6 Rotating the loop: Beyond 90°. What happens to the magnitude and direction of the force on the top wire when the loop is rotated beyond +90°?

Question 7 Rotating the loop: Net force. Can the net force on the loop ever be non-zero? Explain.

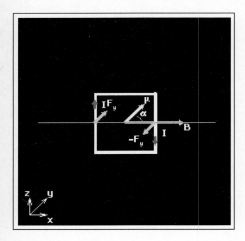

Question 8 Rotating the loop: Torque. What is the direction of the net torque on the loop if it is rotated to a small positive angle?

Question 9 Rotating the loop: Negative angles. What is the direction of the net torque on the loop if it is rotated to a small negative angle?

Question 10 Maximum positive torque. With the magnetic field pointing in the +x-direction, for what angle of orientation does the loop experience the maximum positive torque?

Question 11 Dependence on area. Does the size of the torque depend on the area of the loop? If so, how?

Question 12 General rule. For various orientations, closely examine the relationship between the magnetic field, magnetic dipole moment, and the torque vectors. Measure the torque for various angles between the magnetic field and the dipole moment, and sketch the results.

θ	τ
−180°	
−135°	
−90°	
−45°	
0°	
45°	
90°	
135°	
180°	

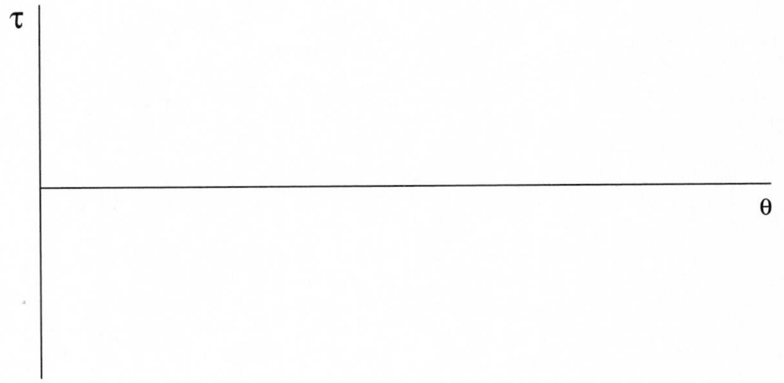

τ

θ

Can you think of a simple vector relationship that summarizes the dependence of the torque on the magnetic dipole moment and the magnetic field?

Question 1 Trajectory. Will the trajectories of the two isotopes be the same or different? Explain.

Sketch the trajectories.

Question 2 Doubling the magnetic field. What happens to the radius of curvature of the trajectories if the magnitude of the magnetic field is doubled? Explain.

Sketch the trajectories.

Question 3 Doubling the velocity. What happens to the radius of curvature of the trajectories if the magnitude of the velocity is doubled? How does this radius compare to the original radius before the magnetic field and the velocity were doubled? Explain.

Sketch the trajectories.

Question 4 Relating curvature to velocity and magnetic field. Using your knowledge of the magnetic force and the mechanics of a particle exhibiting circular motion, derive a relationship between the radius of the particle's trajectory, the particle's velocity, and the magnetic field.

(a) Relation for the acceleration of an object undergoing circular motion:

(b) Relation for the magnetic force on a charged particle:

Combine the two relations using Newton's second law and solve for the radius of the circular orbit.

Question 5 Predicting the curvature. Using the result derived in Question 4, calculate the radius of curvature for both isotopes of carbon. (Remember that the isotopes are singly ionized and that one atomic mass unit is 1.66×10^{-27} kg.)

Question 6 Adjusting the velocity. With what velocity would the neon beam need to be injected into the mass spectrometer for ^{20}Ne to have a radius of curvature equal to that of the previous ^{12}C beam?

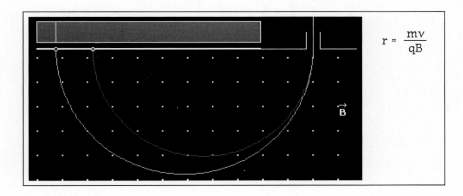

$$r = \frac{mv}{qB}$$

Question 7 Maximum separation for carbon. What is the maximum separation between the two isotopes of carbon?

Parameter settings:

B =

v =

Data:

r_1 =

r_2 =

$r_2 - r_1$ =

Question 8 Maximum separation for neon. Do you think that the maximum separation for neon will be larger or smaller than that for carbon? Is neon harder or easier to separate into its constituent isotopes than carbon? Explain.

Parameter settings:

B =

v =

Data:

r_1 =

r_2 =

$r_2 - r_1$ =

Question 9 Maximum separation for uranium. Is uranium harder or easier to separate into its constituent isotopes than neon? Explain.

Parameter settings:

B =

v =

Data:

r_1 =

r_2 =

$r_2 - r_1$ =

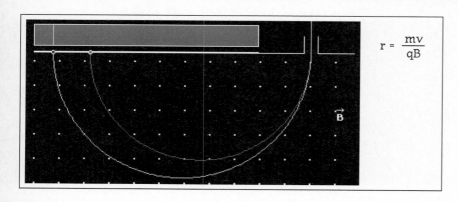

$$r = \frac{mv}{qB}$$

Question 10 Unknown element. Determine the masses of the two isotopes of the unknown element. From your knowledge of chemistry, determine the identity of the unknown element.

Smaller radius:

Larger radius:

Mass of smaller-mass isotope in kg:

Mass of larger-mass isotope in kg:

Mass of smaller-mass isotope in amu:

Mass of larger-mass isotope in amu:

Unknown element:

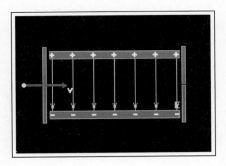

Question 1 Electric force on an electron. If an electron is fired into the region between the charged parallel plates, will the electron be deflected upward or downward by the electric force?

Question 3 Magnetic force on an electron. If an electron is fired into the region between the parallel plates, should the magnetic field be oriented into or out of the screen to create a magnetic force downward?

Question 2 Increasing the electric field. If the magnitude of the electric field is increased, what happens to the curvature of the electron's path between the parallel plates?

Question 4 Increasing the magnetic field. If the magnitude of the magnetic field is increased, what happens to the curvature of the electron's path between the parallel plates?

Question 5 Adjusting the magnetic field. Does the electron deflect up or down?

Therefore, which force is larger?

How should the magnetic field be adjusted for the electron to pass through the device undeflected?

Question 6 Adjusting the electric field. Does the electron deflect up or down?

Therefore, which force is larger?

How should the electric field be adjusted for the electron to pass through the device undeflected?

Question 7 Adjusting the velocity. Does the electron deflect up or down?

Therefore, which force is larger?

How should the velocity of the electron be adjusted for it to pass through the device undeflected?

Question 8 Flipping the electric field. What happens to the electron's path if the direction of the electric field is flipped? Will it still pass through the device undeflected?

Question 9 Flipping the magnetic field. What happens to the electron's path if the direction of the magnetic field is now flipped? Will the electron pass through the device undeflected?

Question 10 Opposite charge. If the sign of the charge of the incident particle is flipped, what happens to the electric force?

Magnitude: Direction:

What happens to the magnetic force?

Magnitude: Direction:

Given that an electron, with negative charge, passes through the device undeflected, what must be changed so that a positron, with positive charge, will pass through undeflected?

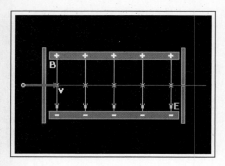

Question 11 Larger mass. If the mass of the incident particle is increased, what happens to the electric force?

Magnitude: Direction:

What happens to the magnetic force?

Magnitude: Direction:

Given that a positron passes through the device undeflected, what must be changed so that a proton, with larger mass, will pass through undeflected?

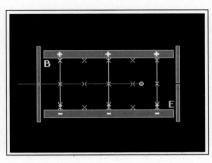

Question 12 Larger charge. If the charge of the incident particle is increased, what happens to the electric force?

Magnitude: Direction:

What happens to the magnetic force?

Magnitude: Direction:

Given that a proton passes through the device undeflected, what must be changed so that a helium nucleus, with twice the electric charge, will pass through undeflected?

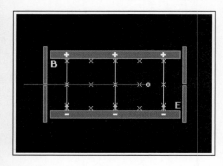

Question 13 Determining the velocity. If a particle passes through a selector undeflected, the magnitudes of the electric and magnetic forces must be equal. Using this observation, determine a relationship between the velocity of undeflected particles and the electric and magnetic fields present in the device.

Relation for magnetic force on a charge q:

Relation for electric force on a charge q:

Set the electric and magnetic forces equal and solve for the velocity.

Question 14 What about neutrons? At what value(s) of velocity, magnetic field, and electric field will a neutron pass through the velocity selector undeflected?

Question 15 Atomic velocities. Is a velocity selector an effective apparatus for determining the velocity of a beam of atoms?

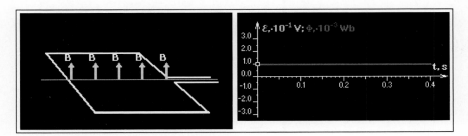

Question 1 Magnetic flux: Magnetic field magnitude.
What happens to the magnetic flux through the loop when the magnetic field is increased to positive values?

Question 3 Magnetic flux: Loop area. What happens to the magnetic flux through the loop when the area of the loop is decreased?

Question 2 Magnetic flux: Magnetic field orientation.
What happens to the magnetic flux through the loop when the magnetic field is flipped to negative values?

Question 4 Magnetic flux: Loop orientation. What happens to the magnetic flux through the loop as the loop rotates relative to the magnetic field? What is the value of the flux after the loop has rotated through 90°? Through 180°?

Question 5 Magnetic flux: Summary. Summarize the dependence of magnetic flux on the magnetic field, the area of the loop, and the relative orientation between them.

13.9 Electromagnetic Induction continued

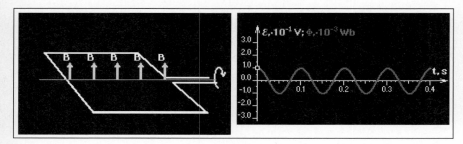

Question 6 Constant flux. Will an EMF be induced when the rotational frequency of the loop is zero?

Question 8 Maximum induced EMF. For what loop orientation(s) is the induced EMF a maximum in magnitude?

Question 7 Rotating the loop. Will an EMF be induced when the rotational frequency of the loop is non-zero?

Question 9 Maximum rate of change of flux. For what loop orientation(s) is the magnetic flux changing most rapidly?

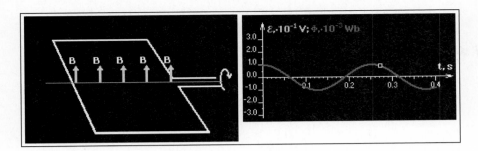

Question 10 No induced EMF. For what loop orientation(s) is the induced EMF instantaneously zero?

Question 11 Zero rate of change of flux. For what loop orientation(s) is the magnetic flux instantaneously not changing?

Question 12 Relating EMF to magnetic flux. Based on your observations, postulate a possible relationship between the induced EMF and the rate of change of the magnetic flux.

Question 13 Dependence of induced EMF on frequency. As the frequency of rotation increases, what happens to the maximum induced EMF?

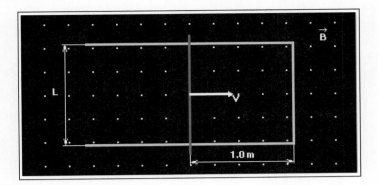

Question 1 Magnetic flux: Stationary bar.

What is the area of the loop?

What is the magnetic flux through the loop?

Question 2 Magnetic flux: Bar moving to the right. What happens to the magnetic flux through the loop as the conducting bar moves to the right?

Question 3 Magnetic flux: Bar moving to the left. What happens to the magnetic flux through the loop as the conducting bar moves to the left?

Question 4 Change in magnetic flux. Complete the following table.

V	$\Phi_{initial}$	Φ_{final}	$\Delta\Phi$
+10			
+7			
+3			
−3			
−7			
−10			

Does the change in magnetic flux depend on the velocity of the bar? Explain.

Question 5 Rate of change of magnetic flux. Complete the following table.

V	$\Delta\Phi$	t	$\Delta\Phi/t$
+10			
+7			
+3			
−3			
−7			
−10			

Does the rate of change of magnetic flux depend on the velocity of the bar? Explain.

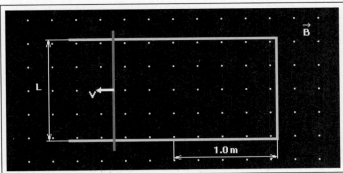

Question 6 Rate of change of area. Construct a relationship between the rate of change of area of the loop and the bar's length and velocity. What is the distance the bar travels in a time Δt?

What is the change in the area of the loop in a time Δt? (Be careful with signs.)

What is the rate of change of the area of the loop?

Question 7 Rate of change of flux. Given the previous results, construct a relationship between the rate of change of magnetic flux through the loop and other relevant variables.

Question 8 Induced EMF. Given the previous result, construct a relationship between the induced EMF in the moving bar and relevant variables.

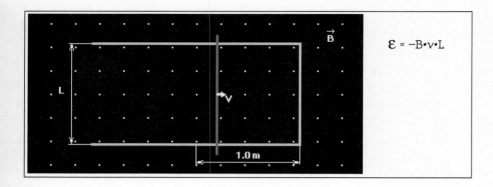

$$\varepsilon = -B \cdot v \cdot L$$

Question 9 Testing the relation. Complete the following table.

B	V	L	EMF
0.1	+10	1.0	
0.1	−5	0.5	
0.1	0	1.0	
0	+10	0.5	
−0.05	−10	0.2	
−0.05	+5	0.5	
−0.05	+10	0.2	

Is the EMF induced in the moving bar always in agreement with the derived relationship?

Question 10 Direction of the induced current. What is the sign of the magnetic flux?

How is the magnetic flux changing as the bar moves?

Will the induced EMF drive current to produce positive or negative magnetic flux?

Which way will the induced current flow in the moving bar?

Question 11 Direction of the induced current, again. What is the sign of the magnetic flux?

How is the magnetic flux changing as the bar moves?

Will the induced EMF drive current to produce positive or negative magnetic flux?

Which way will the induced current flow in the moving bar?

Question 12 Direction of the induced current, one last time. What is the sign of the magnetic flux?

How is the magnetic flux changing as the bar moves?

Will the induced EMF drive current to produce positive or negative magnetic flux?

Which way will the induced current flow in the moving bar?

Question 13 Maximum current. What combination of parameters will produce the maximum magnitude current? What should B equal, and why?

What should v equal, and why?

What should L equal, and why?

What should R equal, and why?

ac CIRCUITS

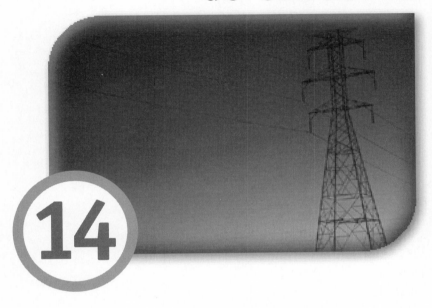

14

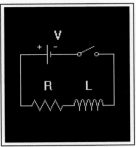

Question 1 A simple circuit. Imagine a circuit consisting of a 2-Ω resistor, a 4-V battery, and a switch. (**Note:** There is no inductor [L = 0] in this hypothetical circuit.) What current will flow through the circuit when the switch is closed?

Question 2 Faraday's law of induction. State as clearly as you can, without using equations, Faraday's law of induction.

Question 3 Closing the switch. When the switch is closed, will the EMF induced in the inductor act in the same direction or the opposite direction of the EMF of the battery? Why?

Question 4 Much later. What current flows through the circuit long after the switch is closed? Why?

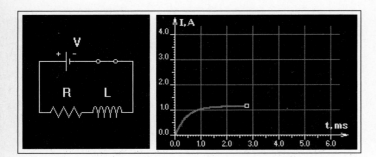

Question 5 Doubling the inductance. When the inductance is doubled, does the time for the current to reach its equilibrium value *increase, decrease,* or *stay the same?* Why?

Question 6 Doubling the resistance. When the resistance is doubled, does the time for the current to reach its equilibrium value *increase, decrease,* or *stay the same?* Why?

Question 7 Inductive time constant—I. With the resistance set to 1.5 Ω, the inductance to 2.5 mH, and the potential difference to 3.0 V, predict the equilibrium current and the inductive time constant.

$I_{equilibrium}$:

Time constant, τ:

Question 8 Inductive time constant—II. Predict the value of the current at $t = \tau_L$ and $t = 2\tau_L$.

$I(\tau_L)$ =

$I(2\tau_L)$ =

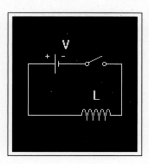

Question 1 Current vs. time. What behavior does the current through the inductor exhibit?

Sketch a graph of I vs. t.

I

t

Question 2 Phase difference. Why does the graph of current vs. time lag 90° behind the graph of charge on the capacitor vs. time?

Question 3 Initial energy. At t = 0 s, is the energy in the circuit in the inductor or the capacitor? Why?

Question 4 Energy flow. After the switch is closed, where does the energy initially stored in the capacitor go?

14.2 The RLC Oscillator continued

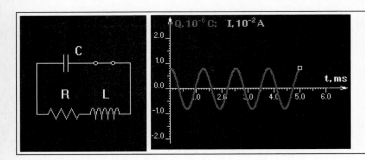

At L = 5 mH, C = 8 mF and R = 0Ω,

I_{max} = _____

Period = _____.

Question 5 Double inductance. What happens to the maximum current through the circuit when the inductance is doubled? Why?

What happens to the period of oscillation when the inductance is doubled? Why?

Question 6 Halve capacitance. What happens to the maximum current through the circuit when the capacitance is halved? Why?

What happens to the period of oscillation when the capacitance is halved? Why?

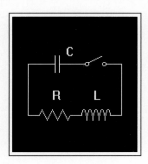

Question 7 Adding resistance. What happens to the behavior of the circuit if resistance is added?

Sketch a graph of I vs. t.

I

t

Question 8 Energy loss? Where does the energy go in a circuit that includes resistance?

Question 9 Mechanical analogy—I. A large inductance makes the circuit respond less rapidly to outside "forces." What aspect of a spring–mass system acts in an analogous way? Why?

Question 10 Mechanical analogy—II. A large capacitance allows the storage of a *large* amount of energy through the application of a relatively *small* potential. Does some aspect of a spring–mass system act in an analogous way? Why?

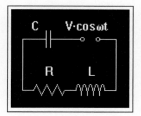

Question 1 Potential difference across the resistor. When attached to a source of alternating electric potential difference, does the current through a purely resistive element lead the potential difference across it by 90°, lag behind the potential difference by 90°, or is it in phase with the potential difference?

Question 2 Potential difference across the inductor. When attached to a source of alternating electric potential difference, does the current through an inductor lead the potential difference across it by 90°, lag behind the potential difference by 90°, or is it in phase with the potential?

Question 3 Potential difference across the capacitor. When attached to a source of alternating electric potential difference, does the current "through" a capacitor lead the potential difference across it by 90°, lag behind the potential difference by 90°, or is it in phase with the potential difference?

Sketch the current in correct phase relation to the given potential difference.

Sketch the current in correct phase relation to the given potential difference.

Sketch the current in correct phase relation to the given potential difference.

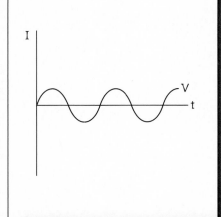

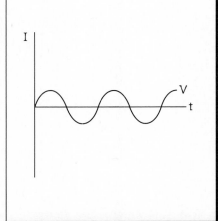

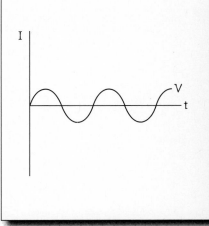

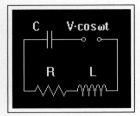

Question 4 X_L. Suppose the driving frequency, ω, is increased. What happens to the rate of change of current through the inductor?

What happens to the potential difference across the inductor?

What happens to the reactance of the inductor?

Question 5 X_C. Now the driving frequency, ω, is increased. What effect does this have on the amount of charge that has time to build up on the capacitor?

What happens to the potential difference across the capacitor?

What happens to the reactance of the capacitor?

Question 6 Phasor diagram. With the driving frequency set to 1400 rad/s, sketch a phasor diagram for the circuit. Set the phasor representing the resistor on the horizontal axis.

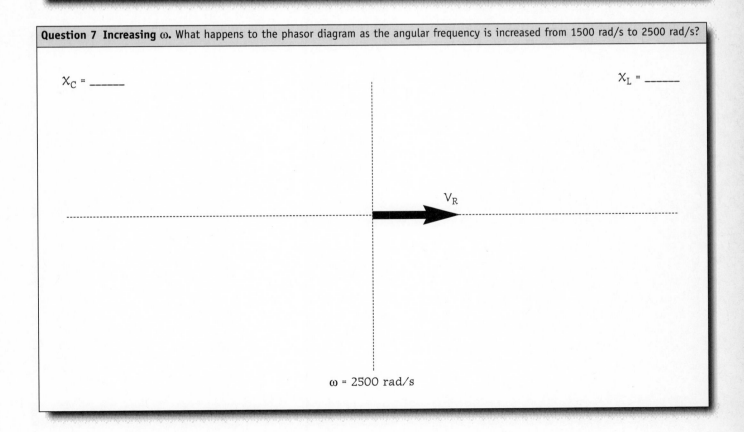

$X_C = 1/\omega C$

$X_C =$ _____

$X_L = \omega L$

$X_L =$ _____

V_R

$\omega = 1500$ rad/s

Question 7 Increasing ω. What happens to the phasor diagram as the angular frequency is increased from 1500 rad/s to 2500 rad/s?

$X_C =$ _____

$X_L =$ _____

V_R

$\omega = 2500$ rad/s

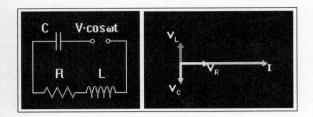

Question 8 Resonance. At what driving frequency will the circuit be at resonance?

Question 9 Resonance curve. How does the shape of the resonance curve change if the resistance of the circuit is reduced? Sketch the resonance curve for $R < 3\ \Omega$.

I

$R = 3.0\ \Omega$

ω_0

ω

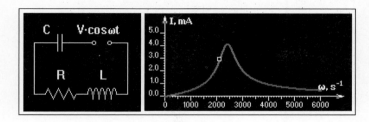

Question 10 Phasor practice. Sketch the phasor diagram for a circuit with a 3.0-mH inductor, a 100-uF capacitor, and driven at 4000rad/sec.

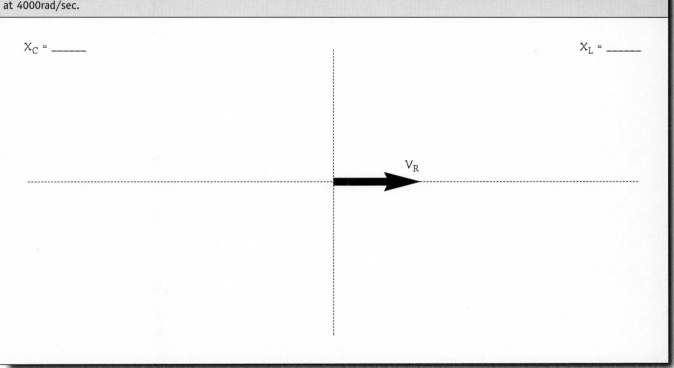

X_C = _____

X_L = _____

V_R

Question 11 Resonance practice. Calculate the resonance frequency for the circuit described in Question 10.

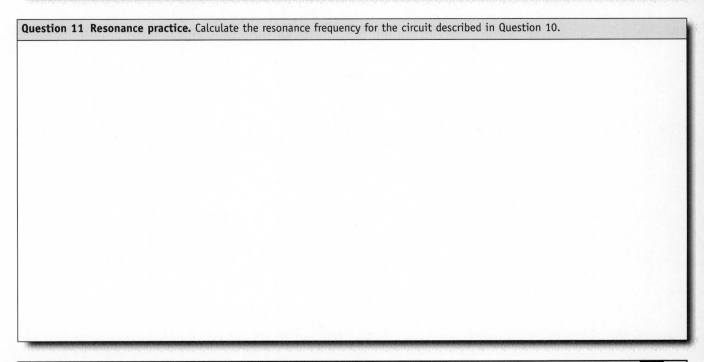

15

GEOMETRIC OBJECTS

Question 1 Speed of light. The index of refraction of water is about 1.35. Determine the speed of light in water.

Question 2 Reflected angle. Set the refractive index of the lower medium to 1.35. Try different incident angles and observe the reflected angles. State a rule that relates the incident and reflected angles. This rule applies to smooth surfaces.

Question 3 Snell's law and the refracted angle. Leave the refractive index of the upper medium at 1.00 and of the lower medium at 1.50. Try different incident angles and observe the refracted angles. Try different incident angles and observe the refracted angles. Show that the incident angle θ_1 and the refracted angle θ_2 are related by Snell's law, $n_1 \sin \theta_1 = n_2 \sin \theta_2$, for two examples where the incident ray moves from the smaller to the larger index of refraction material. Draw each situation before trying the calculations.

Question 4 Snell's law and the refracted angle. Leave the index of refraction of the upper medium at 1.00 and change the index of refraction of the lower medium to 1.60. Choose the incident angle for one example showing that Snell's law also applies when the incident ray moves from the larger to smaller index of refraction material. Draw each situation before trying the calculations.

Question 5 Determine the direction of the refracted ray for light in air incident at 45° on an interface with 1.55 refractive index glass. Draw each situation before trying the calculations.

Question 6 Determine the direction of the refracted ray for light in water (n = 1.35) incident at 30° on a surface with air. Draw the situation before trying the calculations.

Question 1 Total internal reflection. Draw several rays for different incident angles showing how the direction the wave is traveling changes as it moves from the larger refractive index medium at the bottom into the smaller refractive index medium at the top. What is the direction of the refracted wave for the incident critical angle θ_{crit}?

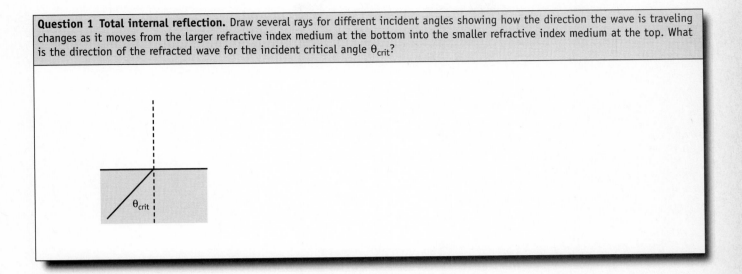

Question 2 Moving from a smaller to larger refractive index medium. Draw several rays for different incident angles showing how the direction the wave is traveling changes as it moves from the small refractive index medium at the top into the large refractive index medium at the bottom. What condition seems to be necessary for total internal refraction to occur?

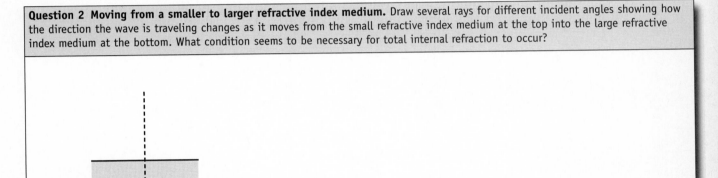

Question 3 Use Snell's law, $n_1 \sin \theta_1 = n_2 \sin \theta_2$, to determine the critical angle for light passing from the lower medium with refractive index 1.60 into the upper medium with refractive index 1.35. Indicate the indices of refraction of the two media and draw the ray representing the direction the wave is traveling at this critical angle before and after reaching the interface between the two media.

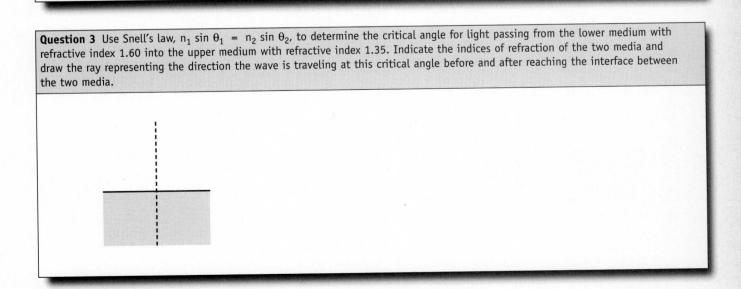

Question 4 Total internal reflection. Use Snell's law to develop a general rule for determining the critical angle θ_{crit} for light passing from the large refractive index medium n_1 (bottom) into the upper small refractive index medium n_2 (top).

Question 5 Fiber optics. A glass fiber used to transmit light-carrying telephone messages has a refractive index of 1.60. If the fiber is surrounded by air, at what angles can the light hit a glass-air interface and be totally reflected? Sketch this special angular region.

Question 6 A coated-fiber optics problem. A glass fiber used to transmit light-carrying telephone messages has a refractive index of 1.60. This fiber is surrounded by a coating with refractive index 1.35. The coating is surrounded by air of refractive index 1.00. At what angles can the light hit a glass-coating interface and not escape the coated fiber into the air? Sketch this special angular region.

Question 1 Suppose light travels from air with refractive index 1.00 into glass with refractive index 1.55. If the incident angle is 30°, determine the angle of the refracted light as it passes through the glass.

Question 2 Suppose light travels from glasslike material with refractive index 1.55 into water with refractive index 1.35. If the refracted angle as the light passes through the water is 37°, determine the angle of the incident light coming from the glass.

Question 3 Suppose you are swimming underwater in a lake with a smooth surface and a flat shoreline (see the figure). While underwater, you see a friend sunbathing on the shore. At what angle are you looking? The index of refraction is about 1.35 for water and 1.00 for air.

Question 4 Suppose that while swimming in water of refractive index 1.35, your keys fall out of your bathing suit. After drying off at the poolside, you see them in the water and decide to retrieve them with a bow and arrow with a magnetic tip. Your eyes are 1.5 m above the water's surface and the pool is 1.5 m deep (see figure). When you look at an angle of 40° below the horizontal, you see the keys. At what angle should you aim the bow, assuming that the arrow does not change direction when entering and traveling through the water?

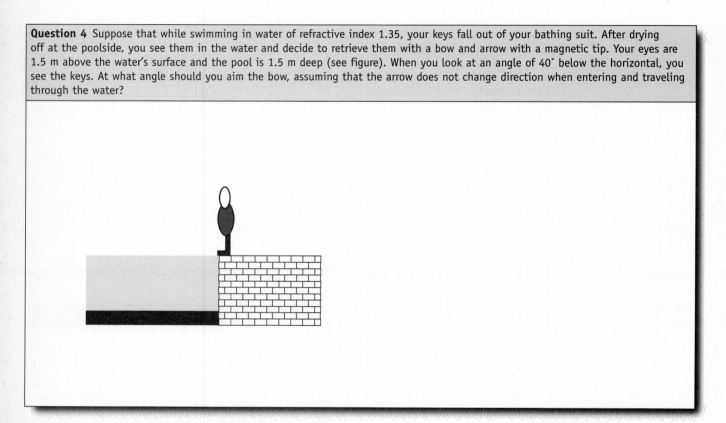

Question 5 You are given an unknown liquid and asked to help identify it by finding its index of refraction. You shine a laser beam so that it first passes through glass and then through the liquid. The light crosses the interface from the glass with 1.60 refractive index to the liquid at an incident angle of 40°. The refracted angle of the light in the liquid is 55°. What is the refractive index of the liquid?

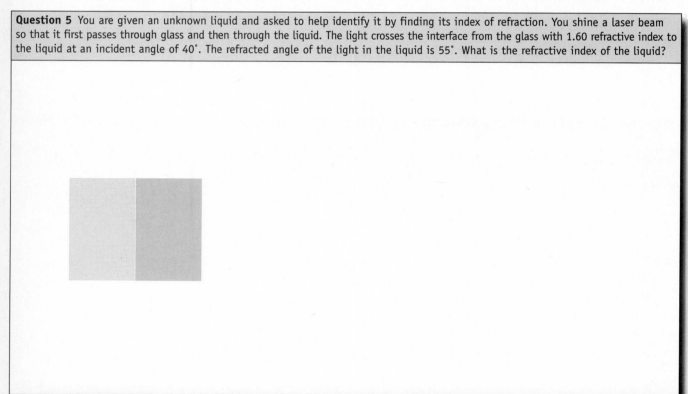

Question 1 Suppose an arrowhead is located 1.00 m (y = 1.00 m) from a plane mirror above the left edge of the mirror (x = 0.00 m). Your eye is about 1.0 m from the mirror and above the middle of the mirror. Draw three rays representing light that travels from the arrowhead toward the mirror and then after reflection toward the region where your eye is located—the rays point in slightly different directions. Determine the point from which the light seems to originate. This is the point where the image of the arrowhead in the mirror is located.

Question 2 Other object locations. Grab the arrowhead with the pointer and move it to different locations. Observe the image location for different object locations. Then, construct a general rule for the location of the image of an object as seen in a plane mirror.

Question 3 Taking your picture in a mirror. Suppose you are standing 2.0 m in front of a mirror and wish to take your picture by aiming a camera at your image in the mirror. What distance setting should you have on your camera lens? Explain.

Question 1 Focal length and radius of curvature. Move the focal length f of the mirror to different values and observe the radius of curvature slider R of the mirror. Devise a rule showing how the mirror's focal length f is related to its radius of curvature R. Note the location of the focal point, the blue cross on the axis of the lens. Try both concave and convex mirrors. The focal point is off the screen for some mirrors.

Question 2 Path of the horizontal ray. Consider light that moves horizontally from the tip of the object arrow toward the mirror. Try different focal-length mirrors and devise a rule for the path followed by that ray after reflection from the mirror. Be sure to consider both concave (positive f) and convex (negative f) mirrors.

Question 3 Ray reflected from center of mirror. Consider light that moves from the tip of the object arrow toward the center of the mirror. Try different focal-length mirrors and devise a rule for the path followed by that ray after reflection from the mirror. Be sure to consider both concave and convex mirrors.

Question 4 Virtual-image ray diagram. As you draw the following diagrams, make them cover most of the space given and use the scale of the drawing to estimate the image distance. Draw a ray diagram using our two special rays and estimate the image location for the given object distances.

50-mm object distance from a +100-mm focal-length mirror:

axis

mirror

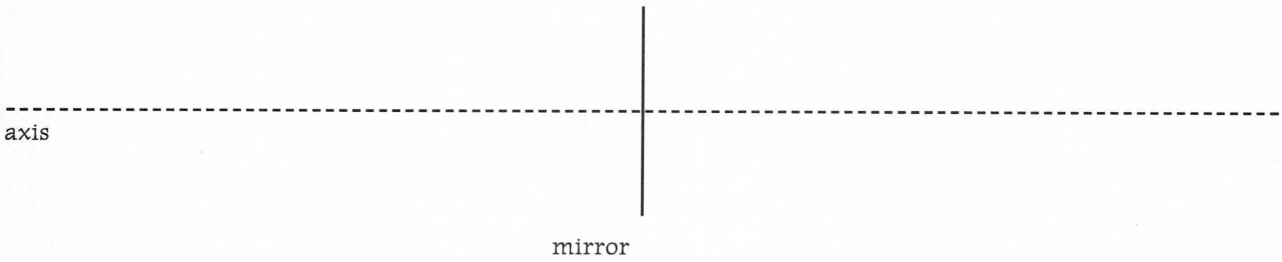

81-mm object distance from a +250-mm focal-length mirror:

axis

mirror

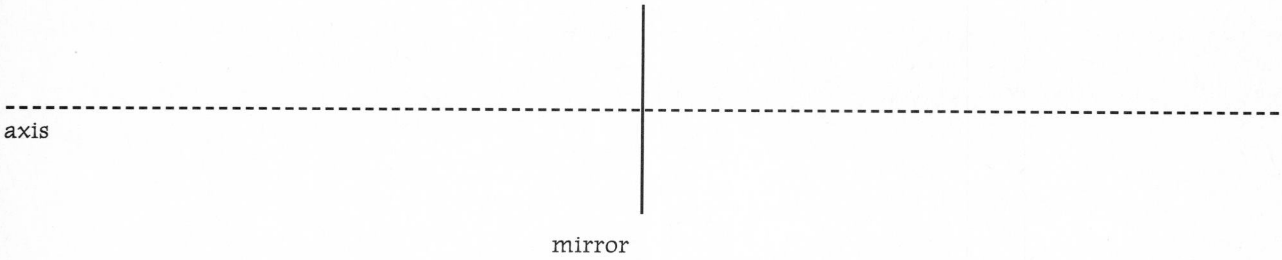

200-mm object distance from a −100-mm focal-length mirror:

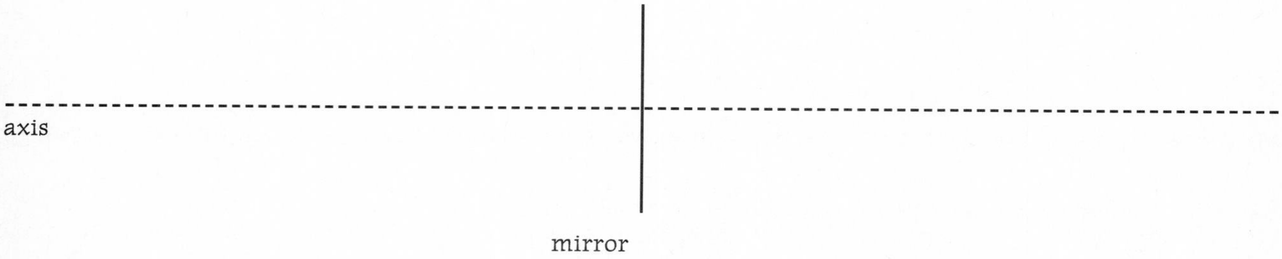

axis

mirror

200-mm object distance from a −250-mm focal-length mirror:

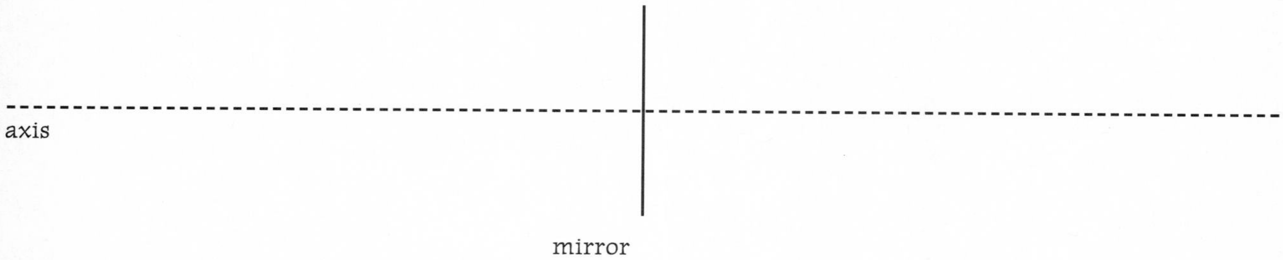

axis

mirror

Question 5 Real-image ray diagram. As you draw the following diagrams, make them cover most of the space given and use the scale of the drawing to estimate the image distance. Draw a ray diagram using our two special rays and estimate the image locations for the given object distances.

250-mm object distance from a +100-mm focal-length mirror:

axis

mirror

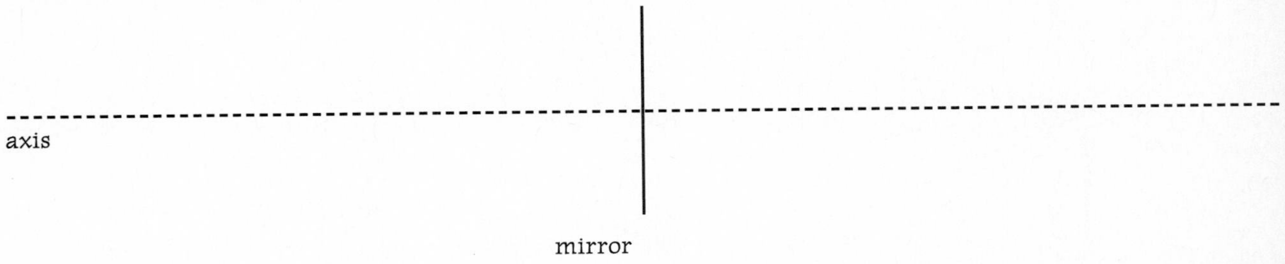

200-mm object distance from a +100-mm focal-length mirror:

axis

mirror

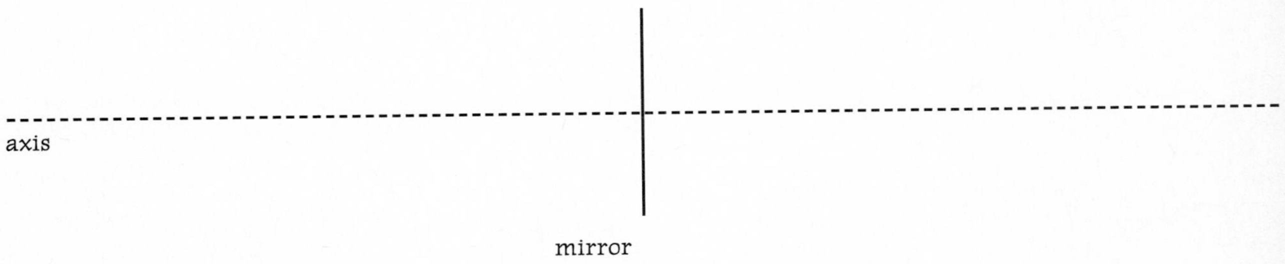

170-mm object distance from a +100-mm focal-length mirror:

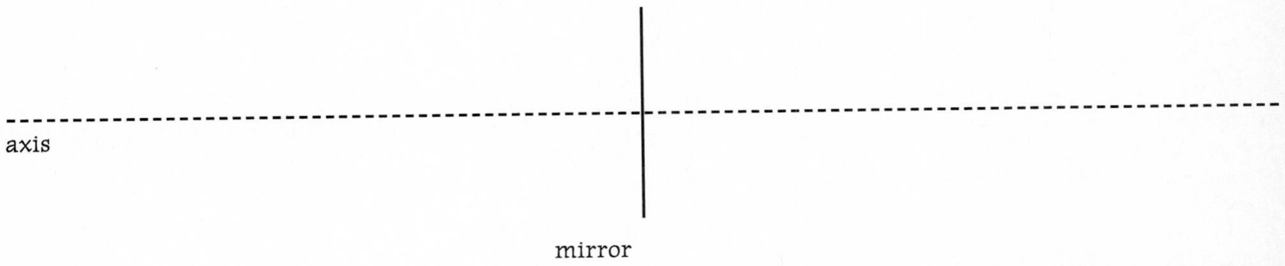

axis

mirror

Question 6 Other rays. The two rays shown in the simulation are convenient for locating mirror images because we can predict their directions if we know the focal point of the mirror. However, many other rays can be drawn to represent the light's direction of travel along other paths (see the figure).

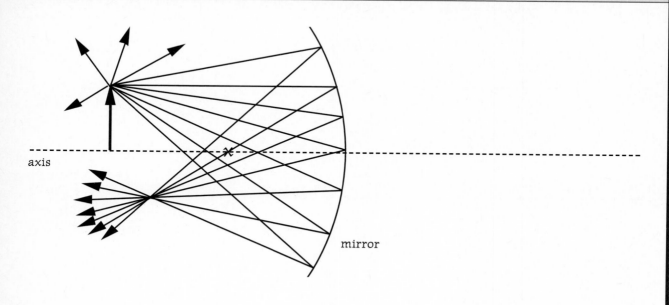

Suppose a cover is placed over the top half of the mirror in the figure as shown here.

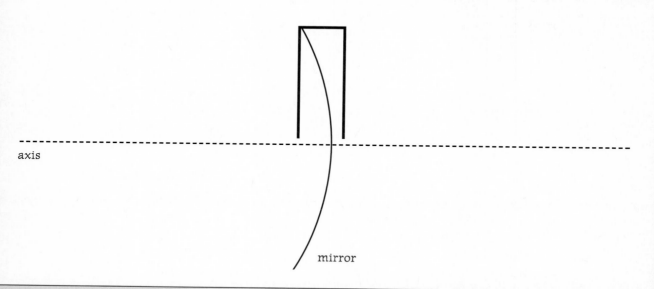

What effect does this have on the image? Explain your reasoning.

Question 1 Use the mirror equation to find the unknown quantity in the following table. You can adjust the simulation to check your answers.

	s (mm)	s' (mm)	f (mm)
(a)	250	_____	100
(b)	50	_____	100
(c)	200	−111	_____
(d)	_____	240	120
(e)	180	_____	100
(f)	_____	−94	−150

Question 2 Surveillance mirrors. Which situation(s) in Question 1 resemble surveillance mirrors used in stores to prevent shoplifting and at the corners of hallways to prevent collisions?

Question 1 Observing image height. Set the focal length of the mirror to f = +100 mm. Move the object so it is the farthest distance from the mirror but can still be seen. Note the relative size of the image and object. Now, with your pointer, move the object toward the mirror. Note carefully the relative sizes of the image and object. Write a qualitative description of your observations concerning these heights. Restrict your experiment to positions that produce observable real images.

Question 2 Linear magnification m. (a) Set the focal length of the mirror to f = +100 mm and the object distance to s = 250 mm. Estimate the ratio of the image height and the object height (h'/h). This is called the linear magnification m. How does your estimate compare to the simulation value given for the linear magnification m? Take the ratio of the image and object positions (s'/s)

(b) Move the object closer to the mirror so that the real image is as far from the mirror as possible but can still be seen. Estimate the ratio of the image and object heights (h'/h) and compare this estimate to the simulation's reported linear magnification m and to the ratio s'/s.

(c) Set the focal length to f = –500 mm and the object position to s = 120 mm. Estimate the ratio of the image height and object height (h'/h). Compare your estimate to the simulation's reported linear magnification m and to the ratio s'/s.

(d) Try focal lengths f = –250, –180, –120, and –100 mm. Change the object distance for each focal length so that the image appears to be half the height of the object and note the value of the linear magnification m and the ratio s'/s for each case.

(e) Finally, state in the form of an equation a rule that relates the ratio of the image and object heights (h'/h), the linear magnification m, and the ratio of the image and object distances s'/s.

Question 3 Why does h'/h = −s'/s? Set f = +100 mm and s = 200 mm. Note that m = h'/h = −s'/s = −1.0. Use the two triangles caused by the ray that reflects from the center of the lens to justify why h'/h = -s'/s (see the figure).

object

image

Question 4 Check h'/h = −s'/s for another triangle. Set f = −170 mm and s = 170 mm. Note that m = h'/h = −s'/s = 0.50. Use the two triangles shown below to justify this equality, including the negative sign in front of s'/s.

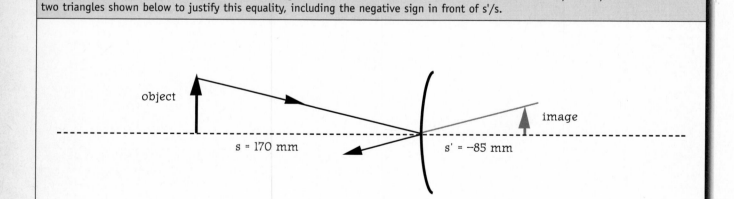

object

image

s = 170 mm   s' = −85 mm

Question 1 Makeup and shaving mirror. A business person asks you to design a mirror that can be used for makeup or shaving. The image formed by the mirror is to be upright and 1.62 times bigger than the object, a user's face. The image is to be 20.9 cm from the object. Determine the focal length needed for the mirror.

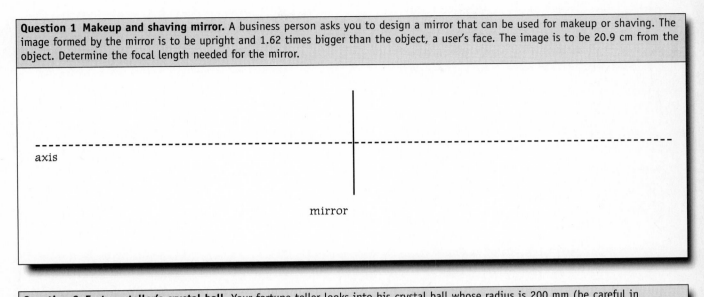

Question 2 Fortune teller's crystal ball. Your fortune teller looks into his crystal ball whose radius is 200 mm (be careful in choosing the focal-length sign—remember the shape of a crystal ball). The teller's eye is 250 mm from the surface of the ball. Determine the location of the image of his eye and the width of the image of the 3.0-cm-wide eye.

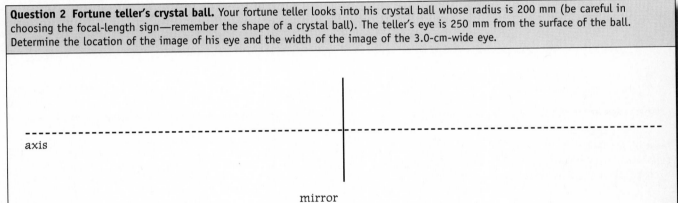

Question 3 Surveillance mirror for ants. To help ants avoid collisions when entering their ant hill, you decide to build a surveillance mirror at the entrance. The mirror is convex with a focal length of –100 mm. Where is the image and what is the image height and orientation of a 2.0-mm-tall ant that is 15 cm from the mirror? Repeat your calculations for a 2.0-mm-tall ant that is 5.0 cm from the mirror.

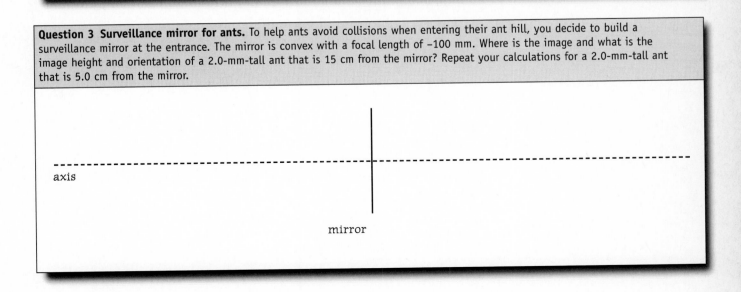

15.8 Spherical Mirrors: Problems continued

Question 4 Inverted light hanging in space. You are asked to design a display for a museum that appears to have an inverted glowing light bulb floating in space. Play around with the spherical mirror simulation to see how you might do this. First produce such a display with the simulation (in the form of object and image arrows). Then provide drawings of the situation and an analysis using the mirror equation and the magnification information so that the museum curator is convinced that you know what you are talking about. **Note:** There are many possible answers for this design.

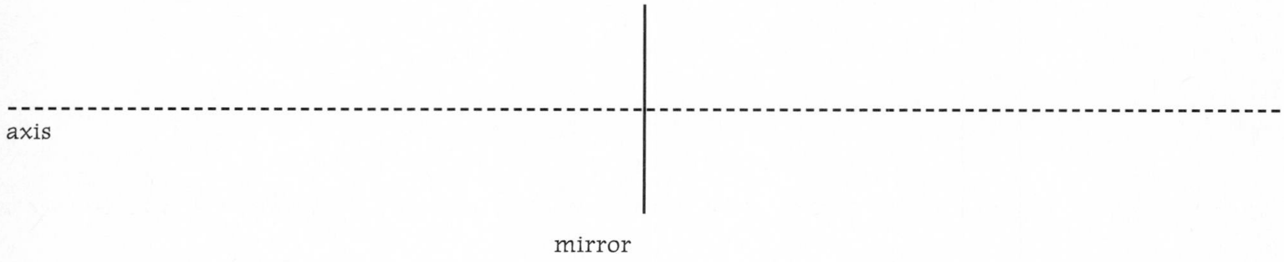

axis

mirror

Question 5 Light beam. You are asked to use a bright light bulb and a large mirror to produce a parallel beam of light that can illuminate a distant sign. Play around with the mirror simulation and decide how you might do this. When finished, show how the mirror equation applies to this situation. Note in particular an object distance that produces a parallel beam of light.

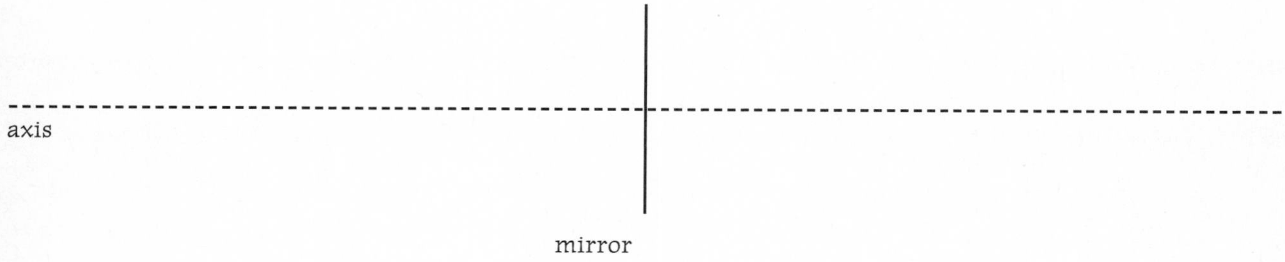

axis

mirror

Question 1 Thin-lens objects and images. Set the focal length of the lens to f = +60 mm (a converging lens) and with the pointer move the lens so that its middle is on a line a little to the left of the center of the simulation screen. Move the object to the left edge of the screen and then pull it slowly toward the lens. Be sure to move it inside the focal point (the blue cross on the axis of the lens). Note the changing position and size of the image.

• Which object–image positions are most like that of a camera?

• Which object–image positions are most like that of a slide projector?

• Which object–image positions are most like that of a magnifying glass?

Question 2 Thin lens ray diagrams—converging lenses. With the previous lens arrangement (f = +60 mm), set the object at the left edge of the screen and move it slowly toward the lens. Observe the two rays that represent light leaving the tip of the arrow. Develop in words a rule for how the direction of these rays is determined. Also develop a rule for determining the location of a real image on the right of the lens and a virtual image on the left.

• Path of ray 1 (on the left of lens, moves parallel to the axis of lens):

• Path of ray 2 (on the left of lens, moves toward the center of the lens):

• How do you decide where a real image is formed on the right side of the lens?

• How do you decide where a virtual image is formed on the left side of the lens?

Be sure to note that light moves away from all points on the object in all directions. The two rays in the simulation indicate the path of only a small portion of the light. The figure below shows a larger number of light rays that focus to form a real-image point.

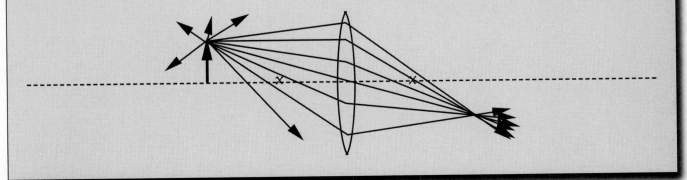

Question 3 Thin-lens ray diagrams—diverging lenses. Set the focal length to f = –60 mm to form a diverging lens. Move the object to the left edge of the screen and pull it slowly toward the lens. Observe the two rays that are shown leaving the tip of the arrow. Develop in words a rule for how the directions of these rays are determined. Also develop a rule for determining the location of the virtual image on the left side of the lens.

- Path of ray 1 (on the left of lens, moves horizontally toward the lens):

- Path of ray 2 (on the left of lens, moves toward the center of the lens):

- How do you decide where a virtual image is formed on the left side of the lens?

Question 4 Find the image. Use ray diagrams to estimate the position of the image of an object for the given object distances. Indicate the type of image (real or virtual) and the orientation of the image relative to the orientation of the object.

300-mm object distance from a +50-mm focal-length lens:

axis

mirror

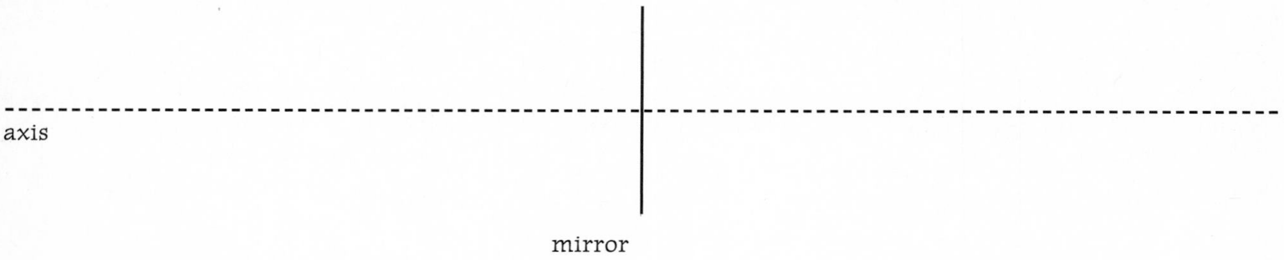

80-mm object distance from a +50-mm focal-length lens:

axis

mirror

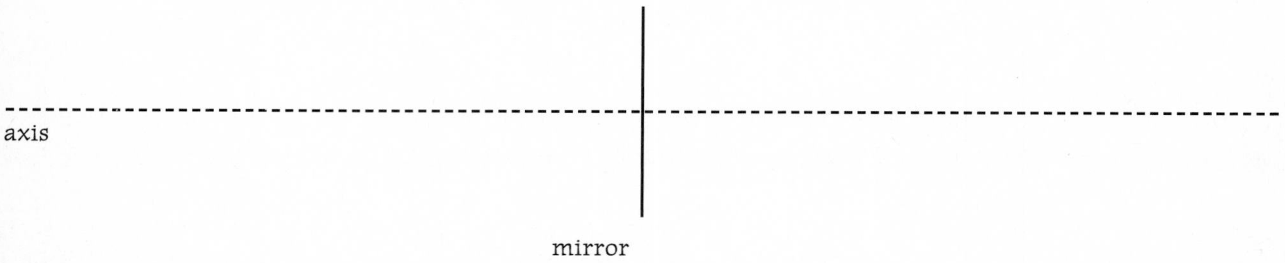

34-mm object distance from a +50-mm focal-length lens:

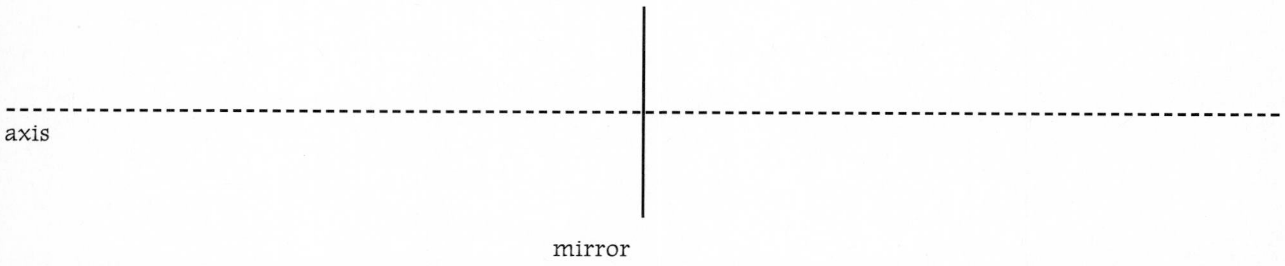

axis

mirror

300-mm object distance from a –100-mm focal-length lens:

axis -

mirror

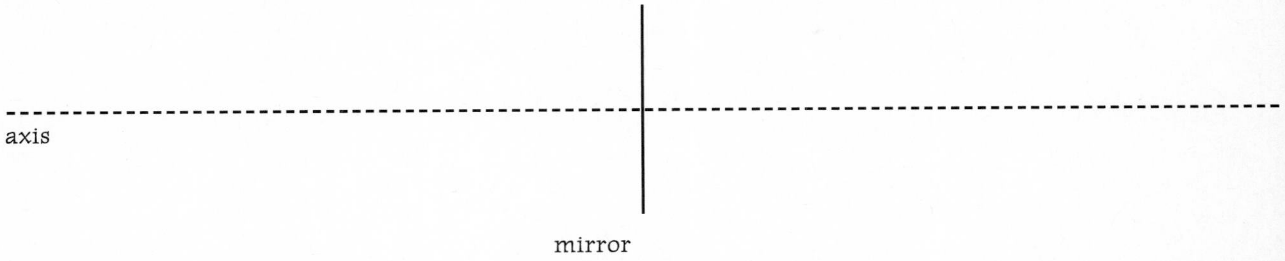

80-mm object distance from a –100-mm focal-length lens:

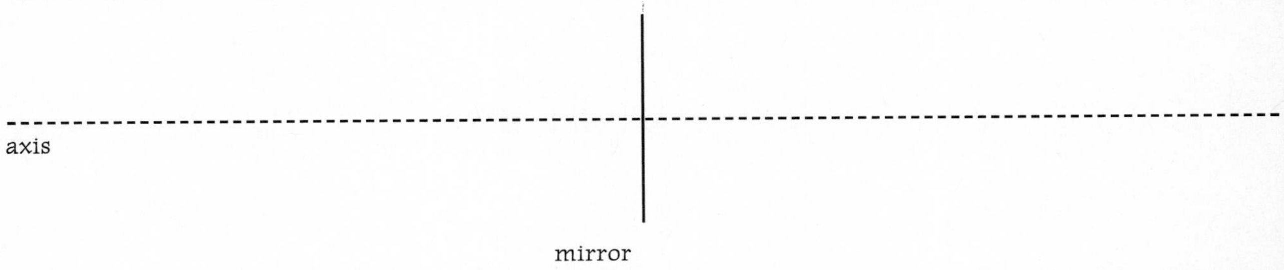

axis -

mirror

Question 1 Thin lens equation—converging lens. The image distance s' is related to the focal length f of the lens and the object distance s by the following equation: 1/s + 1/s' = 1/f. Set the focal length to f = +50 mm (a converging lens with a positive focal length). Try the following object distances and see whether the image distance is at the position predicted by the thin lens equation: (a) s = 200 mm, (b) s = 100 mm, (c) s = 60 mm, (d) s = 40 mm, and (e) s = 30 mm.

Question 2 Negative-image distances. For the last two object distances in Question 1, the image distances were negative. In the simulation, observe the image location for these negative-image distances and compare their location to those for positive-image distances. What does the negative sign mean?

Question 3 Thin-lens magnification. Use the same +50-mm focal-length lens and the same object distances as in Question 1 (200, 100, 60, 40, and 30 mm). In the simulation, note the object and image distances and the linear magnification m of the image. Invent a rule for determining the linear magnification. Interpret the meaning of the linear magnification, including its sign. If you have trouble, consider the object height and image height and orientation when s = 150 mm and when s = 30 mm.

Question 4 Camera image. A camera has a +50-mm focal-length lens. A 2.0-mm-long ant is 200 mm from the lens. Where should the film be located and how large is the image of the ant on the film?

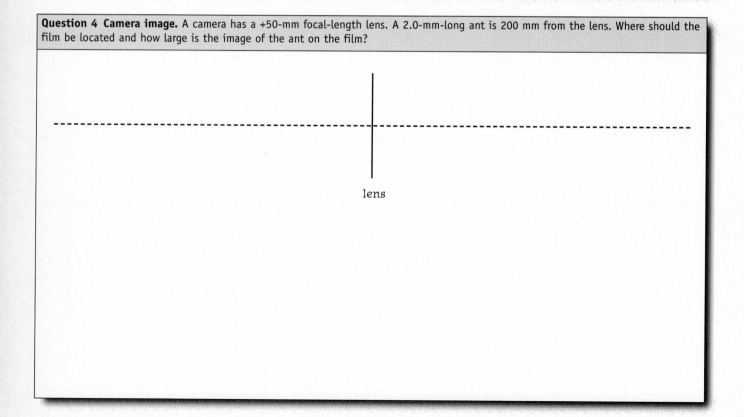

lens

Question 5 Slide projector. A slide projector has a +50-mm focal-length lens. The face of little Sarah occupies 10 mm on a slide that is inserted 55 mm from the lens. Where should the screen be located in order to form a focused image of Sarah on the screen? How large is the image of Sarah's face on the screen?

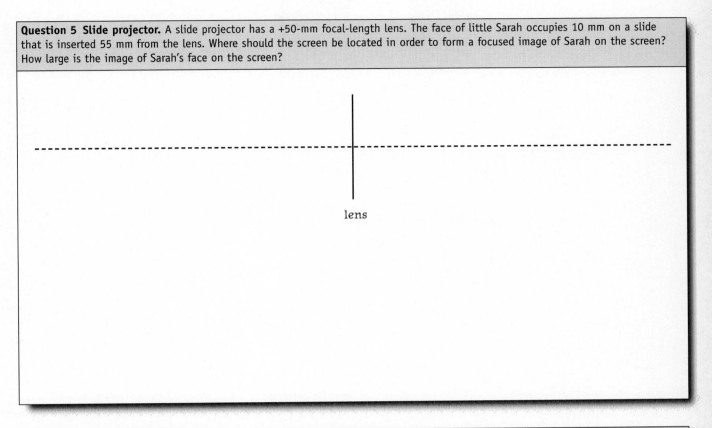

lens

Question 6 Magnifying glass. A magnifying glass has a +50-mm focal-length lens. You look through the magnifying glass at a 2.0-mm-tall ant. You would like the ant's image to be formed at the near point of your eye—200 mm to the left of the lens and from your eye. Where should the ant be located relative to the lens to produce the virtual image? How tall is the image of the ant?

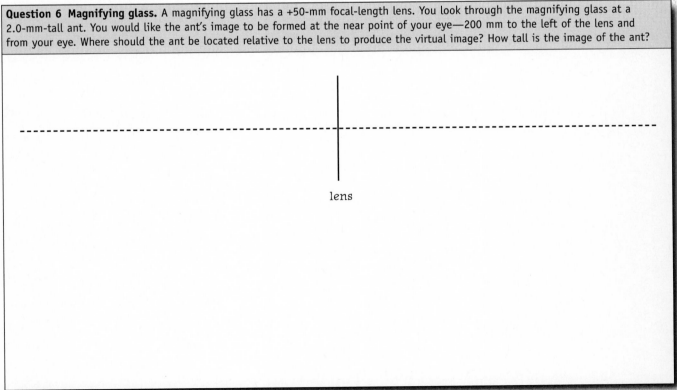

lens

Question 1 Thin-lens equation—diverging lens. The image distance s' is related to the focal length f of the lens and the object distance s by the following equation: $1/s + 1/s' = 1/f$. Set the focal length to $f = -50$ mm (a diverging lens with a negative focal length). Try the following object distances and see whether the image distance is at the position predicted by the thin-lens equation: (a) s = 200 mm, (b) s = 100 mm, (c) s = 40 mm, and (d) s = 30 mm.

Question 2 Negative-image distance. The image distances are negative for all of the object locations in Question 1. Note the image location for these negative-image distances. What does the negative sign mean?

Question 3 Thin-lens magnification. Use the same –50-mm focal-length lens and two of the object distances from Question 1 (200 mm and 40 mm). In the simulation, note the object and image distances and the linear magnification m of the image. Qualitatively, do these image and object heights seem to be related by the linear magnification equation used in Activity 15.10? Explain.

$$m = \frac{image\ height}{object\ height} = \frac{h'}{h} = -\left(\frac{image\ distance}{object\ distance}\right) = -\left(\frac{s'}{s}\right)$$

Question 4 Nearsighted glasses. Your nearsighted pet mouse can focus on objects that are no farther away than 12 cm (120 mm). The mouse needs to see its cheese, which is 30 cm away. What focal-length lenses for the mouse eyeglasses will form an image 12 cm from the glasses for the 30-cm-distant cheese? If the cheese is 10 mm tall, how tall is the image of the cheese as seen through the lenses?

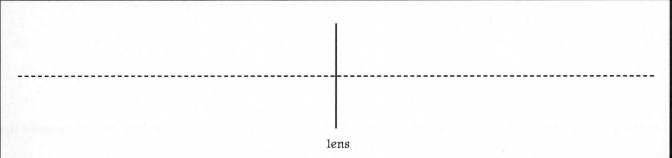

lens

©1999 Addison Wesley Longman, Alan Van Heuvelen and Paul D'Alessandris

Question 1 Two-lens image location. Set the focal length of lens 1 to +40 mm (+0.040 m) and the focal length of lens 2 to +35 mm (+0.035 m). Set x_1 = 75 mm and x_2 = 275 mm. We now use a general procedure to find the final image produced by the two-lens system.

First image location: Use the thin-lens equation to find the image produced by the first lens. The object of the first lens is 75 mm left of the +40-mm focal-length lens.

lens 1

Second object location: The image of the first lens is the object of the second lens. To find this object distance, we must determine the distance of the first image from the second lens. In this example, the lenses are separated by $x_2 - x_1$ = 275 mm − 75 mm = 200 mm. Since the image of the first lens is a distance s_1' = 86 mm to the right of the first lens, its distance from the second lens is 200 mm − 86 mm = 114 mm. In general, the object distance for the second lens is $s_2 = (x_2 - x_1) - s_1'$.

Second image location: Use the thin-lens equation to find the image produced by the second lens. The object of the second lens is 114 mm left of the 35-mm focal-length lens.

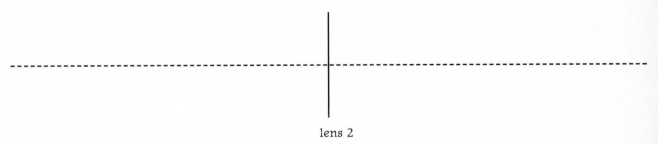

lens 2

Question 2 Image magnification. Determine the linear magnification for the two-lens system.

$$m_{net} = \frac{\text{final image height}}{\text{original object height}} = \frac{h_2'}{h_1} = -\left(\frac{s_1'}{s_1}\right)\left(\frac{s_2'}{s_2}\right)$$

Question 3 Locating and sizing another two-lens image. Set the focal lengths for both lenses to +50 mm. Set x_1 = 60 mm and x_2 = 200 mm.

First image location: Use the thin-lens equation to find the image produced by the first lens. The object of the first lens is 60 mm left of the +50-mm focal-length lens.

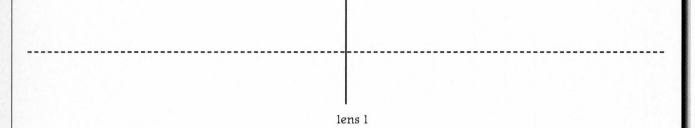

lens 1

Second object location: The image of the first lens is the object of the second lens. Determine the object distance for the second lens. **Note:** If you get a negative sign for s_2, it means the object is on the right side of the lens—on the right side after the light has passed through the lens. Strange! Include the negative sign in your next calculation. In general, the object distance for the second lens is: $s_2 = (x_2 - x_1) - s_1'$.

Second image location: Use the thin-lens equation to find the image produced by the second lens.

Image Magnification: Determine the linear magnification for the two-lens system.

$$m_{net} = \frac{\text{final image height}}{\text{original object height}} = \frac{h_2'}{h_1} = -\left(\frac{s_1'}{s_1}\right)\left(\frac{s_2'}{s_2}\right)$$

Question 4 Microscope. Set the focal length of the first lens to +50 mm and the focal length of the second lens to −100 mm. Set the first lens at x_1 = 60 mm and the second lens at x_2 = 200 mm. Determine the position of the final image and the magnification of the two-lens system.

First image location: Use the thin-lens equation to find the image produced by the first lens.

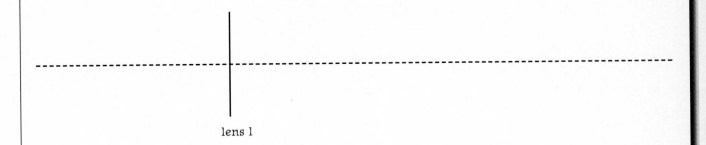

lens 1

Second object location: The image of the first lens is the object of the second lens. Determine the object distance for the second lens. In general, the object distance for the second lens is: $s_2 = (x_2 - x_1) - s_1'$.

Second image location: Use the thin-lens equation to find the image produced by the second lens.

lens 2

Image Magnification: Determine the linear magnification for the two-lens system.

$$m_{net} = \frac{\text{final image height}}{\text{original object height}} = \frac{h_2'}{h_1} = -\left(\frac{s_1'}{s_1}\right)\left(\frac{s_2'}{s_2}\right)$$

Question 1 The telescope. Set the focal length of the first objective lens to +150 mm and the focal length of the second eyepiece lens to + 30 mm. The distance between the lenses is adjusted automatically to the sum of the focal lengths (150 mm + 30 mm = 180 mm in this example). Adjust the angle of the light from the distant object to +0.05 rad. We now use our general two-lens image location procedure to find the final image of that distant object.

First image location: Use the thin-lens equation to find the image produced by the first lens.

Second object location: The image of the first lens is the object of the second lens. Determine the object distance for the second lens.

Second image location: Use the thin-lens equation to find the image produced by the second lens.

Question 2 Angular magnification of a telescope. Suppose the object of the first lens is off axis so that incoming rays make an angle θ_1 with the axis. The ray that passes through the middle of a thin lens does not change direction and passes through the first image point.

From the drawing, we see that

(1) $\tan \theta_1 = h_1'/s_1' = h_1'/f_1$

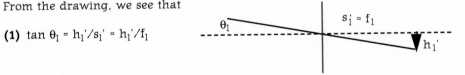

since $s_1' = f_1$. The image of lens 1 is the object for lens 2. Thus the height of object 2, h_2, equals the height of image 1 h_1'. Light leaving object 2 is shown in the sketch below. The angle θ_2 that it makes with respect to the optical axis is determined from the following equation:

(2) $\tan \theta_2 = h_2/s_2 = h_2/f_2$

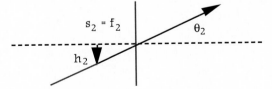

since $s_2 = f_2$. Combining Eqs. (1) and (2) and using the small angle approximation ($\tan \theta \approx \theta$ for small angles), we find that $\theta_1 \approx h_2/f_1$ and $\theta_2 \approx h_2/f_2$. The **angular magnification of the telescope** is $M = -\theta_2/\theta_1 = -f_1/f_2$. For this problem, the angular magnification is −5.0.

Question 1 Accommodation.

Set the object distance slider to s = 30 cm. Press on the "Normal" eye button. Leave the other buttons off (unchecked). You will see two light rays representing light coming from an object that is 30 cm in front of the eye. The light passes through the lens of the eye and is focused as a real image on the retina at the back of the eye.

Now, press the "Infinity" button on and off. The object will jump between infinity and 30 cm. As you do this, watch the image location, then the shape of the lens of the eye, and finally the focal length of the lens. This is called **accommodation.** Does the image position change? If not, how does light from an object 30 cm in front of the lens and light from an object infinitely far from the lens manage to focus at the same place?

Question 2 Focused and unfocused images.

Turn on the "Nearsighted" eye button. Place the object slider at 12 cm (s = 12 cm). The lens of the eye forms a pointlike blue image of the object at the surface of the back of the eye—at the retina. Now, leave the object at the same position and turn on the "Farsighted" eye button. The image is now formed somewhat behind the retina. Why would this image appear blurred or unfocused to the eye?

Question 3 Near point.

Move the object distance slider to s = 40 cm. Turn on the "Normal" type of eye button. Now, move the object distance slider (the s slider) so that the object moves closer to the lens of the eye. What is the nearest object distance **(the near-point distance)** for which the image is still focused on the retina? As the object moves closer to the lens than this near point, does the image move farther in front of the retina or farther behind it?

Question 4 Near point for other types of vision.

(a) Find the near-point distance for the farsighted person in the simulation.

(b) Find the near-point distance for the nearsighted person in the simulation.

(c) Estimate the near-point distance for your own eye.

Question 5 Far point.

(a) Move the object distance slider to s = 50 cm. Leave the "Glasses off" and turn on the "Nearsighted" type of eye button. Now, slowly move the object distance slider so that the object moves farther from the lens of the eye. What is the farthest object distance (the **far-point distance**) for which the image is still focused on the retina? If the object is farther from the lens than the far point, where does the image form—in front of the retina or behind it?

(b) Find the far-point distance for the simulation's normal eye.

(c) Find the far-point distance for the simulation's farsighted eye.

Question 6 Thin-lens equation for eye's vision. Create and solve two different problems that show that the simulation is consistent with the thin-lens equation. Give all of the numbers and settings used and show how they are consistent with the equation.

Question 1 Glasses for a farsighted person to see near objects.

Make the following simulation settings: "Farsighted" eye, "Glasses off" and "s = 20 cm" object distance. Light from the nearby object passes through the lens of the eye and forms an unfocused image *behind* the retina. What type of eyeglass lens allows the eye to form a focused image on the retina? You can answer this question in a special way by answering the following questions.

(a) Determine the near-point distance of this farsighted eye.

(b) Use the thin-lens equation to determine the focal length of eyeglass lens that forms an image of the near object (s = 20 cm) to the left of the eyeglass lens and at (or beyond) the eye's near point. This distance image formed by the eyeglass lens becomes the object of the eye's lens. This new object is far from the eye, and the farsighted eye can produce a focused image of this new object that is formed by the eyeglasses.

Question 2 Glasses for a nearsighted person to see distant objects.

Make the following simulation settings: "Nearsighted" type of eye, "Glasses off," and "Infinity" checked. Light from the distant object passes through the lens of the eye and forms an unfocused image in *front* of the retina. What type of eyeglass lens allows the eye to form a focused image on the retina? You can answer this question in a special way by answering the following questions.

(a) Determine the far-point distance of this nearsighted eye.

(b) Use the thin-lens equation to determine the focal length of eyeglass lens that forms an image of a distant object (s = infinity) to the left of the eyeglass lens and at (or nearer than) the eye's far point. This nearby image of the eyeglass lens becomes the object of the eye's lens. Since the new object is nearer the eye, the nearsighted eye can produce a focused image of this nearer object.

16

PHYSICAL OPTICS

Question 1 The central n = 0 bright band. Set the wavelength to 400 nm and the source separation to d = 2.0 mm. The light from the two sources when it reaches the screen causes alternating bright bands and dark bands. Why is the light bright at position y = 0.0, the center of the screen? This is called the n = 0 bright band.

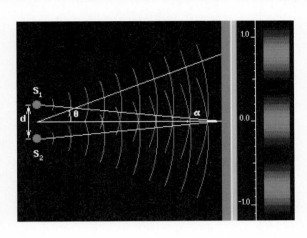

Question 2 The n = 1 bright band. With λ = 400 nm and d = 2.0 mm, use the figure above to help explain why the light is again bright at position y = 0.80 mm.

Question 3 The n = 2 bright band. With λ = 400 nm and d = 2.0 mm, explain why the light would again be bright at position y = 1.60 mm (not shown in the figure above or in the simulation).

Question 4 The angular deflection θ_n of the nth bright band. Use the figure below to see that the angular deflection θ_n of the light traveling toward the nth bright band is given by the equation $\sin \theta_n = n \lambda/d$, where d is the separation of the light sources and λ is the wavelength of the light.

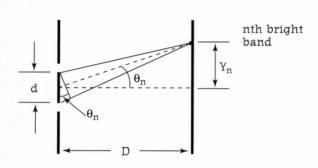

Question 5 Bright-band positions on a screen. Use the figure above to see that the position y_n of the nth bright band on the screen is given by the equation $\tan \theta_n = y_n/D$, where D is the distance of the light sources from the screen and y_n is the distance on the screen of the nth bright band from the central maximum.

Question 6 Small-angle approximation. You just found that $\sin \theta_n = n \lambda/d$ and $\tan \theta_n = y_n/D$. For small angles (10° or less), $\sin \theta = \tan \theta$. This approximation is usually true for two-source interference involving light but is not true in general for longer wavelength two-source interference (e.g., for sound waves). Assuming this is true for two-source interference of light waves, show that the separation of fringes on the screen is $\Delta y = \lambda D/d$.

Question 7 Predict the separation of the bright bands. You just found that the bright bands are separated by a distance $\Delta y = \lambda D/d$. Predict the separation of the bright bands for two 500-nm turquoise light sources separated by 2.0 mm when observed on a screen 4.0 m from the sources.

Question 1 Effect of source separation on the band pattern. Set the wavelength to $\lambda = 600$ nm and the source separation to $d = 3.0$ mm. The light from the two sources when it reaches the screen causes alternating bright bands and dark bands. The pattern is shown on the right side of the simulation screen.

When the sources are moved closer to each other, the position y_1 of the first bright band from the central maximum at $y_0 = 0.0$ **(a)** increases, **(b)** remains the same, or **(c)** decreases. Justify your answer.

Question 2 Effect of wavelength on the band pattern. Set the wavelength to $\lambda = 400$ nm and the source separation to $d = 2.0$ mm. The light from the two sources when it reaches the screen causes alternating bright bands and dark bands. The pattern is shown on the right side of the simulation screen. Note the separation Δy of the central bright band and the first bright band above it.

When the wavelength of the light is increased, the position y_1 of the first bright band from the central maximum **(a)** increases, **(b)** remains the same, or **(c)** decreases. Justify your answer.

Question 1 Separation of bands on a screen. Set the wavelength to $\lambda = 400$ nm (violet light) and the source separation to $d = 2.0$ mm. The light from the two sources when it reaches the screen 4.0 m from the sources causes alternating bright bands and dark bands. The distance Δy between the central bright band and the first bright band at its side (above it on the simulation screen) is 0.80 mm. Determine the distance between the central bright band and the first bright band if the wavelength is changed to 630 nm.

Question 2 Separation of bands on a screen. Determine the distance on the screen between the central bright band and the first bright band with the light wavelength at 630 nm and the slit separation now adjusted to 3.0 mm.

Question 3 Separation of bands on a screen. By what fraction will the separation of the central bright band and the first bright band change if the wavelength is decreased from 630 nm to 420 nm and the separation of the sources is decreased from 3.0 mm to 1.0 mm? Start by recording the initial value of y_1. Then, try to calculate in your head the change in y_1 when the wavelength and source separation are made. Finally, check the final y_1 by changing the simulation sliders.

Question 4 Separation of bands on a screen. You are asked to help with an art exhibit in which you are to provide on a screen bands of 500-nm turquoise light that are separated by 2.0 mm. Determine the separation between two synchronized light sources that produces the desired bands on a screen 4.0 m from the sources.

Question 5 Separation of bands on a screen. You find that you can only produce bands on a screen for the art exhibit from sources separated by 3.0 mm. What wavelength light should you use to provide bands on the screen with a separation of 0.92 mm for a screen 4.0 m from the sources?

Question 6 Angular deflection and position on screen of nth bright band. (a) Determine the angular deflection to the fourth bright band to the side of the central maximum for 600-nm yellow light sources separated by 2.0 mm. **(b)** Determine the distance from this fourth bright band to the side from the central maximum when observed on a screen 4.0 m from the source.

Question 1 The central m = 0 bright band. Set the wavelength to 600 nm (yellow light) and the source separation to d = 2.0 × 10⁻³ mm. Why do we see bright light straight ahead at the center of the screen (at the 0.0 position)? This is called the m = 0 bright band. Does the position of this band depend on the wavelength of the light or on the slit separation? Explain.

Question 2 The m = 1 bright band. With λ = 600 nm and d = 2.0 x 10⁻³ cm, why is the light bright at position y₁ = 1.50 cm?

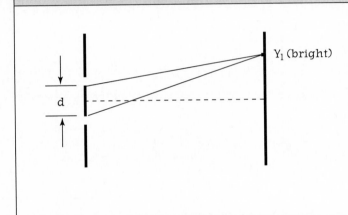

Question 3 The m = 2 bright band. With λ = 600 nm and d = 2.0 × 10⁻³ cm, why is the light bright at position y₂ = 3.0 cm?

Question 4 The angular deflection θ_m of the nth double-source bright band. Explain why light traveling toward the mth bright band at an angular deflection θ_m is given by the equation $\sin \theta_m = m\lambda/d$, where d is the separation of the light sources and λ is the wavelength of the light. (**Hint:** Look at the figure in Question 4 in the worksheet for Activity 16.1.)

Question 5 Bright-band positions on a screen. Explain why light traveling from the grating toward the mth bright band on the screen is given by the equation $\tan \theta_m = y_m/D$, where D is the distance of the grating from the screen (in the simulation, D = f where f is the focal length of the lens) and y_m is the distance on the screen of the mth bright band from the central maximum.

Question 6 Small-angle approximation. For small angles (10° or less), $\sin\theta = \tan\theta$. This approximation applies for the simulation geometry (note that y_m is much less than $D = f$ and θ_m is small). However, for many real gratings, the angular deflection of the first and second bright bands may be large and the two equations must be used separately. Assuming that the angular deflection is small, show that the separation of bright bands on the screen is $\Delta y = \lambda\,f/d$, where the distance D to the screen equals the lens focal length f.

Question 7 Effect of source separation on the band pattern. Set the wavelength to 600 nm (yellow light) and the source separation to $d = 3.0 \times 10^{-3}$ cm. The light from the the grating slits, when it reaches the screen, causes a series of bright bands. The pattern is shown on the right side of the simulation screen.

When the slits are moved closer to each other, the position y_1 of the first bright band from the central maximum at $y_o = 0.0$ **(a)** increases, **(b)** does not change, or **(c)** decreases. Why does this happen?

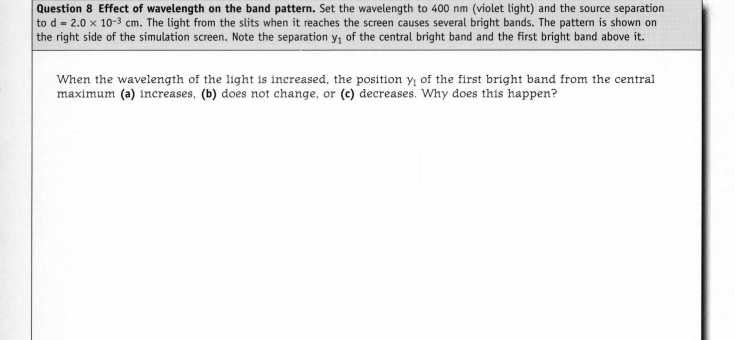

Question 8 Effect of wavelength on the band pattern. Set the wavelength to 400 nm (violet light) and the source separation to d = 2.0×10^{-3} cm. The light from the slits when it reaches the screen causes several bright bands. The pattern is shown on the right side of the simulation screen. Note the separation y_1 of the central bright band and the first bright band above it.

When the wavelength of the light is increased, the position y_1 of the first bright band from the central maximum **(a)** increases, **(b)** does not change, or **(c)** decreases. Why does this happen?

Question 1 Separation of bands on a screen. Set the wavelength to 420 nm (violet light) and the source separation to $d = 2.1 \times 10^{-3}$ cm. The light passing through the slits reaches the screen 50 cm from the slits and causes on the screen a series of bright bands separated from each other by 1.0 cm. **(a)** Show that this band separation is predicted by one of the grating equations. **(b)** Determine the distance on the screen between the central bright band and the first bright band at the side if the wavelength is increased from 420 nm to 630 nm, the wavelength of red light from a helium–neon laser.

Question 2 Separation of bands on a screen. With the wavelength still at 630 nm, if you change the slit separation from 2.1×10^{-3} cm to 1.4×10^{-3} cm (don't do it yet), what wavelength of light causes the distance on the screen between the central bright band and the first bright band at the side to remain at 1.5 cm?

Question 3 Separation of bands on a screen. Determine the separation of the central bright band and the first bright band at the side if the wavelength is 690 nm and the separation of the slits is 3.0×10^{-3} cm. When finished, check the value of y_1 by changing the simulation sliders.

Question 4 Separation of bands on a screen. You are asked to help with an art exhibit in which you are to provide on the screen bright bands of 480-nm turquoise light with a separation of 2.0 cm between adjacent bands. Determine the separation between grating slits that produces the desired bands on a screen 50 cm from the slits. (The light passes through a 50-cm focal-length lens just after leaving the grating.) When finished, adjust the sliders to check your work.

Question 5 Separation of bands on a screen. You find that you can only produce bands on a screen for the art exhibit from sources separated by 2.5×10^{-3} cm. What wavelength light should you use to provide bands with a separation of 1.2 cm on a screen 50 cm from the sources? When finished, adjust the sliders to check your work.

Question 6 Angular deflection and position on screen of fourth bright band. (a) Determine the angular deflection of the fourth bright band to the side of the central maximum for 600-nm yellow light passing through a grating with 400 slits/cm. **(b)** Determine the distance of this fourth bright band to the side of the central maximum when observed on a screen 50 cm from the source. When finished, set the simulation to these settings to check your answers.

Question 1 Effect of wavelength on the first dark band m = 1 position on the screen. Set the wavelength to 400 nm (violet light) and the slit width to d = 0.30 mm. Note the positions of the first m = 1 dark bands on each side of the central maximum. Design your own experiments to determine how the positions of these m = 1 dark bands are affected by the wavelength of light. Provide numbers that support your conclusion.

Question 2 Effect of slit width on the first dark band m = 1 positions on the screen. Set the wavelength to 500 nm (turquoise light) and the slit width to d = 0.50 mm. Note the positions of the m = 1 dark bands on each side of the central maximum. Design your own experiments to determine how the positions of these m = 1 dark bands are affected by the slit width d. Provide numbers that support your conclusion.

SUMMARY: **The Mathematics of Single-Slit Diffraction**

- **Angular deflection to bright bands.** The angular deflection θ_m from the center of the slit to the mth dark band on the screen is determined from the equation $\sin \theta_m = m \lambda/d$, where λ is the wavelength of the light and d is the width of the slit.

- **Dark-band position on screen.** The position x_m on a screen of the center of the mth dark band from the center of the central maximum is determined from the equation $\tan \theta_m = x_m/L$, where θ_m is the angular deflection from the center of the slit to the mth dark band and L is the distance from the slit to the screen.

- **Small-angle approximation.** Often, the angular deflection of light to the dark bands is very small. In that case, $\sin \theta_m = \tan \theta_m$. We can set the two expressions above equal to each other and obtain the equation $m \lambda/d = x_m/L$. This equation can be used to quickly determine one of the quantities if the other quantities are known.

Question 3 Dark-band positions on a screen. Predict the location of the first and second dark bands on the screen and the angular deflection from the slit to these dark bands for 600-nm light passing through a 0.40-mm slit. The screen is 10 m from the slits. After your prediction, move the sliders to check your prediction.

Question 4 Wavelength. Predict the wavelength of light that produces the third dark band (the m = 3 dark band) 30 mm from the center of the central bright band after passing through a 0.40-mm wide slit. The screen is 10 m from the slits. After your prediction, move the sliders to check your prediction.

Question 5 Wavelengths and slit widths. Use the diffraction equations to predict three different wavelength and slit width combinations that produce the second dark band 30 mm from the center of the central bright band. The screen is 10 m from the slits. After your predictions, move the sliders to check your predictions.

Question 1 The m = 1 dark ring on the screen. Set the wavelength to 700 nm (red light) and the hole radius to R = 0.30 mm. Note the radius of the first m = 1 dark ring on the screen. Design your own experiment to determine how the radius of the m = 1 dark ring on the screen is affected by the wavelength of light. Provide approximate numbers to support your conclusion.

Question 2 The m = 1 dark ring on the screen. Set the wavelength to 600 nm (yellow light) and the hole radius to R = 0.30 mm. Note the radius of the m = 1 dark ring on the screen. Design your own experiment to determine how the radius of the m = 1 dark ring on the screen is affected by the radius R of the hole. Provide approximate numbers that support your conclusion.

SUMMARY: **The Mathematics of Circular-Hole Diffraction**

- **Angular deflection to dark rings.** The angular deflection θ_m from the center of the hole to the mth dark ring on the screen is determined from the equation $\sin \theta_m = 1.22 \, m \, \lambda/2R$, where λ is the wavelength of the light and R is the radius of the circular hole.

- **Dark band position on screen.** The radius r_m on a screen of the mth dark ring is determined from the equation $\tan \theta_m = r_m/L$, where θ_m is the angular deflection from the center of the circular hole to the mth dark ring and L is the distance from the hole to the screen.

- **Small-angle approximation.** Often, the angular deflection of light to the dark rings is very small. In that case, $\sin \theta_m = \tan \theta_m$. We can set the two expressions above equal to each other and obtain the equation $1.22 \, m \, \lambda/2R = r_m/L$. This equation can be used to quickly determine one of the quantities if the other quantities are known.

Question 3 Dark ring positions on a screen. Predict the location of the first dark ring on the screen and the angular deflection from the hole to this dark ring for 500-nm turquoise light passing through a 0.19-mm hole. The screen is 10 m from the slits. After your prediction, move the sliders to check your prediction.

Question 4 Radius of hole. When 630-nm red light shines on a small circular hole, a diffraction pattern is formed with a first dark-ring radius of 25.6 mm (about two inches in diameter). The screen is 10 m from the slits. Determine the radius of the circular hole. After your prediction, move the sliders to check your prediction. **Note:** The dimensions of very small objects can be measured by diffraction. For example, scientists at Los Alamos Scientific Labs measured the radius of body cells and the radius of the nuclei of these cells using diffraction. This diffraction was used to develop a technique to detect cervical cancer.

Question 5 Wavelengths and circular-hole radii. Use the diffraction equations to predict three different wavelength and circular-hole radius combinations that produce an m = 1 dark ring of radius 21 mm. The screen is 10 m from the slits. After your predictions, move the sliders to check your predictions.

Question 1 Effect of angular separation of sources on resolving power. Start with the wavelength at $\lambda = 600$ nm, the shutter opening at $D = 1.5$ cm, and the angular separation of the sources $\theta = 10.0 \times 10^{-5}$ rad. Can you see on the screen the image of the two point objects? Now, decrease only the angular separation θ of the sources in several steps to the minimum allowed value. Observe the pattern formed on the screen. How does decreasing the angular separation of the sources affect your ability to "see" the images of the two objects on the screen? Explain.

Question 2 Effect of shutter size on resolving power. Set the wavelength to $\lambda = 600$ nm, the shutter opening to $D = 1.5$ cm, and the angular separation of the sources to $\theta = 5.0 \times 10^{-5}$ rad. Can you see the images of the two point objects on the screen? How does decreasing the shutter size to 1.0 cm and 0.50 cm affect your ability to "see" the images of the two objects on the screen? Explain.

Question 3 Effect of wavelength on resolving power. Set the wavelength to $\lambda = 400$ nm, the shutter opening to $D = 0.60$ cm, and the angular separation of the sources to $\theta = 10.0 \times 10^{-5}$ rad. Can you see the image of the two point objects on the screen? Now, increase only the wavelength λ in 100-nm steps and observe the pattern formed on the screen. How does increasing the wavelength affect your ability to resolve the images of the two objects on the screen? Explain.

Question 4 The separation of the images on a screen. Set the wavelength to 600 nm (yellow light), the shutter opening to D = 1.4 cm, and the angular separation of the sources to 5.0×10^{-5} rad. Decide whether the centers of the images on the screen are the correct distance apart. The screen is 20 cm from the lens.

Question 5 Width of the images. The 600-nm light from the point sources illuminates the circular opening with shutter diameter d = 1.4 cm. Images are formed on a screen 20 cm from the lens. Use the circular-hole diffraction equation to determine the radius of the first dark ring surrounding one of the images on the screen. Then, compare your work with the image size of one image on the simulation screen.

The **resolving power** of an optical instrument is a measure of its ability to produce separate images of two nearby point objects. Diffraction is the ultimate limit of resolving power. The accepted criterion for resolution is the Raleigh criterion:

$$\theta_{\text{angular separation of objects and images}} > 1.22\ \lambda/D$$

According to this criterion, two images are just resolved if the center of the central maximum of one diffraction pattern falls on the first dark ring of the other diffraction pattern.

Question 6 Binary stars. Predict the minimum shutter diameter that can resolve the 400-nm violet light from binary stars with an angular separation of 3.6×10^{-5} rad. When finished with your prediction, set the shutter diameter to this value and see whether the images are barely observable.

Question 7 Moon rocks. Your home telescope has a maximum shutter opening of 1.5 cm. Determine the closest distance of two shiny rocks on the moon 3.8×10^8 m from the earth that can be resolved with your telescope. Assume that the telescope is most sensitive to 600-nm yellow light. When finished with your prediction, set the sliders to check your work.

Question 8 Car headlights. Estimate the maximum distance that two car headlights can be for you to distinguish the lights while looking through a 1.0-cm-diameter telescope lens. Assume that the light wavelength is 550 nm. When finished with your estimate, set the slider settings to check your work.

Question 1 Angle dependence of transmitted intensity. In the wave theory of light, the light intensity I is proportional to the square of the amplitude A of the light wave I = (constant) A^2. Set the orientations of both Polaroids to 0°. The difference in the orientation of the two Polaroids is given the symbol $\Delta\phi$. Observe the changing intensity of the light leaving the second Polaroid as you turn the second Polaroid from 0° to 90°. Confirm that the intensity of the light decreases by $\cos^2 \Delta\phi$ and not by $\cos \Delta\phi$.

Question 2 Transmitted intensity for different Polaroid orientations. Unpolarized light of intensity I_0 is incident on the first of two Polaroid films. **(a)** If you set the Polaroid orientations to $\phi_1 = \phi_2 = 16°$, what is the intensity of the transimitted light? After your prediction, check your results with the simulation.

(b) If you set the Polaroid orientations to $\phi_1 = 16°$ and $\phi_2 = 32°$, what is the intensity of the transmitted light? After your prediction, check your results with the simulation.

(c) If you set the Polaroid orientations to $\phi_1 = 16°$ and $\phi_2 = 46°$, what is the intensity of the transmitted light? After your prediction, check your results with the simulation.

(d) If you set the Polaroid orientations to $\phi_1 = 16°$ and $\phi_2 = 76°$, what is the intensity of the transmitted light? After your prediction, check your results with the simulation.

(e) If you set the Polaroid orientations to $\phi_1 = 16°$ and $\phi_2 = 106°$, what is the intensity of the transmitted light? After your prediction, check your results with the simulation.

Question 3 Angle for certain transmitted intensity. Unpolarized light of intensity I_0 is incident on the first of two Polaroid films. **(a)** Set the orientation for the first Polaroid to $\phi_1 = 30°$. What orientation should the second Polaroid have so that the transmitted intensity through both Polaroids is 0.5 I_0? After your prediction, check your results with the simulation.

(b) Set the orientation for the first Polaroid to $\phi_1 = 30°$. What orientation should the second Polaroid have so that the transmitted intensity through both Polaroids is 0.3 I_0? After your prediction, check your results with the simulation.

(c) Set the orientation for the first Polaroid to $\phi_1 = 30°$. What orientation should the second Polaroid have so that the transmitted intensity through both Polaroids is 0.1 I_0? After your prediction, check your results with the simulation.

Question 4 Transmitted intensity for different Polaroid orientations. Unpolarized light of intensity I_0 is incident on the first of two Polaroid films. **(a)** If you set the Polaroid orientations to $\phi_1 = 30°$ and $\phi_2 = 76°$, what is the intensity of the transmitted light? After your prediction, check your results with the simulation.

(b) With the second Polaroid orientation still at $\phi_2 = 76°$, what is the transmitted intensity through the second Polaroid if you now change the first Polaroid's orientation from $\phi_1 = 30°$ to $\phi_1 = 16°$? After your prediction, check your results with the simulation.

(c) With the first Polaroid orientation still at $\phi_1 = 16°$, what is the transmitted intensity through the second Polaroid if you now change its orientation from $\phi_2 = 76°$ to $\phi_2 = 136°$? After your prediction, check your results with the simulation.

©1999 Addison Wesley Longman, Alan Van Heuvelen and Paul D'Alessandris

MODERN PHYSICS

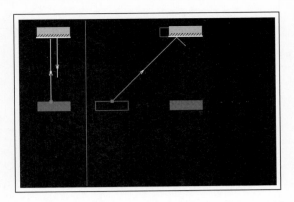

Question 1 Distance traveled by the light pulse, as measured on the earth. How does the distance traveled by the light pulse on the moving light clock compare to the distance traveled by the light pulse on the stationary light clock?

Question 2 Time interval required for light pulse travel, as measured on earth. Given that the speed of the light pulse is independent of the speed of the light clock, how does the time interval for the light pulse to travel to the top mirror and back on the moving light clock compare to on the stationary light clock?

Question 3 Time interval required for light pulse travel, as measured on the light clock. Imagine yourself riding on the light clock. In your frame of reference, does the light pulse travel a larger distance when the clock is moving, and hence require a larger time interval to complete a single round-trip?

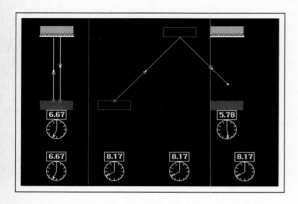

Question 4 The effect of velocity on time dilation. Will the *difference* in light pulse travel time between the earth's timers and the light clock's timers increase, decrease, or stay the same as the velocity of the light clock is decreased?

Will the distance the light pulse travels, as measured by an observer riding on the light clock, change?	Will the distance the light pulse travels, as measured by an observer on the earth, change?

Will the time of travel, as measured by the light clock's timers, change?	Will the time of travel, as measured by the earth's timers, change?

Final answer:

Question 5 The time dilation formula. Using the time dilation formula, predict how long it will take for the light pulse to travel to and fro between mirrors, as measured by an earth-bound observer, when the light clock has a Lorentz factor (γ) of 1.2. The proper time (Δt_{proper}) is

The Lorentz factor (γ) is

The time measured on the earth (Δt) is

Question 6 The time dilation formula, one more time. If the time interval between departure and return of the light pulse is measured to be 7.45 ms by an earth-bound observer, what is the Lorentz factor of the light clock as it moves relative to the earth? The proper time (Δt_{proper}) is

The time measured on the earth (Δt) is

The Lorentz factor (γ)

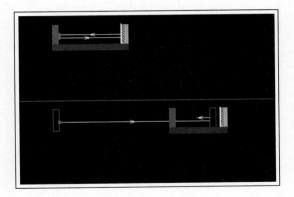

Question 1 Round-trip time interval, as measured on the light clock. Imagine riding on the left end of the light clock. A pulse of light departs the left end, travels to the right end, reflects, and returns to the left end of the light clock. Does your measurement of this round-trip time interval depend on whether the light clock is moving or stationary relative to Earth? Explain

Question 2 Round-trip time interval, as measured on the earth. Will the round-trip time interval for the light pulse as measured on the earth be longer, shorter, or the same as the time interval measured on the light clock?

Which time interval, the one measured by the light clock's timer or the earth's timers, is the proper time interval?

Question 3 Why does the moving light clock shrink? You have probably noticed that the length of the moving light clock is smaller than the length of the stationary light clock. Is the round-trip time interval measured on the earth currently equal to the product of the proper time interval and the Lorentz factor?

Could the round-trip time interval as measured on the earth be equal to the product of the Lorentz factor and the proper time interval if the moving light clock were the same size as the stationary light clock?

Question 4 The length contraction formula. A light clock is 1000 m long when measured at rest. How long would an earth-bound observer measure the clock to be if it had a Lorentz factor of 1.3 relative to the earth? The proper length (l_{proper}) is

The Lorentz factor (γ) is

The length measured by an earth-bound observer (l) is

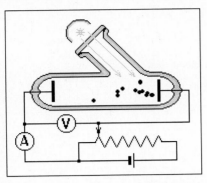

Question 1 The effect of intensity. What will happen to the number of electrons that are ejected from the metal as the intensity (brightness) of the light is increased? Explain.

Question 2 Positive applied potential. What will happen to the current if the battery provides a positive potential on the collecting plate relative to the emitting plate? Explain.

Question 3 Negative applied potential. What will happen to the current if the battery provides a negative potential on the collecting plate relative to the emitting plate? Explain.

Question 4 Energy conservation. Consider the motion of an electron from when it first leaves the emitting plate until it is stopped and turned around by the action of the stopping potential. The electron just barely misses making it to the collecting plate.

Construct an energy bar chart for this motion, defining the emitting plate as zero potential.

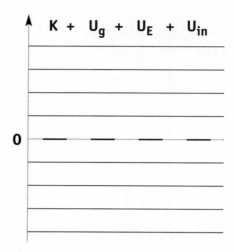

Initial Energy + Work =

$$K + U_g + U_E + W$$

Final Energy

$$K + U_g + U_E + U_{in}$$

Translate your bar chart into a mathematical relationship between the electron's kinetic energy when it leaves the emitting plate and the applied potential difference.

Question 5 Stopping potential vs. intensity. If you increase the intensity of the incoming light, will the stopping potential *increase, decrease,* or *stay the same?* If you increase the intensity, what happens to the number of photons?

If you increase the intensity, what happens to the energy of each photon?

Does the stopping potential depend on the number or energy of the photons?

Final answer:

Question 6 Intensity vs. current. If you decrease the intensity of the incoming light, will the current *increase, decrease, or stay the same?* If you decrease the intensity, what happens to the number of photons?

If you decrease the intensity, what happens to the energy of each photon?

Does the current depend on the number or energy of the photons?

Final answer:

Question 7 Stopping potential vs. wavelength. If you decrease the wavelength of the incoming light, will the stopping potential *increase, decrease* or *stay the same?* As the wavelength is decreased, what happens to the photon energy?

As the wavelength is decreased, what happens to the electron energy (after absorption)?

As the wavelength is decreased, what happens to the potential needed to stop the electron?

Question 8 Threshold wavelength.

What happens to the strength with which electrons are bound to the metal as wavelength increases?

What happens to photon energy as wavelength increases?

Construct an argument explaining why long wavelength light is unable to free electrons.

Question 9 Work function. Determine the work function for the metal in the simulation.

17.3 Photoelectric Effect continued

Question 10 Predicting the stopping potential.

What is the work function for the metal?

What is the energy of a 450-nm photon?

Predict the stopping potential required when 450-nm light is focused on the emitting plate.

Question 1 Momentum conservation. In a classical collision between two identical billiard balls, one initially moving and the other stationary, is the momentum transferred to the stationary ball larger for a *head-on collision* or a *glancing collision*?

Head-on Collision

Initial	Final

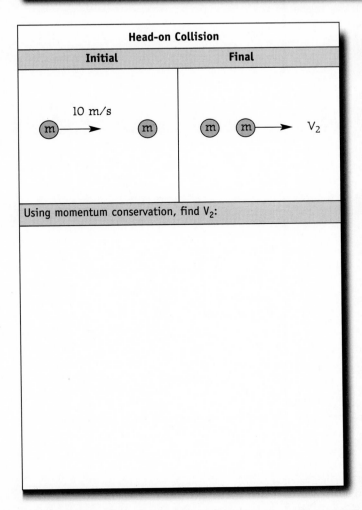

Using momentum conservation, find V_2:

Glancing Collision

Initial	Final

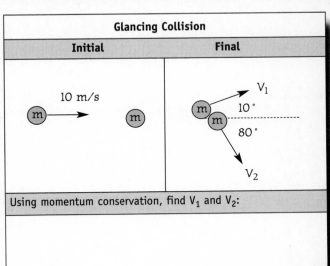

Using momentum conservation, find V_1 and V_2:

Determine the momentum change of the initially stationary ball for both collisions.

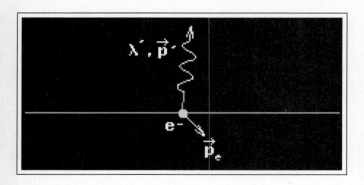

Question 2 Scattered photon wavelength. Predict the wavelength of a 0.035-nm photon after colliding with a stationary electron, if the scattered photon is detected at 83° from its initial direction of travel.

Question 3 Photons scattering from protons. Predict the wavelength of a 0.035-nm photon after colliding with a stationary proton, if the scattered photon is detected at 83° from its initial direction of travel.

Question 4 Resolution of Intensity Peaks. Imagine you have at your disposal a photon detector that can only measure photon wavelength with 2% precision. If you have an incident beam of 0.45-nm x rays, below what angle will your detector not be able to resolve the difference between the scattered and unscattered peaks? Will the scattered photons have wavelengths larger or smaller than 0.45 nm?

What wavelength is 2% longer than 0.45 nm?

Into what angle will photons with the above wavelength be scattered?

Question 5 Resolution vs. incident wavelength. If you use shorter wavelength x rays, will you be able to use your detector at angles smaller than 51°? Does the shift in wavelength ($\lambda'-\lambda$) depend on the initial wavelength, assuming the angle is held constant?

If the wavelength decreases, and the shift remains constant, what happens to the percentage shift of the wavelength?

Will the detector work at less than 51°? Why?

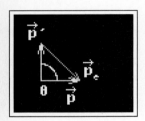

Question 6 Electron momentum. Find the magnitude and direction of the electron's momentum after a collision with a 0.09-nm incident photon, assuming the photon scatters by 90°. (**Hint:** Make use of the momentum diagram.)

Find the photon's initial and final momentum.

Initial: Final:

Find the magnitude of the electrons momentum by
trigonometry.

Find the direction of the electron's momentum by trigonometry.

Question 7 Maximum momentum transfer. To provide the greatest momentum transfer to the electron, what wavelength photon should be incident and at what angle should you scatter the photon? (Only use values that the simulation allows.)

Angle	Wavelength
Does the photon transfer more momentum to the electron at small scattering angles or at large ones?	Does the incident photon have more momentum at short wavelength or long wavelength?
	At what allowed wavelength in the simulation does the photon have the most momentum?
At what allowed angle in the simulation is the maximum momentum transferred to the electron?	
	At what allowed wavelength does the photon transfer the most momentum to the electron?

Final answer:

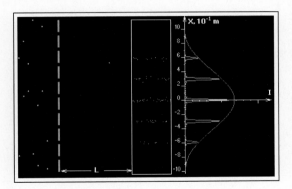

Question 1 Atomic spacing. In order to spread the interference maxima as far apart as possible, should you choose a crystal in which the atoms are spaced by 0.10 nm ($d = 1.0 \times 10^{-10}$m) or 0.15 nm ($d = 1.5 \times 10^{-10}$m)? Explain.

Question 2 Electron's velocity. In order to spread the interference maxima as far apart as possible, should you fire slow electrons or fast electrons? Explain.

Question 3 Minimum resolution. At what speed and atomic spacing will the resulting interference pattern be hardest to resolve, i.e., will have the smallest spacing between maxima? Explain.

Question 4 Analyzing the interference pattern. Set the electron velocity and atomic spacing to generate the largest separation between maxima. Measure the distance between maxima. From this measurement, and the interference relationship used for light, calculate the wavelength of the incident electrons. What velocity and atomic spacing generate the largest separation between maxima?

Velocity:

Spacing:

Measure the distance between maxima:

Calculate the angel between maxima:

Using the diffraction grating equation, calculate the electron's wavelength.

Question 5 The de Broglie relation. What does the de Broglie relation predict for the wavelength of electrons traveling at 1.5×10^7 m/s? Are the effects of special relativity important?

What is the momentum of the electron?

Using the de Broglie relation, calculate the electron's wavelength.

Does the result of the de Broglie relation agree with the result calculated through analyzing the interference pattern?

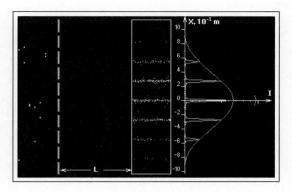

Question 6 Detector placement. If 2.00×10^7 m/s electrons are fired at a crystal lattice with interatomic spacing of 0.123 nm, how far from the central maximum should a detector be placed to record the intensity in the m = 2 peak? Are the effects of special relativity important?

Calculate the electron's momentum.

From the de Broglie relation, calculate the electron's wavelength.

From the diffraction grating equation, calculate the angle of the m = 2 peak.

Calculate the distance of the m = 2 peak from the central maximum.

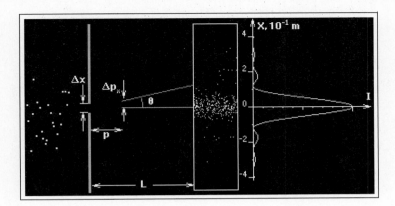

Question 1 The de Broglie relation. What does the de Broglie relation predict for the wavelength of an electron traveling at 2.0×10^7 m/s? What is the electrons momentum?

What is the electron's wavelength?

Question 2 Diffraction minimum. Using the wavelength calculated above, determine the location of the m = 1 diffraction minimum when the electrons pass through an aperture of width 0.30 nm. What is the relationship for determining the location of diffraction minima?

Determine the location of the m = 1 minimum.

Question 3 Uncertainty in x-momentum. When passing through the aperture, the electron's position is specified to be in a region of space of width 0.30 nm. Given the uncertainty in position, what is the minimum uncertainty in x-momentum possible for the electron?

Question 4 Time-of-flight. Now long will it take an electron moving at 2.0×10^7 m/s to reach the screen?

Question 5 X-velocity. Given the x-momentum of our hypothetical electron, what is its x-velocity?

Question 6 X-displacement. Given the time-of-flight and the x-velocity, what is the x-displacement of the electron when it hits the screen? How does this compare to the spread of landing positions predicted by the diffraction equation?

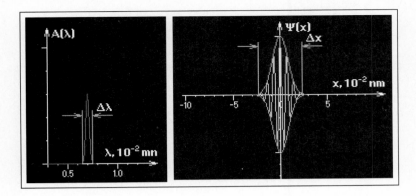

Question 1 Changing the spread of wavelengths. What will happen to the spatial extent of the resultant waveform when a smaller spread of wavelengths are superimposed?

From the de Broglie relation, what effect does a smaller spread in wavelength have on the "spread" in momentum?

From the Heisenberg uncertainty relation, what effect does this have on the spatial extent of the wave form?

What if a larger spread of wavelengths are superimposed?

Question 2 Changing the central wavelength. Will the spatial extent of the resultant wave form change when the spread of wavelengths superimposed are centered on a longer wavelength? Explain.

Question 3 Building a wave packet — I. What is the spatial extent of a wave packet built from plane waves centered around $\lambda = 1.0 \times 10^{-2}$ nm with $\Delta \lambda = 0.2 \times 10^{-2}$ nm?

Question 4 Building a wave packet — II. What spread of wavelengths is necessary to represent an electron with momentum approximately 8.3×10^{-23} kg m/s and spatial extent 4.0×10^{-2} nm?

From the de Broglie relation, what is the approximate wavelength of the electron?

Thus, what spread of wavelengths is necessary to "build" the electron's wave packet?

18

ATOMIC PHYSICS

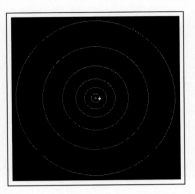

Question 1 Absorption. Does it take more energy for the electron to jump from the ground state to the second orbit or from the ground state to the third orbit? Given your answer, which transition requires a shorter-wavelength photon?

Question 2 Emission. Excite the electron from the ground state to the fifth orbit by absorbing a photon. How will the wavelength of the emitted photon, as the electron returns to the ground state, compare with the wavelength of the absorbed photon, which originally excited the electron into the fifth orbit?

Question 3 Longest wavelength. Which electron transition will emit the longest-wavelength photon?

Question 4 Predicting wavelengths. In order to jump from the second energy level to the fifth energy level, how much energy must the electron absorb? Assuming this energy is transferred to the electron through photon absorption, what wavelength photon must be absorbed? Find the energies of the relevant levels.

Second level:

Fifth level:

Energy difference:

Wavelength of photon:

Question 5 The green line. The transition from the second to the fifth energy level required a photon of wavelength 434 nm to be absorbed, which is blue. Adjacent to this blue line in the spectrum of hydrogen is a green line. This line is also due to a transition involving the second level. What other level is involved in the green line transition, the fourth level or the sixth level? Does the green line represent a longer-wavelength or shorterwavelength photon?

Does the green line represent a higher-energy or lower-energy photon?

Is a higher or lower energy level than the fifth level involved in the transition?

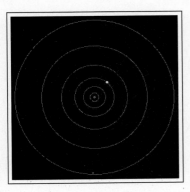

Question 6 Predicting transitions. One day while reflecting on the spectrum of hydrogen, you turn your attention to the infrared line at 1875 nm. What electron transition produces this line? What energy photon has a wavelength of 1875 nm?

What two energy levels differ by an amount equal to the energy calculated above?

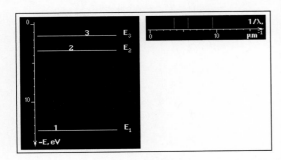

Question 1 Increasing E_2. If the energy of level 2 is increased, how many of the three spectral lines will shift? Which ones? In which direction(s) will each line shift?

λ_{31}:

λ_{32}:

λ_{21}:

Question 2 Decreasing E_3. If the energy of level 3 is decreased, how many of the three spectral lines will shift? Which ones? In which direction(s) will each line shift?

λ_{31}:

λ_{32}:

λ_{21}:

Question 3 Verifying the wavelengths. Given that $E_1 = 13.6eV$, calculate the three wavelengths of light emitted by the atom you have constructed. Do your calculations agree with the simulation?

$E_1 = -13.6\ eV$ $\lambda_{31} = $ _____

$E_2 = $ _____ $\lambda_{32} = $ _____

$E_3 = $ _____ $\lambda_{21} = $ _____

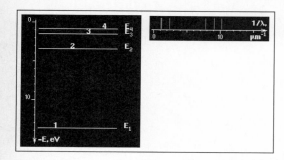

Question 4 Four-level system. How many different wavelengths of light will be emitted by an atom with four distinct electron energy levels? Explain.

Question 5 Increasing E_2 in a four-level system. If the energy of level 2 is increased in a four-level system, which of the *six* spectral lines will shift?

λ_{41}:

λ_{42}:

λ_{43}:

λ_{31}:

λ_{32}:

λ_{21}:

Question 6 Decreasing E_4. If the energy of level 4 is decreased, which of the six spectral lines will shift? In which direction(s) will each line shift?

λ_{41}:

λ_{42}:

λ_{43}:

λ_{31}:

λ_{32}:

λ_{21}:

Question 7 Verifying the wavelengths. Given that $E_1 = -13.6$ eV, calculate the six wavelengths of light emitted by the atom you have constructed. Do your calculations agree with the simulation?

$E_1 = -13.6\ eV$

$E_2 = $ _____

$E_3 = $ _____

$E_4 = $ _____

$\lambda_{41} = $ _____

$\lambda_{42} = $ _____

$\lambda_{43} = $ _____

$\lambda_{31} = $ _____

$\lambda_{32} = $ _____

$\lambda_{21} = $ _____

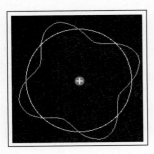

Question 1 Electron phase. Observe the relative phase of the electron as it starts its second circle around the nucleus. Do you think the second pass of the electron around the nucleus will be in phase or out of phase with the first pass? Explain.

Question 2 Standing waves. Does the electron wave interfere constructively, creating a stable standing wave, or destructively, creating a disturbance with an amptitude of zero? Explain.

Question 3 Finding a standing wave. Vary the radius of the electron's path until you find a radius at which the electron will interfere constructively, i.e., form a standing wave. Find as many standing waves as possible. What are the radii of the standing waves? List all stable radii.

Question 4 Allowed wavelengths. Derive a relationship for the allowed wavelengths of electron waves in terms of the radius of the orbit.

Express the relationship between distance traveled and wavelength when the electron arrives at each point along its path in phase with its previous passing.

Express the distance traveled by the electron in one path around the nucleus in terms of the radius of the orbit.

Relate allowed wavelength to radius.

Question 5 Angular momentum. Using the result derived in Question 4, and the de Broglie relation between wavelength and linear momentum, show that Bohr's hypothesis (that the angular momentum of the electron must be a multiple of $h/2\pi$) is simply the result of the electron's wavelike nature.

Express the result of Question 4.

Express the de Broglie relation between wavelength and linear momentum.

Combine these two results and solve for angular momentum $L = mvr$.

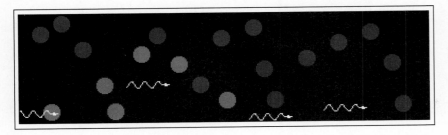

Question 1 Absorption. At any given time, the number of photons inputted into the cavity must be equal to the number that have passed through the cavity without exciting an atom plus the number still in the cavity plus the number of excited atoms. Verify this conservation law by stopping the simulation and counting photons.

$$N_{in} \overset{?}{=} N_{art} + N_{remaining} + N_{excited}$$

____ = ____ + _____ + _____

Question 2 Direction of spontaneous emission. During spontaneous emission, does there appear to be a preferred direction in which the photons are emitted? Explain.

Question 3 Lifetime of excited state. Does there appear to be a constant amount of time in which an atom remains in its excited state? Explain.

Question 4 Stimulated emission. Carefully describe what happens when a photon interacts with an excited atom. Pay careful attention to the phase and direction of the subsequent photons. (Can you see why this is called stimulated emission?)

Phase:

Direction:

Question 5 Pumping. Approximately what pumping level is required to achieve a population inversion? Remember, a population inversion is when the number of atoms in the excited state is at least as great as the number of atoms in the ground state.

Question 6 Photon emission. Although most photons are emitted toward the right in the simulation, occasionally one is emitted in another direction. Are the photons emitted at odd directions the result of *stimulated* or *spontaneous* emission? Explain.

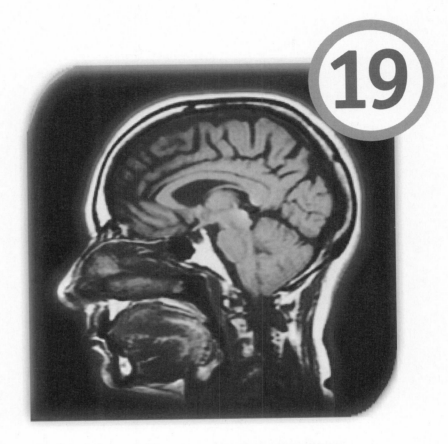

NUCLEAR PHYSICS

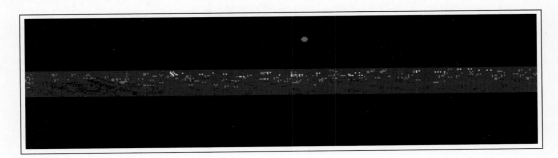

Question 1 Enough information? Does the result of one scattering event provide enough information to identify the radius of the atoms? Explain.

Question 2 Enough information now? Does the result of ten scattering events provide enough information to identify the radius of the atoms? Explain.

Question 3 Constructing a relationship. Construct a relationship between the ratio $N_{unscattered}/N$ and the effective atomic radius. Make sure your relationship agrees with common sense in the appropriate limits.

As the effective atomic radius approaches zero, does your result approach 1.0?

As the effective atomic radius approaches 10 Å, does your result approach zero?

Question 4 R_{atom} =? Rewrite your relationship in the form of "R_{atom} = _____."

Question 5 Precision. Using your scattering data and the relationship derived in Question 4, calculate a tentative value for the atomic radius.

$N_{unscattered}$ =

N =

R_{atom} (prediction) =

If the number of unscattered projectiles had been one larger, what value would the relationship predict for the atomic radius?

In light of these two answers, is your data sufficient to determine the atomic radius to the requested precision of 0.5 Å?

Question 6 Predicting the radius. Using your scattering data and the relationship derived above, predict the atomic radius.

$N_{unscattered}$ =

N =

R_{atom} =

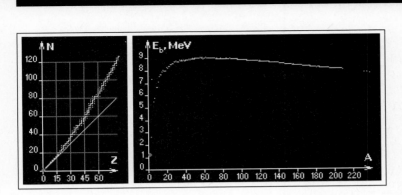

Question 1 ¹H + neutron? If you add a neutron to a hydrogen nucleus, will the resulting nucleus be stable? What is the name of this nucleus?

Question 2 ¹H + proton? Create a simple hydrogen nucleus again. If you add a proton, will the resulting nucleus be stable?

Explain why a neutron is "safe" to add while a proton is not.

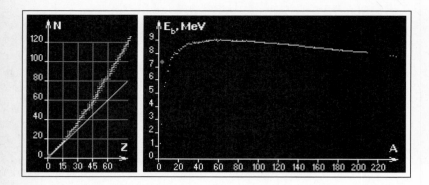

Question 3 **³He?** In addition to 2 protons, include a neutron in the nucleus. Is the resulting nucleus stable?

Question 4 **⁴He?** If you add another neutron to the previous nucleus, giving rise to a nucleus with 2 protons and 2 neutrons, will the resulting nucleus be stable? Will it be more or less stable than the previous nucleus?

Question 5 **⁴He + neutron?** Based on what you have learned so far, if you add another neutron to ⁴He will the resulting nucleus be stable? If so, will it be more or less stable than ⁴He?

Question 6 N = Z? The following nuclei are stable: ^{2}H, with 1 proton and 1 neutron; ^{4}He, with 2 protons and 2 neutrons; ^{12}C, with 6 protons and 6 neutrons; ^{14}N with 7 and 7, ^{16}O with 8 and 8, and many other nuclei with an equal number of protons (Z) and neutrons (N). Is this a general rule of nature? Is stability guaranteed if the number of protons equals the number of neutrons (N = Z)? Create the following nuclei. Are they stable?

$^{12}_{6}$C

$^{14}_{7}$N

$^{16}_{8}$O

$^{26}_{13}$Al

$^{52}_{26}$Fe

$^{164}_{82}$Pb

Does N = Z guarantee stability?

Question 7 Forming ^{3}He. Determine the amount of energy released if ^{1}H and ^{2}H are fused to form ^{3}He. Determine the binding energy of ^{1}H.

Determine the binding energy of ^{2}H.

Determine the binding energy of ^{3}H.

How much energy is released?

Question 8 Forming ^{4}He. Another reaction taking place in the center of stars is ^{3}He + ^{3}He –> ^{4}He + ^{1}H + ^{1}H. Determine the amount of energy released by this fusion reaction. Determine the binding energy of ^{3}He.

Determine the binding energy of ^{4}He.

Determine the binding energy of ^{1}H.

How much energy is released?

Question 9 Fission. At the other end of the nuclear size spectrum are the extremely large nuclei. Examine the reaction in which uranium fractures into cerium and zirconium.

$$^{235}_{92}\text{U} \longrightarrow {}^{140}_{58}\text{Ce} + {}^{94}_{40}\text{Zr} + \text{neuron}$$

Is this reaction allowed by energy considerations? If so, how much energy is released? Determine the binding energy of $^{235}_{92}\text{U}$.

Determine the binding energy of $^{140}_{58}\text{Ce}$.

Determine the binding energy of $^{94}_{40}\text{Zr}$.

How much energy is released?

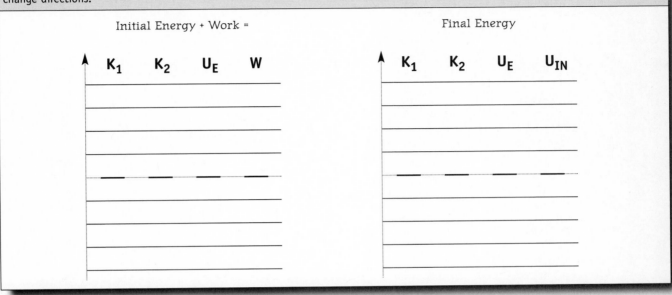

Initial state:

$^1H \longrightarrow \qquad \longleftarrow ^1H$

$v = 0.03c \qquad\qquad v = 0.03c$

Final state:

$^1H \qquad\qquad ^1H$

$\longleftarrow \quad d \quad \longrightarrow$

Question 1 Energy bar chart. Construct an energy bar chart for the first half of this collision. Start your analysis when both ^1H nuclei are travelling at $v = 0.03c$ and are very far apart and end your analysis when the ^1H nuclei instantaneously stop and change directions.

Initial Energy + Work =

$K_1 \qquad K_2 \qquad U_E \qquad W$

Final Energy

$K_1 \qquad K_2 \qquad U_E \qquad U_{IN}$

Question 2 Energy conservation. Translate your energy bar chart into a mathematical relationship.

Solve this relationship for the *distance of closest approach,* d, the distance between the nuclei when they instantaneously stop.

Question 3 Fusion. In a symmetric collision (both ^1H nuclei traveling at the same speed), how large must the speed be to allow fusion to take place? Assume fusion takes place is $d \leq 10^{-15}$m.

Initial state: Final state:

^{1}H → v = 0.04 C   ← ^{1}H v = 0.04 C   ← ^{2}H e^+ →   v →

Question 4 Q-value. Calculate the Q-value, the amount of energy released in the fusion reaction.

^{1}H:

     Mass energy =

     Kinetic energy =

     Total energy =

^{1}H:

     Mass energy =

     Kinetic energy =

     Total energy =

Initial state:

     Total mass energy =

     Total kinetic energy =

     Total initial energy =

^{2}H:

     Mass energy =

     Kinetic energy =

     Total energy =

e^+:

     Mass energy =

     Kinetic energy =

     Total energy =

v:

     Mass energy =

     Kinetic energy =

     Total energy =

Final state:

     Total mass energy =

     Total kinetic energy =

     Total final energy =

     Q =

Question 5 Fusion? The ^{1}H + ^{1}H reaction achieves fusion when each ^{1}H nucleus is launched at $v = 0.04c$. Will the two ^{3}He nuclei also fuse at this speed? Explain.

Question 6 ^{3}He fusion. In a symmetric collision (both ^{3}He nuclei travelling at the same speed), how large must the speed be to allow fusion to take place?

$v = 0.032$ C $v = 0.032$ C

Question 7 Fusion. If the two nuclei are launched at the same speed, 0.032 c, will they undergo fusion?

Find d, the distance of closest approach.

Is d less than 1.0×10^{-15}m? Should fusion occur?

Why does the formula derived in Question 2 not give a correct result?

Initial state: Final state:

^{12}C ⟶   ⟵ ^4He ^{16}O ⟶ γ ⟶

Question 8 A Final Q-value. Calculate the Q-value of the ^{12}C + ^4He reaction.

^{12}C:

        Mass energy =

        Kinetic energy =

        Total energy =

^4He:

        Mass energy =

        Kinetic energy =

        Total energy =

Initial state:

    Total mass energy =

    Total kinetic energy =

    Total initial energy =

^{16}O:

        Mass energy =

        Kinetic energy =

        Total energy =

γ:

        Mass energy =

        Kinetic energy =

        Total energy =

Final state:

    Total mass energy =

    Total kinetic energy =

    Total final energy =

Q =

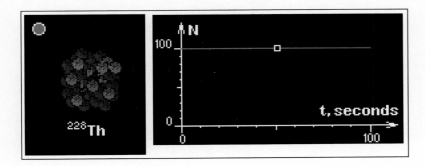

Question 1 Radioactive? *Based only on the data you have collected,* does it appear that ^{228}Th is radioactive? Explain.

Question 2 Decay process. Based on your observations, does ^{228}Th decay via the *alpha, beta-minus,* or *beta-plus* process?

If alpha decay, the resulting nucleus is

$$^{228}\text{Th} \xrightarrow{\alpha} \underline{\qquad}$$

If beta-minus decay, the resulting nucleus is

$$^{228}\text{Th} \xrightarrow{\beta^-} \underline{\qquad}$$

If beta-plus decay, the resulting nucleus is

$$^{228}\text{Th} \xrightarrow{\beta^+} \underline{\qquad}$$

Question 3 Half-life.

Over what time scale does ^{228}Th decay?

Estimate the half-life of ^{228}Th.

Question 4 ^{224}**Ra.** Determine the decay process and estimate the half-life of ^{224}Ra.

If alpha decay, the resulting nucleus is

$$^{224}\text{Ra} \xrightarrow{\alpha} \underline{\hspace{2cm}}$$

If beta-minus decay, the resulting nucleus is

$$^{224}\text{Ra} \xrightarrow{\beta^-} \underline{\hspace{2cm}}$$

If beta-plus decay, the resulting nucleus is

$$^{224}\text{Ra} \xrightarrow{\beta^+} \underline{\hspace{2cm}}$$

Over what time scale does ^{224}Ra decay?

Estimate the half-life of ^{224}Ra.

Question 5 ^{14}**C.** Determine the decay process and estimate the half-life of ^{14}C.

If alpha decay, the resulting nucleus is

$$^{14}\text{C} \xrightarrow{\alpha} \underline{\hspace{2cm}}$$

If beta-minus decay, the resulting nucleus is

$$^{14}\text{C} \xrightarrow{\beta^-} \underline{\hspace{2cm}}$$

If beta-plus decay, the resulting nucleus is

$$^{14}\text{C} \xrightarrow{\beta^+} \underline{\hspace{2cm}}$$

Over what time scale does ^{14}C decay?

Estimate the half-life of ^{14}C.

Question 6 ^{13}**N.** Determine the decay process and estimate the half-life of ^{13}N.

If alpha decay, the resulting nucleus is

$$^{13}\text{N} \xrightarrow{\alpha} \underline{\hspace{2cm}}$$

If beta-minus decay, the resulting nucleus is

$$^{13}\text{N} \xrightarrow{\beta^-} \underline{\hspace{2cm}}$$

If beta-plus decay, the resulting nucleus is

$$^{13}\text{N} \xrightarrow{\beta^+} \underline{\hspace{2cm}}$$

Over what time scale does ^{13}N decay?

Estimate the half-life of ^{13}N.

Initial state:

Final state:

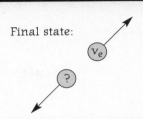

Question 1 Initial state. What are the initial electric charge, baryon number, electro-lepton number, muon-lepton number, and tau-lepton number for this interaction?

Proton <_____, _____, _____, _____, _____>

              Charge: _____

          baryon number: _____

        e–lepton number: _____

        μ–lepton number: _____

        τ–lepton number: _____

Electron <_____, _____, _____, _____, _____>

              Charge: _____

          baryon number: _____

        e–lepton number: _____

        μ–lepton number: _____

        τ–lepton number: _____

Initial state: <_____, _____, _____, _____, _____>

Question 2 Unknown particle. Determine the "numbers" on the unknown outgoing particle. From this information, determine the identity of the unknown particle.

Electron neutrino <____, ____, ____, ____, ____>

              Charge: _____

          baryon number: _____

        e–lepton number: _____

        μ–lepton number: _____

        τ–lepton number: _____

Unknown particle <____, ____, ____, ____, ____>

              Charge: _____

          baryon number: _____

        e–lepton number: _____

        μ–lepton number: _____

        τ–lepton number: _____

Unknown particle
identity is _____.

Initial state:

Final state:

n̄

?

Question 3 Unknown particle, once again.

Antiproton <__ __ __ __ __>

Antineutron <__ __ __ __ __>

Antimuon <__ __ __ __ __>

Unknown particle <__ __ __ __ __>

Initial state <__ __ __ __ __>

Unknown particle identity is: _____

Initial state:

Final state:

?

Question 4 Unknown particle, one last time.

Antiproton <__ __ __ __ __>

Antidelta⁺⁺ <__ __ __ __ __>

Pion <__ __ __ __ __>

Unknown particle <__ __ __ __ __>

Initial state <__ __ __ __ __>

Unknown particle identity is: _____

20

QUANTUM MECHANICS

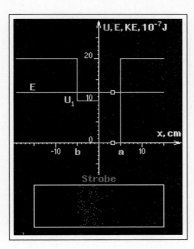

A particle of energy 12×10^{-7} J moves in a region of space in which the potential energy is 10×10^{-7} J between the points −5 cm and 0 cm, zero between the points 0 cm and +5 cm, and 20×10^{-7} J everywhere else.

Question 1 Range of motion. What will be the range of motion of the particle when subject to this potential energy function?

Question 2 Turning points. Clearly state why the particle cannot travel more than 5 cm from the origin.

Question 3 Probability of detection. Assume we measure the position of the particle at several random times. Is there a higher probability of detecting the particle between −5 cm and 0 cm or between 0 cm and +5 cm?

In which region is the particle traveling slower?

In which region does the particle spend more time?

In which region is the particle more likely to be detected?

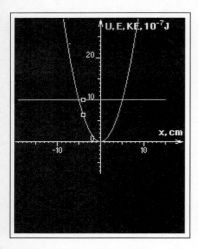

Turn off the strobe display and select the **Harmonic** potential. Select a particle energy of 10×10^{-7} J and a spring constant of 8×10^{-4} N/m. Run the simulation.

Question 4 Range of motion.

What is the range of motion of the particle?	What will happen to the range of motion of the particle if its energy is doubled?

Question 5 Kinetic energy.

Sketch the graph of the particle's kinetic energy vs. position.	Explain why the graph has this shape.

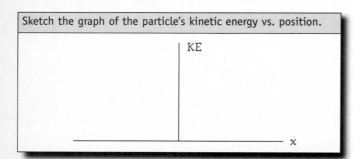

Question 6 Most likely location(s). Assume the position of the particle is measured at several random times.

Where is the particle traveling the slowest?	Where is the particle most likely to be detected?

©1999 Addison Wesley Longman, Alan Van Heuvelen and Paul D'Alessandris

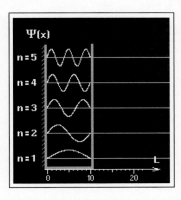

Question 1 Standing waves. From your study of mechanical waves, what is the longest wavelength standing wave on a string of length L?

Question 2 The de Broglie relation. What is the momentum of the longest-wavelength standing wave in a box of length L?

What is the de Broglie relation between momentum and wavelength?

Combine the de Broglie relation and the expression for the longest standing wavelength to relate the momentum to the box length, L.

Question 3 Ground-state energy. Assuming the particle is not traveling at relativistic speeds, determine an expression for the ground-state energy.

What is the relation between particle energy and momentum, in a region of no potential energy?

Combine the above relation and the result from Question 2 to determine the energy of the longest standing wave.

Explain why the longest standing wave has less energy than all other standing waves.

Question 4 Increasing L. If the size of the box is increased, will the ground-state energy increase or decrease?

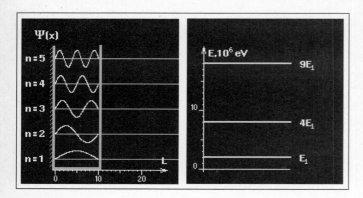

Question 5 The correspondence principle: Large size.
In the limit of a very large box, what will happen to the ground-state energy and the spacing between allowed energy levels? Explain.

Explain why quantum effects are not noticeable in everyday, macroscopic situations.

Question 6 The correspondence principle: Large mass.
In the limit of a very massive particle what will happen to the ground-state energy and the spacing between allowed energy levels? Explain.

Explain why quantum effects are not noticeable in everyday, macroscopic situations.

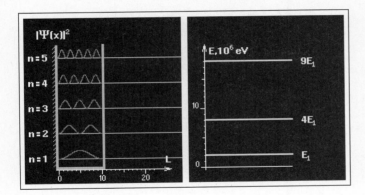

Question 7 Ground-state probability. If a measurement is made of the particle's position while in the ground state, at what position is it most likely to be detected?

Question 8 Probability: Dependence on mass and size. The most likely position to detect the particle, when it is in the ground state, is in the center of the box. Does this observation depend on either the mass of the particle or the size of the box?

Question 9 Probability: Dependence on energy level. The most likely position to detect the particle, when it is in the ground state, is in the center of the box. Does this observation hold true at higher energy levels?

Question 10 The correspondence principle: large n. In the limit of large n, what will happen to the spacing between regions of high and low probability of detection?

Explain why quantum effects are not noticeable in everyday, macroscopic situations.

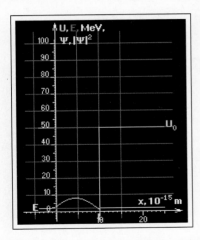

Question 1 Infinite well. If the potential well is infinitely deep, determine the ground-state energy.

Is this also the ground-state energy in the finite well?

Question 2 First excited state. If the potential well is infinitely deep, determine the energy of the first excited state (n = 2).

Is this also the energy of the first excited state in the finite well?

Question 3 "Forbidden" regions. Since the wave function can penetrate into the "forbidden" regions, how will the wavelength of the wave function in the finite well compare to the wavelength of the wave function in the infinite well?

Will the energy of the first excited state in the finite well be greater than or less than the energy of the first excited state in the infinite well? Why?

Question 4 More shallow well. If the depth of the potential well is decreased from 50 MeV to 25 MeV, what will happen to the penetration depth?

What will happen to the wavelength of the wave function?

What will happen to the energy of the n = 3 state?

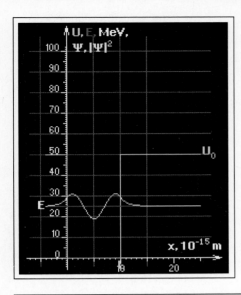

Question 5 Penetration depth (δ). Complete the following table.

m	δ
0.5	
1.0	
2.5	
3.5	
4.5	
(m_p)	$(\times 10^{-15} m)$

What happens to the penetration depth as the mass of the particle is increased?

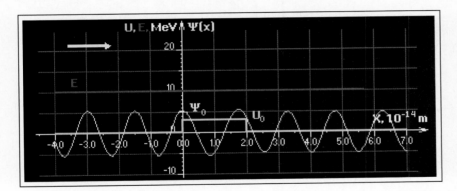

Question 1 Creating a potential barrier. If a potential barrier of a few MeV is created, what will happen to the transmission probability of the particle? Explain.

Question 2 Raising the barrier. What will happen to the transmission probability when the potential equals, and then exceeds, the initial energy of the particle? Will the particle be able to be transmitted through the barrier? Explain.

Question 3 Barrier width. If the width of the barrier is decreased, what effect will this have on the transmission probability? Explain.

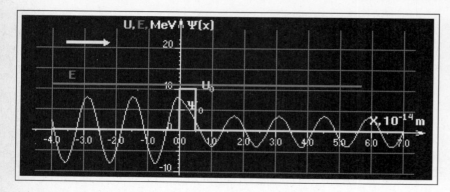

Set the potential height to 11 MeV, the incident energy to 10 MeV, and the barrier width to 0.5×10^{-14} m.

Question 4 Functional effect of barrier width on transmission probability.

Record the transmission probability.

Double the barrier width and record the new transmission probability. Continue to double the width and record the new transmission probabilities.

L	T
0.5	
1.0	
2.0	
4.0	
($\times 10^{-14}$m)	

Sketch a graph of T vs. L.

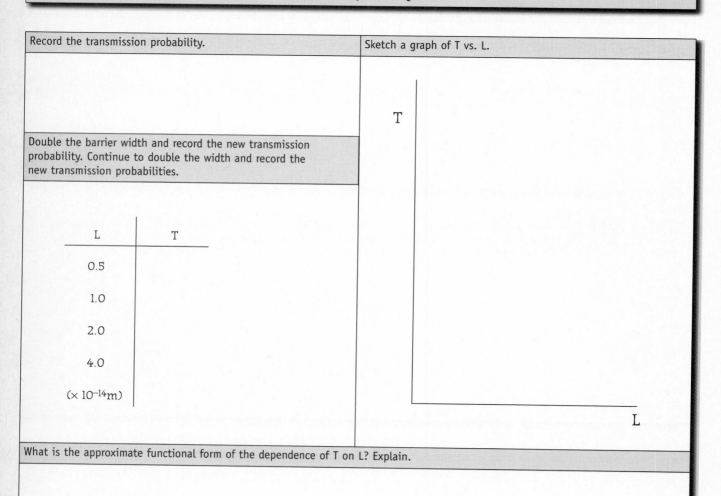

What is the approximate functional form of the dependence of T on L? Explain.

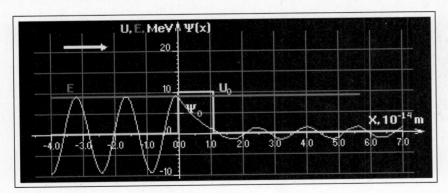

Set the potential height to 9 MeV, the incident energy to 10 MeV, and the barrier width to 1.1×10^{-14} m.

Question 5 Tricky question. If the barrier width is slowly increased to 2.3×10^{-14} m, what will happen to T? Describe what you discover.

Question 6 Doubly tricky question. If you continue to increase the barrier width to 4.7×10^{-14} m, what will happen to T? Describe what you discover.

Question 7 Explanation. From your careful observation of the wave function, formulate an explanation as to why the transmission probability does not always decrease when the barrier gets wider.

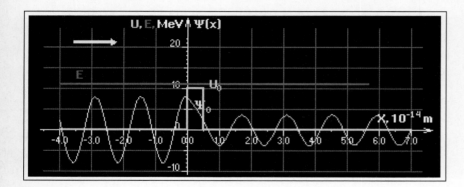

Question 8 Scattering from potential wells. What will happen to the transmission probability if the potential is dropped to a negative value, i.e., a potential well is formed? Can the particle get reflected from a potential well? Explain.

Question 9 No Longer a Tricky Question. Continue to lower the potential energy in the well. Why does the transmission probability have maximas at −4 MeV and −10 MeV? Explain.

PART IV

ActivPhysics User Guide

About *ActivPhysics*

ActivPhysics 2 is a collection of guided, interactive activities that present Electricity and Magnetism, Optics and Modern Physics for use in introductory college or university physics courses or high school courses that emphasize problem solving. All the activities are simulation based.

ActivPhysics 2 contains many features that convey concepts and information in a visual, interactive way, unlike most traditional methods.

This CD-ROM can be used alone, but the accompanying *ActivPhysics 2* Workbook is strongly recommended.

Navigating *ActivPhysics*

ActivPad
Launches *ActivPad,* an interactive notebook you can use to keep notes and create customized links to any place in *ActivPhysics 2* or the World Wide Web.

Help
Outlines navigation features and provides tips on how to integrate the product into your course.

Main
Brings you back to the main menu of the unit you are in.

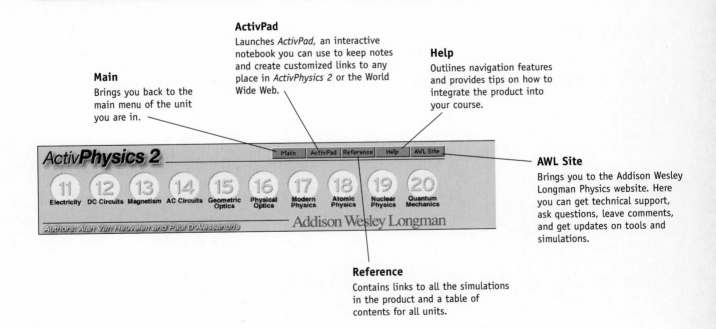

AWL Site
Brings you to the Addison Wesley Longman Physics website. Here you can get technical support, ask questions, leave comments, and get updates on tools and simulations.

Reference
Contains links to all the simulations in the product and a table of contents for all units.

Units and Activities

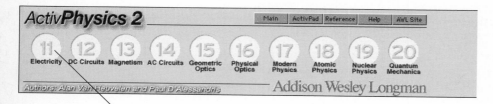

You can move to a unit by selecting one of the
unit names or numbers along the middle of the
menu. Once you have made your selection, the
titles of the activities for that unit will appear
in the frame on the right side (see below).
Simply click on an activity to launch it. The
activity will appear in the frame on the right,
and all simulations will appear on the left.

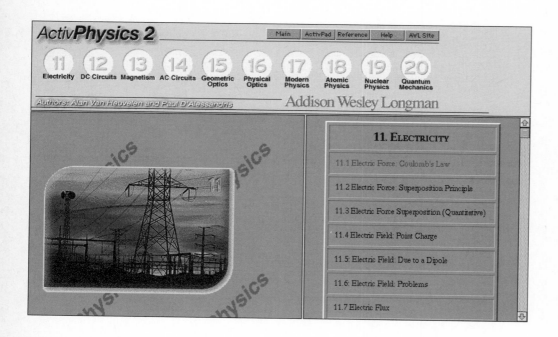

Navigating an *ActivPhysics* Activity

The Help button in the main menu brings you to a sample interactive activity that illustrates what each button link in an *ActivPhysics* activity does. This interactive Help activity is a great way to learn how to use the *ActivPhysics* interface. It is recommended that you review this section before working with an *ActivPhysics* activity.

  Objective button links to a description of the goals of the activity.

  Simulation button launches interactive simulation for the activity.

  Advisor button links to information and tips to help you complete the activity.

Some *ActivPhysics* activities contain computer tools to help you solve problems and make predictions:

Force Diagram Tool:
Allows you to create force diagrams on the screen. Note that the tails of the force arrows should attach at the place the flow is exerted on the object of interest.

Bar Chart Predictor:
Allows you to qualitatively predict the initial and final work-energy terms in a work-energy process.

Using the Simulations

 Simulations are launched by clicking on this icon.

The simulations contain sliders and controls that allow you to alter the conditions of the physical system represented by the simulation. Simulations can be accessed through the on-screen activity or through the Reference section.

As you roll the cursor over the simulation screen, information about the simulation, including descriptions of what the various controls do, appears at the bottom of the interface screen.

To get simulation help, click anywhere on the simulation. (In Windows, right mouse click).

Using ActivPad

ActivPad is an on-line, interactive notepad you can use to keep notes and "bookmark" places in *ActivPhysics*. You can also use *ActivPad* to create hyperlinks to sites on the World Wide Web. *ActivePad* is ideal for creating lecture notes or custom homework problems, because you can have instant hyperlinks to *ActivPhysics* tools or other Web sites.

Students Use *ActivePad* to:

keep your notes about the various activities, questions you want to ask an instructor or TA later, etc.;

post your answers to *ActivPhysics* questions and paste in material from *ActivPhysics*, or graphs and charts from other programs;

"bookmark" places in *ActivPhysics* and, if you have a live Web connection, to add links to physics sites or other related material on the Web. You can also link to your course home page if one has been posted.

Instructors Use *ActivPad* to:

Organize your lecture notes and class demonstrations. Type your notes into *ActivPad* and/or use the active linking feature to create links to the simulations or other portions of *ActivPhysics* that you want to show in class.

Create new questions or problems to accompany the existing *ActivPhysics* simulations. You can save your *ActivPad* assignment to a server where your students can access it.

Save links to physics resources on the Web, including your course home page.

To Set Up *ActivPad* on Windows

In Netscape 4:

1. With *ActivPhysics* 2 open, from the **Edit** menu select **Preferences.**
    A Preferences window opens.

2. Under **Category** at the left side of the Preferences dialog box, select
    Navigator by clicking on the plus symbol. Then, click on the **Applications**
    sub-category to open the Applications dialog area on the right side of the
    Preferences window.

3. On the right side of the dialog box, click the button labeled **New Type...**

4. In the dialog box enter:
    Description of Type: **ActivPad**
    File Extension: **led**
    MIME Type: **application**
    Application to use: Click the **Browse** button and locate *ActivPad* 1.0 by
    browsing your hard drive for the application.

5. Click **OK** to close the dialog box and return to the Preferences window.

6. Close the Preferences dialog box by clicking OK.

In Internet Explorer 4:
Internet Explorer 4.01 on the Windows platform cannot be configured to
automatically launch *ActivPad*. If you plan to use this application while
running *ActivPhysics* 2, please locate and launch *ActivPad* from your hard
drive. For more information, please click the "AWL Site" button on your
toolbar in *ActivPhysics*.

To Set Up ActivPad on Macintosh

In Netscape 4:

1. With *ActivPhysics* open, from the **Options** menu select **General Preferences.**
    A Preferences window opens.

2. Select the **Helpers** tab and click the **[New]** button.

3. In the dialog box type:
    Description: ActivPad
    MIME Type: **application/led**
    Suffixes: **led**
    Select **Application** in the **Handled By** box

4. Select *ActivPad* as the application by clicking the Browse button to locate
    the *ActivPad* application on your hard drive and then clicking **Open.**

5. Click the File Type pop-down menu and select **LDDC.**

6. Click OK to close the Helpers dialog box.

7. Click OK to close the Preferences window.

In Internet Explorer 4:

1. With *ActivPhysics* open, from the **Edit** menu select **Preferences.**
   A Preferences window opens.

2. Locate the **Receiving Files** category in the list on the left side of the window and click the arrow to open the sub-menu, if it is not already open. Under Receiving Files, select **File Helpers.**

3. In the File Helper Settings dialog area on the right, click the **Add...** button. A new dialog box will open titled **Edit File Helper.**

4. In the area of the dialog box labeled **Representation** type:
   Description: ActivPad
   Extension: **led**
   MIME Type: **application/led**

5. In the area of the dialog box labeled **File Type,** click the **Browse...** Locate the *ActivPad* application on your hard drive and then click **Open.** The File type field should automatically be filled in with the type LDDC and the File creator field should read Apad.

6. In the bottom area of the dialog box labeled **Handling,** open the pull-down menu and select View With Application. The application name and icon should then appear below the menu. If it does not, click the Browse... button in the Handling area and repeat the procedure in item 5 above.

7. Click OK to close the Edit File Helpers dialog box.

8. Click OK to close the Preferences window.

Managing Your *ActivPad* Documents

ActivPad documents are like any other documents that you save on your computer. You can save them all in one folder, or in various locations. You decide where an *ActivPad* document will be stored when you name and save it.

If you work with *ActivPhysics* and *ActivPad* on more than one computer, be sure to see "Sharing *ActivPad* Documents."

Taking Notes in *ActivPad*

Note taking using *ActivPad* is straightforward. The program behaves much like a regular word processor.

1. In the **Main** menu bar, launch *ActivPad* by clicking on the *ActivPad* button.

ActivPad does not launch from within Internet Explorer. If *ActivPad* is not launched from the Main Menu, locate the *ActivPad* application on your hard drive and launch it from there.

Cutting and Pasting in *ActivPad*

You can cut and paste material from other documents into *ActivPad*. This includes material from *ActivPhysics*, word processing documents, clip art, graphics, charts and tables from spreadsheets, etc. Simply open the document you want to paste from, copy the material, then open your *ActivPad* document and paste the material in.

ActivPad is not a full math processor, so check the pasted material for accuracy when cutting and pasting formulas or other math text.

Depending on your computer's memory allocations, you may not be able to have many documents open at once. You may have to open and close documents while copying and pasting.

Windows users using Netscape cannot paste images into *ActivPad* directly from *ActivPhysics*; those using Internet Explorer can do so.

Creating a Link in *ActivPad*

Make sure that both *ActivPad* and *ActivPhysics* (or the Web document you want to link to) are open. It is easiest to create the link if you can see the *ActivPad* document you are working with and the document you want to link to at the same time. To do this you can reduce the size of the windows of each application in such a way that they are side by side or one on top of the other.

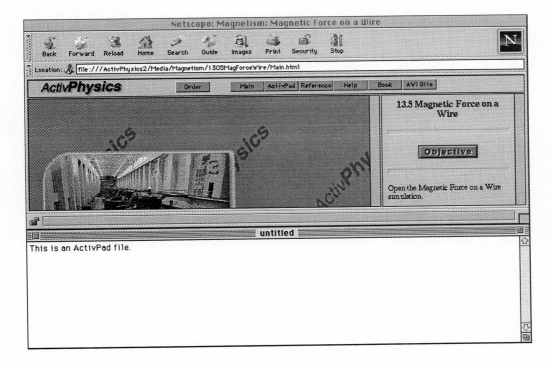

Grab Current

Grab Current is a method to "bookmark" useful resources in *ActivPhysics*
or on the Web.

1. With *ActivPad* open, go to the spot in *ActivPhysics* or on the Web to which
    you want to create an *ActivPad* link.

2. From the ActivLinks pull-down menu, choose **Grab Current URL.** The link
    will appear in your *ActivPad* document.

Drag and Drop

Drag and Drop is helpful when you want to grab many links from one page
and put them into a single *ActivPad* document.

1. With *ActivPad* open, select the place in *ActivePhysics* or on the Web that
    contains the link you want to add to *ActivPad*. *Do not activate the link.*

2. Select the link and drag it over to the open *ActivPad* document and
    release the mouse. The link will appear in your *ActivPad* document.

3. Double-click on the new link to activate it.

You need to have either *ActivPhysics* or a Web connection open in order
for your links to work (depending on where they point to).

You can delete any links that you have created in *ActivPad* by simply
selecting them and hitting the delete key.

ActivPad links will open any framed links full screen instead of in their
original framed window.

Customizing Your *ActivPad* Links

When you bring a link into *ActivPad* from *ActivPhysics* or the Web you will
get a link label that shows the title of the link, information about the link's
point of origin, etc.

You can rename the label or customize it so that the link is represented by
an image. You may want to do this to make the link easier to remember, to
connect an image to a link for study purposes (e.g., an image of a graph
linking to material about the physical phenomena it represents), or to
make your *ActivPad* document visually interesting if you are using it for
demonstration purposes.

Creating a Link Represented by an Image

1. Paste the image you want to use to represent a link into the *ActivPad* document (See "Cutting and Pasting in *ActivPad*" for help with this.)

2. Select the place in *ActivPhysics* or on the Web that contains the link you want to connect to the image. *Do not activate the link.*

3. Select the link (Right click for Windows; click and hold for Mac) until the pop-up link menu appears. From the menu, select **Copy this Link Location.**

4. Return to the image you pasted in the *ActivPad* document. Select the image.

5. From the **ActivLinks** menu, select **Edit ActivLink.** A new window will open.

6. Highlight all of the text in the URL line of this window, and then select **Paste.** This replaces the old link information with the new information you copied from your desired link. If there is no text in this line simply select **Paste.**

7. You have now created an image link in *ActivPad*, which works like every other *ActivPad* link. Remember that the document you are linking to must be open, whether it is *ActivPhysics* or a web browser.

Changing a Link's Label

1. Select the link in *ActivPad.*

2. Go to the menu bar at the top of the screen and open the **ActivLinks** menu. From that menu, select **Edit ActivLink.** A new window will open.

3. Replace any text in the title line of this window with whatever text you want to change it to.

4. Your link still goes to the same location it originally did, but now has the title of your choice. Remember that the document you are linking to must be open, whether it is *ActivPhysics* or a web browser.

Sharing *ActivPad* Documents

Standardizing *ActivPad* Links

If you intend to use *ActivPad* documents on a different computer or to share *ActivPad* documents with other *ActivPhysics* users, you should use *ActivPad's* standardizing feature.

When an ActivLink is created, *ActivPad* records a URL, or digital address, so that the program will later be able to retrieve that same location on the CD-ROM or Web. Because different computers are configured differently, this address varies from computer to computer. While one computer may have the CD-ROM drive designated as drive D, another may call it drive G, and yet another (a Macintosh, for example) does not use a letter to denote its CD-ROM drive. Thus the same *ActivPhysics* home page may have several different addresses, depending on the computer it is being viewed on:

    Your computer: file///D|/ActivPhysics2.html
    PC 2: file: ///E|/ActivPhysics2.html;
    Web server: http://www.phys.university.edu/ActivPhysics2.html
    Macintosh: file://ActivPhysics_2_CD/ActivPhysics2.html

ActivPad's standardizing feature will automatically replace the first part of these URL's with a variable name like "$ActivPhysics2$." Thus, the URLs from above will be recorded in *ActivPad* as follows:

    Your computer: $ActivPhysics2$ActivPhysics2.html
    PC 2: $ActivPhysics2$ActivPhysics2.html
    Web server: $ActivPhysics2$ActivPhysics2.html
    Macintosh: $ActivPhysics2$ActivPhysics2.html

Now all standardized links will work properly when shared among the above users.

Make sure that everyone is using the same variable name.

You do not need to standardize links to the World Wide Web.

Standardizing ActivPad Hyperlinks

You should standardize *ActivPad* hyperlinks if you intend to do any of the following:

Share *ActivPad* documents with other users.

Distribute *ActivPad* documents as class notes or custom homework sets.

Use *ActivPad* documents on multiple computers.

You must perform the following steps with the *ActivPhysics* home page open.

To Standardize *ActivPad* Documents

1. Launch *ActivPad* by clicking the **ActivPad** button on the Main Screen of *ActivPhysics*.

2. From the **ActivLinks** menu choose **ActivLink Preferences.** A window appears listing *ActivPhysics* in a **Variable** box.

3. Click on the **Grab** button to the right of the **ActivPhysics Variable box.**

4. Click the check box under the **Standardize New URL's** heading, if a check is not already there.

5. To test: From the **ActivLinks** menu, select **Grab Current Location.** The following hyperlink should be inserted into the current *ActivPad* document:

    URL:$ActivPhysics2$ActivPhyiscs2.html

If the link is not inserted properly, check your **ActivLink Preferences** to make sure that the **Standardized new URL's with this prefix** checkbox is checked.

Getting Help with *ActivPhysics*

If you find that you need help or technical support:

Try reading the section of this User Guide that covers the part of *ActivPhysics* about which you have a question. There is also a README file and a Help file on the *ActivPhysics* CD-ROM. You may find an answer to your question in one of these.

Addison Wesley's physics web site (http://www.awl.com/physics) is also a good source for updates on new products, technical information, frequently asked questions, and user comments.

If your problem is related to installation or defective media, please contact Addison Wesley's Technical Support Division via e-mail at mailto:techsprt@awl.com, or by phone at 847 486-2111. The hotline is staffed from 9 a.m. to 4 p.m., Monday through Friday (Eastern time). If you do not get through immediately, please leave them a message describing your problem. A software technician will return your call. Please note that Technical Support provides installation guidance and defective media replacement only. Questions on program usage should be directed to Addison Wesley Longman Physics via our web site. If you are a student, you can also direct questions on program usage to your professor or lab coordinator. Also check the product support web site: http://techsupport.awl.com.

ActivPhysics 2   Quick Start Card

Installation for Windows 95 or NT 4.0
1. Place the CD-ROM in the CD-ROM drive. A launcher window will open.
   If the launcher window does not open automatically when you insert the ActivPhysics CD-ROM, you should open the *ActivPhysics* CD-ROM via Windows Explorer, then double-click the "Launcher" or "Launcher.exe" application.
2. Choose from and install either the Netscape 4.04 or Internet Explorer 4.01 Internet browser and the ActivPhysics 2 plug-ins onto your hard drive.. If you use Microsoft Internet Explorer (version 4.0 or higher), or if Netscape Navigator (version 3.0 or higher) is already installed on your machine, you do not need to install an Internet browser from this CD-ROM.
3. After this installation, click "RUN" from the launcher window to launch ActivPhysics 2.

See the on-line Help to get more information on how to use *ActivPhysics*

Installation for Macintosh
1. Insert the ActivPhysics CD-ROM into your CD-ROM drive. A window will open.
2. Choose from and install either the Netscape 4.04 or Internet Explorer 4.01 Internet browser
   If you have Internet Explorer (version 4.0 or higher) or Netscape Navigator (version 3.0 or higher) already installed on your machine, can omit this step.
3. Install *ActivPhysics2* – this will install the required plug-ins and ActivPad on your hard drive.
4. Launch ActivPhysics by double-clicking the "ActivPhysics2.html" icon.

See the on-line Help to get more information on how to use *ActivPhysics*.